# THE OPEN SEA: ITS NATURAL HISTORY

## PART II

# FISH AND FISHERIES

THE OPEN SEA: ITS NATURAL HISTORY

*PART II*

# FISH & FISHERIES

*With chapters on Whales, Turtles*

*and Animals of the Sea Floor*

*by*

*SIR ALISTER HARDY*

M.A., D.SC., F.R.S.

*Fellow of Merton College,*
*Hon. Fellow of Exeter College*
*and Linacre Professor of Zoology*
*and Comparative Anatomy*
*in the University*
*of Oxford*

WITH WATERCOLOUR AND LINE DRAWINGS
BY THE AUTHOR
68 PHOTOGRAPHS IN BLACK AND WHITE
BY DOUGLAS WILSON AND OTHERS
AND DIAGRAMS AND MAPS

HOUGHTON MIFFLIN COMPANY BOSTON
THE RIVERSIDE PRESS CAMBRIDGE
1959

# CONTENTS

# PLATES IN COLOUR

## PLATES IN BLACK AND WHITE

# EDITORS' PREFACE

IN OUR Preface to *The World of Plankton*, the first part of Sir Alister Hardy's distinguished contribution to the New Naturalist series on the subject of The Open Sea, we made much of the author's enthusiasm. As we explained, it was in a burst of enthusiasm that he found that he had so much to say about the sea that he had to write us two books instead of one. This second volume completes his enterprise.

Alister Hardy's first contribution, on the World of Plankton, described a world almost unknown and very strange to the ordinary naturalist. In this new volume he gives his message from much more familiar ground. Indeed, he starts by saying that, "There can be no better introduction to the fish and fisheries of the sea than the sight of a full-sized commercial trawl being emptied of its catch." But if he starts from the familiar, he is soon once again in a little explored realm. After leading the reader through a most compelling exposition of the history and habits of fishes in general, he introduces him to the latest scientific discoveries about the life of important commercial species, such as herring, cod and plaice, in particular.

In a most easy and well thought out way he gives us a picture of the pure natural history of fish and refreshes it with a clear and up-to-date development of its implications for the fishing industry. Indeed, the book is an admirable blend of the theoretical and the practical.

It is also notable for being so admirably illustrated by its author. The line drawings from his own hand figure over 200 species of animals, and in the plates more than 100 others are reproduced in colour from his paintings, all of which were executed from living examples or freshly-caught specimens before their colours had had time to fade.

Particularly absorbing and interesting are his chapters on fish parasites and on the problem of over-fishing; but he does not fear to pursue the sea serpent and the possibility that eskimos in kayaks may have reached our shores from Greenland alive.

Sir Alister's last chapter, "The Ecologists and the Future", is a fitting culmination to this masterly two-book study of marine biology. It shows that we, as ransackers of the sea (to use the old Norse word for research) are just at the beginning of a new age of discovery, just at the start of the proper appreciation, identification and classification of the communities of life of two-thirds of the surface of the earth. From this beautiful synthesis of nature's network in the seas around Britain, naturalists all over the world can learn, not only how tidily and keenly dedicated biologists are pushing into the unknown and enlarging our organised knowledge but also how much there is still to do for generations to come in this challenging field of science.

THE EDITORS

# AUTHOR'S PREFACE

ALTHOUGH this book forms the second part of *The Open Sea*, it has deliberately not been called Volume II. Each part may be regarded, if a reader so desires, as an entirely independent work complete in itself; yet the second follows from the first and the two were planned together as a whole. The division between them is a logical and natural one. The first dealt with the world of plankton and the physical background behind it all; the second treats of the fish (and fisheries) and all the other animals of the sea which depend directly or indirectly upon the plankton for their support.

As this part is being published only some two years, after the appearance of the first, I should perhaps explain that it has not been hurriedly put together in just that time. It was originally intended that one volume should have covered the whole natural history of the open sea; and it was, in fact, first written in this way, but then found to be nearly twice the length it should have been, with quite a lot left out which I had hoped to include. It had consequently to be cut in two and the halves considerably rewritten to give each the desired balance and completeness. As a sideline to a busy professorial life the two parts together have taken some ten years to produce; but then it has not meant just the writing: the drawings have taken much time with many visits to marine laboratories and trips to sea.

Once more I wish to express my gratitude to the publishers and editors for their kind forbearance over my delay in completing the whole work and for all the trouble they have taken in its production.

Again I have the pleasure and privilege, as I had in Part I, of acknowledging that which will, of course, be obvious to every reader: the great contribution made to my book by the series of brilliant photographs taken by that master of marine picture-making, Dr. Douglas P. Wilson. I am indeed lucky to have his continued collaboration in Part II. His fame as a photographer of sea animals is so thoroughly established that it needs no emphasis here; I would, however, like to draw the attention of the general reader, who may not be so familiar with his research, to his powers of observation and his patience which have enabled him to make such remarkable studies as those illustrated, for example, by his pictures of the courtship of the

xi

dragonet (Plate XXIII) or of the cuckoo wrasse (Plate XXI), of nest
protection by the black sea-bream (Plate XXII) or the digging of the
red band-fish (Plate XX). And here I may acknowledge another
addition which he has made to the book in kindly allowing me to quote
from some of his excellent accounts of fish behaviour such as that of the
capture of prey by the electric ray *Torpedo* (p. 183) or by the angler
fish (p. 194); these show well what an acutely observant naturalist
he is.

In addition to those by Dr. Wilson there are a number of other
excellent photographs in the black-and-white plates which will be
acknowledged as they occur. A few, however, of the more remarkable
of these, which have been taken by unconventional means, should be
mentioned here. Among them I am lucky to be able to reproduce
(in Plate V) two electronic flash studies of flying fish in the air taken
by Dr. H. E. Edgerton, of the Massachusetts Institute of Technology.
Then there are the pictures of the sea-floor taken by Dr. Vevers's
underwater camera (Plate IX) or by Dr. Barnes's television apparatus
(Plate XII), and those unique shots of a seine-net in action from the
film taken on the sea-bed by that pioneer frogman, the late Commander Hodges; this film was made for the Fisheries Division of the
Scottish Home Department who have kindly allowed me to reproduce
three pictures from it (Plate XIV). In contrast to these underwater
studies are the photographs of whales taken from the air. The one of
the fin whales blowing (Plate XXVIII) was taken from a helicopter
in the Antarctic by Mr. M. Vardy, a whale-spotting pilot attached to
the Floating Factory Ship, *Southern Harvester;* those of the humpback
whales (Plate XXIX) were taken by Mr. S. Fowler from a plane engaged in fishery exploration flights off the coast of Western Australia
and were published in the *Australian Journal of Marine and Freshwater
Research*, Vol. 4., from which I reproduce them by the kind permission
of the Commonwealth Scientific and Industrial Research Organisa-
tion.

As to the coloured drawings, they have been made as far as possible
from living specimens; this is so in regard to all the invertebrate
animals, but many of the fish have not been available for study in
aquaria and these have been drawn from freshly-caught specimens.
I have to thank Dr. C. E. Lucas C.M.G., Director of the Fishery
Investigations of the Scottish Home Department, for kindly allowing me
to accompany their new Fishery Research Ship *Explorer* on a trawling
survey over the northern North Sea in the summer of 1956 and so
enabling me to make watercolour drawings as soon as the fish came
out of the trawl; it was on that voyage that all the drawings in Plates

12, 13 and 14 were made, together with some in other plates (1, 2, 5, 9, 10, 11 and 15). I am very glad to acknowledge the valuable help I received during that voyage from Mr. Sidney Devlin, Senior Scientific Assistant, who, from his wide experience, taught me much about the North Sea fish that I did not know before. The other coloured drawings were made in the Marine Laboratories of Plymouth, Millport, Aberdeen and Cullercoats, and in the Mevagissey Aquarium. I am once more most grateful to the Sun Engraving Company for the fine craftsmanship which has made such excellent reproductions of my watercolours; from visiting their Works I know what a great deal of trouble has been taken over the individual blocks to get results as near as possible to the originals.

Regarding text-figures I again thank Dr. Marie Lebour and the Council of the Marine Biological Association for kindly allowing me to include again some of her excellent drawings of plankton animals feeding on young herring (Fig. 21, p. 54); similarly, I thank the Council for permission to reproduce drawings by Mr. L. R. Brightwell and the late Dr. G. A. Steven, of the lemon dab (Fig. 91, p. 203). I also gratefully acknowledge the permission given by Messrs. J. M. Dent and Son Ltd., to produce five of the drawings of fishing boats by the late Mr. Ernest Dade from that splendid selection of his sketches in *Sail and Oar*. (Figs. 17, 65, 66, 68 and 69).[1] Then I must again thank Sir Gavin de Beer and members of the staff at the British Museum (Natural History), particularly Dr. F. C. Fraser and Mr. N. B. Marshall, for kindly allowing me to make many black-and-white drawings from specimens in the museum collections; I am similarly indebted to Dr. Bennet Rae, of the Marine (Fisheries) Laboratory at Aberdeen who has kindly let me draw some of the fish in his collection. I also wish to express my appreciation of the care and skill with which Mr. J. F. Trotter has redrawn the various graphs and maps for publication.

Coming now to the text, I gratefully record, as I did in my preface to Part I, my indebtedness to my old friend—and once my Oxford tutor—Sir Julian Huxley for his careful reading of the typescript and for the many valuable comments he made which helped in its improvement. I am also greatly indebted to Dr. Denys Tucker of the British Museum (Natural History) for kindly reading the whole proofs and giving me much help and advice from his special knowledge of the British fishes, and, incidentally, saving me from not a few slips of syntax. The chapter on "Fish in General" was read by Dr. Margaret Brown (now Mrs. Varley) and that on whales by Dr. N. A. Mackintosh;

[1] I had made every effort to trace the relatives of Mr. Dade to obtain their permission also, but without success.

I am most grateful to them for a number of helpful suggestions which they made. Regarding the last chapter I must acknowledge that some of what I have written concerning ecology, although now a little rearranged, was said before in very similar terms in my presidential address to Section D (Zoology) of the British Association at their meeting of 1949. Dr. Sheina Marshall has been most kind in going through the page proofs with great care and so saving me from many slips and misprints which I had myself failed to find.

I will end, as I did my preface to Part I, by drawing attention to two important points. Zoologists will find the authorities for the different specific names given after these names in the index and not in the text where they are left out to avoid undue elaboration; and non-zoologists will find a glossary, immediately before the index, giving a simple explanation of the few technical terms which have been unavoidably used.

A.C.H.

# CHAPTER I

# INTRODUCTION

*Including a summary of the
earlier volume : Part I*

THERE can be no better introduction to the fish and fisheries of the sea than the sight of a full-sized commercial trawl being emptied of its catch. Let us watch for a moment as the net is pulled up to the trawler's side after being dragged along the sea-bed for three hours or so.

The modern trawl, a gigantic netting bag with an oblong mouth some eighty feet across, is much more artful than might appear at first sight. Its upper lip, or head-rope, is raised by a row of floats, while the heavier lower lip, or foot-rope, sweeps the bottom; and its opening is spread wide by the corners being pulled sideways by wooden otter-boards which sheer outwards like kites as they are towed along. Now the trailing foot-rope, being much longer than the stretched head-rope above, curves backwards *well behind it* and shows us just what a cunning device the trawl is; by the time the fish on the bottom are disturbed they find themselves actually covered by a roof of moving net and are, in fact, almost half-way down the bag already, for the floor of the sea in front acts like an extension of the mouth. Perhaps its unknown inventor smiled as broadly as his trawl when he thought of it; if we could ride as frogmen on top of the net as it moves forward, it might almost appear as if the fish were carried down its throat on an endless conveyor belt. The bag tapers behind to a narrow cylinder, the cod-end, where its catch accumulates. The sketch in Fig. 1, shows this trawl in action; it is called an otter-trawl.

As the two thick towing warps are wound in, the otter-boards come into view and are drawn up to the steel gallows, which project slightly over the side: one towards the bows and another towards the stern; being heavily bound with iron and bridled with chains, the boards rattle and clank noisily into place. All at once we see, abeam of us, a flash of silver as the cod-end breaks the surface; it floats because so many of the fish are swollen, almost to bursting, as their air-bladders (buoyancy chambers) are violently distended by being dragged up so quickly through zones of decreasing pressure. A little time before this and we would have seen but a few gulls circling the ship: now, drawn as if by magic from miles around, wheeling, excited, and screaming birds fill the air and repeatedly swoop down to peck at the fish through the meshes of the net.

The head-rope is drawn up and, after much clutching and heaving, the deck-hands pull sufficient of the trawl over the side to allow a rope to be passed around its middle; and now the 'cod-end', distended and heavy, is hoisted from the sea. It is swung in-board over a gently rolling deck which has been divided by low wooden partitions into 'pounds' to receive the fish; or, if our ship is a very modern one, they would be of gleaming aluminium. For a moment or two the huge bulging mass hangs, dripping and swaying, level with our eyes. What a sight it is! Through the netting, which is stretched to the utmost, stick out fins, spines, tails and gaping mouths, while here and there, large round eyes stare out in unexpected places to give the whole a queer and gruesome look. At the bottom of the bag is an opening tied up tightly with a special kind of knot; now an end of this is pulled, and, in a flash, an avalanche of fish cascades on to the deck. The great heap spreads sideways as its slippery components slide and slither in all directions, filling one pound and overflowing into others. Flapping, writhing and gasping, they form a stream of pitiable creatures in distress, but, before

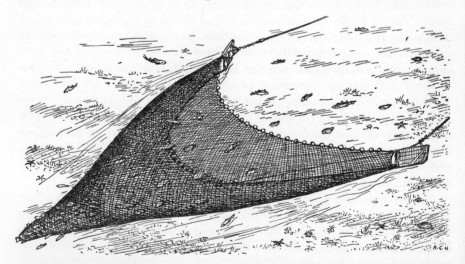

FIG. 1. The otter-trawl in action. For simplicity of illustration the older type is shown; usually today the otter boards are separated from the mouth of the trawl by long cables so that they would be out of the picture on either side—an arrangement shown in the sketch in Fig. 72 (p. 157).

FIG. I. *continued.*

long, they will be still, as they pass, with little bouts of quivering, into the fixity of death. Plate XIII (p. 162) shows the scene.

Many of the fish appear glistening white as they lie belly-upwards; but as many, top-side up, show the colours of a host of different kinds. Cod, haddock, whiting and coal-fish show green, grey, buff and black; here and there may be a striped or spotted cat-fish and, if our haul has been far enough to the north, we may get a few scarlet Norway haddocks (*Sebastes*), or 'soldiers' as the fishermen call them, or if further to the south perhaps a red gurnard. On the way up the trawl may have caught a herring and a mackerel or two to give a touch of blue or brighter green to the medley, or a male dragonet in courtship dress may flash with rainbow hues. Then there are the flatfish: dark brown plaice flecked with orange spots, speckled turbot and brill, smooth sand-coloured soles, or large skates and rays dappled with a bolder camouflage design; and there are some dogfish, of course. All these are in just one haul, perhaps more than two thousand fish.

In case I may be thought to exaggerate, let me give a few figures. I have recently returned (August 1956) from a three weeks' cruise in the new Scottish Fishery Research Ship *Explorer* whilst she was conducting, along with other work, a survey of the stocks of fish in the northern North Sea; using a standard trawl she made half-hour hauls at fourteen positions spread across the area lying between the north of Scotland, Shetland and the Norway deeps; and all the fish caught were measured and recorded. The smallest catch numbered 137 and the largest 1,244, while an average for the fourteen hauls was 536; this would mean an average of over 3,000 fish if the hauls had been of three hours' duration, as with a commercial trawler, instead of only half-an-hour. Now our trawl on the research ship had, for the purpose of special investigations, a small-mesh net fitted to its upper side to capture the younger fish escaping through its wider standard meshes; and this caught in addition to those just mentioned an average of 654 smaller fish, which

F&F—B

would amount to nearly 4,000 in three hours. These small fish are normally taken by a commercial trawl but, thanks to the new and wider regulation meshes, are now allowed to escape through the netting to grow up to a marketable size[1]; they must, however, be included in any estimate we are making of the richness of life in the sea.

As to variety, the different kinds of fish caught on our voyage in the *Explorer* numbered from eleven to nineteen species per haul. Plate 12 (p. 141) reproduces a watercolour sketch which I made of a small part of one of these trawl hauls as soon as it had been tipped on to the deck; I did a little re-arranging to get as many different fish into the one view as I could, but, apart from that, it is typical of the appearance of such a catch. Plates 13, 14 and 15 (pp. 194, 195 and 210) give further selections of North Sea fish from other grounds sampled on the same cruise; here the commoner species, such as cod, haddock and whiting, which would provide a general background similar to that in Plate 12, have been left out in order to show more clearly the form and colour of the more interesting kinds typical of the different areas; and some of the more characteristic invertebrate animals taken with them are also shown.

But now to return to the catch of our trawler; here, too, will be a profusion of other animals dragged up with the fish from the sea floor: perhaps rose-coloured anemones, crimson starfish, variegated brittle-stars, sea-urchins, hermit crabs in whelk shells, and buff and orange rock-lobsters, to mention only the more striking forms. If we could have sewn a small gauze net, like a butterfly-net, on the top of the trawl, as we did with Dr. Stanley Kemp on the old *Discovery*,[2] we should have caught hosts of small shrimp-like crustaceans (amphipods, cumaceans, copepods, etc. which were described in the previous volume). These swarm over the sea-bed like insects in a hayfield, swimming up in clouds as they are disturbed by the foot-rope of the trawl; they, too, must be added to our rough assessment of the sea's productivity, together with all the animals which, as we know from using a special kind of dredge, may be found burrowing below the surface of the bottom and so escaping the trawl.

Like the first volume, which dealt largely with the plankton, this second one is written as much for the general reader as the zoologist.

[1]To be strictly accurate and fair to the industry, I must qualify this statement slightly. *Some* of the fish caught in our small-mesh net would actually have been able to escape through the meshes of a trawl of the old type, for the meshes of our net were even finer than those normally used by a trawler of former days. Nevertheless the stock saved by the new regulations has been considerable.

[2]In this, Kemp told me, he followed a practice initiated by E. W. L. Holt who is referred to on P. 15.

It aims at giving, as far as possible, a non-technical account of the natural history of the fish and other more strange kinds of life which we see brought up in a trawl or dredge from the hidden world of the sea-floor; it will also deal with the fish which swim up nearer the surface, and with the whales and porpoises, and will include those rare vertebrate visitors to our seas from warmer or colder climes: turtles and the walrus. Again, as in the former volume, I will not try to present a detailed systematic account of all the animals one by one in turn; rather will I hope to sketch a broader picture of how the different kinds live and play their part in the various communities of this underwater world. The sea-bed varies widely in character and we find correspondingly different faunas as we pass from rock to gravel, or from sand to mud; but everywhere it is the wealth and variety of life that surprise us when first we see a dredge or trawl come up.

Is there anywhere on land, in our wild countryside, where life is so prolific?—where a net of similar span to our trawl could pick up so much animal life in a three-hours' sweep at walking pace? No, not even supposing that all the animals encountered were actually caught, unless perhaps in a very large sea-bird rookery—and we come back again to the unrivalled richness of the sea. For any naturalist who is a good sailor, a good mixer, and one who does not mind roughing it a bit, there can be no more rewarding experience than that of taking a trip on a trawler which is going to fish on one of the rougher trawling grounds where there will be a rich and varied fauna. For those who have not the opportunity or inclination for such a voyage, something of the same pleasure, only on a smaller scale, may be obtained in an hour or two with a simple naturalist's dredge used from a rowing or motor boat in the shallow waters off the coast; it is indeed surprising, as we shall presently see (p. 100), how many different kinds of animal may come up in a dredge of only two foot span, which has been on the bottom for but five minutes.

If we did not already know the answer, we might well ask why there was not a trace of plant-life, not a frond of seaweed, in the trawl. What at first sight appear to be feathery weeds, prove on closer examination to be animals having an extraordinarily plant-like form[1]. In the sea, light is so quickly absorbed by the water that, at the depth of some twenty fathoms, from which our trawl came, it is too dim to allow plants to grow. The sea-floor, at this and greater depths, is an entirely animal world, yet all its wealth of life must primarily depend for its support upon an even greater bulk of plants; in our first volume we saw how they form invisible pastures near the surface and, in

[1]See p. 95.

addition, provide a supply of food which is always sinking to nourish the animals below.

As in a magazine serial, I ended the earlier volume by saying that its theme would "*be continued in our next*"; so I shall introduce this volume by giving a short summary of the earlier plot and characters, to enable any reader, who has not yet read the former part, to have an impression of the whole. Those who already know the story may like to skip the next few paragraphs and go on again at the top of page 12; or, perhaps, they may be glad to have a brief résumé before proceeding to the rest. While this second volume is a continuation of the first, each, if the reader so desires, may be regarded as an entirely separate book.

The plants of the open sea are exceedingly small, so small that they can only be seen with a microscope. They are suspended in untold billions through the top ten fathoms or so where there is sufficient light for them to thrive and multiply. They are microscopic because their very smallness gives them a great advantage in the struggle for life. The smaller an object is, the larger is its surface area *in relation to its volume*. Relative to their body-mass these little plants have more surface, than have larger forms, for absorbing the rarer but essential mineral salts which may be in short supply. This higher proportion of surface to volume also means a greater frictional resistance to sinking and so helps them to keep up longer in the upper sunlit zone. Each is made up of but a single living unit or cell, and they are mainly either diatoms or flagellates. Many of the former are provided with fine spines like thistle-down to give them parachute support; the flagellates, on the other hand, are provided with little whip-like processes (flagella) which, when set in motion, act like helicopter rotors to keep them up. Fig. 2, opposite, is a sketch to give an impression of the variety of form to be seen in this vegetation when viewed through a microscope.

Feeding upon these little plants and, like them, scattered through the water, are vast numbers of tiny animals of many different kinds. There are hosts of shrimp-like crustaceans no bigger than the smallest insects, little snails which support themselves by flapping wing-like fins, swimming worms and many other even more unusual creatures. They are often so numerous that thousands may be collected by pulling a small tow-net—a conical net of fine silk gauze—through the water for only some five or ten minutes. All these little specks of life, plants and animals together, are known collectively as the *plankton*. This term, taken directly from the Greek word meaning 'that which is

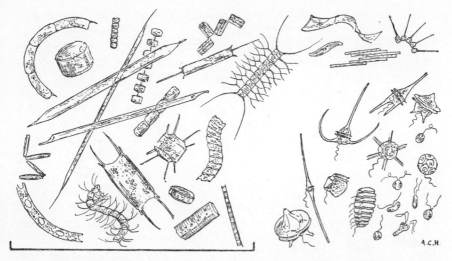

FIG. 2. The small plants of the plankton (phytoplankton) as seen through a microscope (magnified ×50). Flagellates of various kinds are shown in the group at the right-hand lower corner; all the rest are diatoms. They may be further identified by reference to Part 1 where they are all illustrated and named. The line below the diatoms represents 1/20th of an inch.

made to wander'[1] is used to denote this category of life which is passively carried along by the flow of ocean currents and tidal streams. It is convenient to have such a general term to distinguish all this drifting life on the one hand from the more active swimming creatures of the sea, the fish and whales, which can migrate at will against the currents, and, on the other, from the more sedentary animals living on the sea-bed. These two other categories, the swimmers and bottom dwellers, are sometimes given the collective terms of *nekton* and *benthos* respectively, to match the term plankton.

The animals of the plankton are not, like the plants, limited to the upper layers of the water. In addition to those which feed upon the plants are many others which prey upon these vegetarians, and yet others still more voracious which in turn devour these. Little medusae (miniature jelly-fish), comb-jellies, arrow-worms and many kinds of crustacea are the principal predators of the plankton; in this connection, we must also not forget the growing and hungry young fish which, before they are large and strong enough to swim against the currents, are carried along as part of this drifting community. The animal-life extends downwards, and there is, as we have seen, a continuous rain

[1]It is often translated as just 'wandering', but it really means more than this; see p. 5 of Part I.

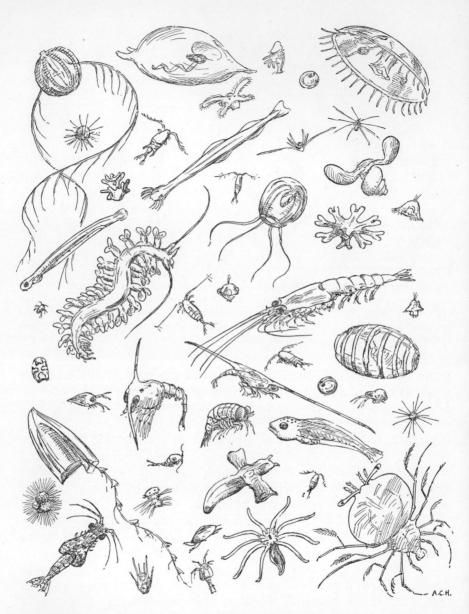

FIG. 3. A selection of animals from the plankton (zooplankton) magnified variously from 2 to 8 times. A sketch to show the range of form from protozoa to young fish; eleven different phyla (main divisions) of the animal kingdom are represented. The various members may readily be identified and named by referring to the illustrations in Part I.

of the dead and dying, from the world of little plants above, to nourish the creatures of the depths. Many plankton animals, both plant-eaters and predators, make extensive vertical migrations up from the lower to the surface layers at night and down again at dawn. Some idea of the great diversity found in the animal plankton is indicated in Fig. 3 opposite.

Many years ago I used the following illustration in a broadcast talk.[1] "If we look out of the window," I said, "at snowflakes falling through a fog we might imagine we were looking at the plankton through the porthole of a submarine coming up through the water. The snowflakes would represent the plankton animals and the fog would be the tiny plants, invisible as individuals but in their multitudes obscuring the clarity of the water. For the simile to be complete, I have suggested that the submarine must be rising—this because we must not suppose that all the plankton animals are falling like the snowflakes: some are moving hither and thither, but each—until it dies—has some means of preventing itself from sinking." Since then, I have sometimes wondered if, in using this illustration, I exaggerated the density of the plankton, for in truth I have never looked through the porthole of a submarine; indeed a typical submarine, I believe, has no such window. Now, however, I do know that the plankton can indeed look just like a snowstorm, for I have recently seen it on a viewing screen in the cabin of the *Calanus*, the research vessel of the Millport Marine Station, as Dr. Barnes's remarkable underwater television camera was suspended on a cable some two hundred feet below the ship. The 'snowflakes' went whirling across the screen and, every moment or so, one or two would come for a fraction of a second into focus and be recognised as members of one or another group of plankton animals. This wonderful invention now enables us not only to see the plankton in deep water but to watch the bottom-dwellers crawling over the sea-floor; more will be said later about underwater exploration with both television and photographic cameras (p. 139).

To summarise the natural economy of the sea in its simplest terms I will reproduce, in Fig. 4 overleaf, a diagrammatic sketch from the earlier volume. In the water near the surface we have all the conditions suitable for plant growth: sunlight, the gases oxygen and carbon dioxide dissolved into it from the atmosphere, and the necessary mineral salts, phosphates, nitrates etc., brought in from the land. The sea is indeed like a great culture medium, and the little plants of the plankton—called collectively the *phytoplankton* (Greek *phuton*, a

[1] I am quoting from the *Listener* of April 29, 1931.

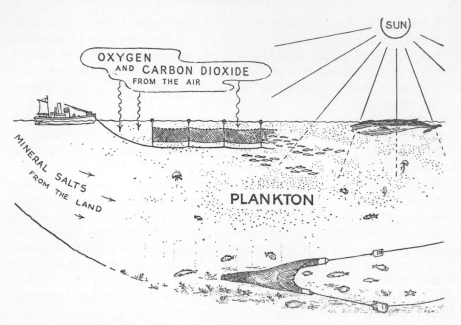

FIG. 4. A diagrammatic sketch illustrating the general economy of the sea, reproduced from Part I.

plant)—are spread through its upper layers; upon these, as we have just seen, graze the members of the animal plankton or *zooplankton* (Gk. *zoön*, an animal). Some fish, such as herring, sprat and mackerel, feed directly on the zooplankton, so also do the basking sharks and the still larger whalebone whales; the largest of these whales, the rorquals, such as the huge blue and fin whales, specialise in feeding upon the krill (euphausiacean shrimps) which, though large for plankton animals, are but an inch or so in length. From this teeming world of planktonic life there sinks the rich supply of nourishment to the animals on the sea-bed which are equipped with all manner of devices for collecting it; and these in turn not only support a host of worms, crustaceans, starfish and many less familiar creatures, but also form the food of the bottom-living fish that we have just seen brought up in such great variety. The entire wealth that man takes from the sea by trawling, or by letting out miles of drift nets for herring, or by harpooning the great whales for oil, is ultimately dependent upon the plankton for its production. We see how important is a study of this small drifting life for an understanding of the natural history of our fish and consequently in showing us some of the factors governing the success or failure of the fisheries.

The plankton is not always uniform in composition over long distances on end; it is often patchy in its distribution, continually varying both in quantity and kind. Here may be a dense production of the little plants and relatively few animals, while some five or ten miles away may be a great concentration of small crustacea which have grazed down the plants to relative paucity. As the ocean currents flow, the patterns of distribution change; areas of rich production and of scarcity are continually on the move. At one time the herring food may be concentrated in a belt against the coast, while next year at the same season it may be fifty or more miles to seaward; there may now be plenty of food suitable for the newly-hatched baby fish, but on the next such critical occasion there may be a shortage.

The world of plankton, quite apart from its economic interest, presents a fascinating field of study. In addition to those animals which spend all their days in this drifting community, there are many of the young stages of bottom-living animals (or larvae as they are called) which spend only a part of their life in the upper layers; this they do so as to spread the species far and wide by riding in the moving waters for a time. Many members of the plankton provide the phosphorescence of the sea whose biological meaning is still so much a mystery. Our former volume dealt with all this planktonic life in its many different aspects: its variety, patchiness, seasonal changes, vertical migrations, phosphorescence, and extension into the great depths; and it also dealt with the movement of the waters.

A knowledge of the ocean currents is, of course, very important in helping us to understand not only the distribution of the fishes' planktonic food, but also the drift of their floating eggs and newly-hatched fry. As our book proceeds we shall frequently have to consider these water movements, so that it will be well to reproduce here two of the charts from Part I for convenient reference: these are Figs. 5 and 6, showing respectively the general surface currents of the North Atlantic and, in more detail, those of the North Sea and English Channel. For an account of the measurement of these currents and for a discussion of their causes the former volume (Chapter 2) should be consulted; here we will just remind ourselves of the great influence, upon our coastal waters, of the warm Gulf Stream—or the North Atlantic Current as it is more correctly called on this side of the Atlantic. A stream of Atlantic water flows into the North Sea from the north and a lesser one enters via the Channel from the south; the relative strength of the two may vary from year to year and this may alter the pattern of swirls and eddies where they meet one another or where one impinges upon the irregularities of a coast.

To return to the present volume, we see that it deals with all the other life of the open sea which is dependent upon the plankton: the

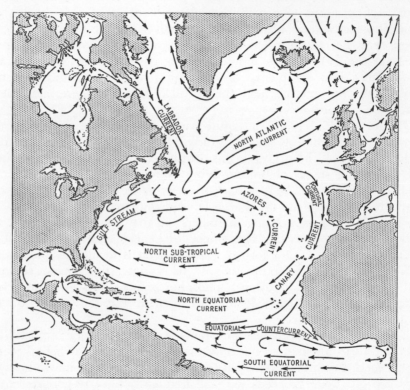

FIG. 5. The surface currents of the North Atlantic Ocean. Drawn with kind permission, from Admiralty chart No. 5310 (1949), omitting some of the detail, and reproduced from Part I.

nekton and benthos—or, in other words, the swimming fish and whales and the crawling or sedentary animals of the sea-bed. The squids and cuttlefish might indeed more logically be treated here, but they were in fact included in Part I with the deep-water fish because they were linked with the plankton in a general account of life in the ocean depths. Here, as our title shows, we shall deal also with the fisheries. Our fishermen now catch over a million tons of fish every year; man becomes a major predator and his activities, whether we regard him as part of wild nature or not, must certainly form a part of our natural history of the sea.

The recent expansion of the fisheries has indeed had a most profound influence upon the development of our young science of oceanography. It is well at the beginning of this second volume to

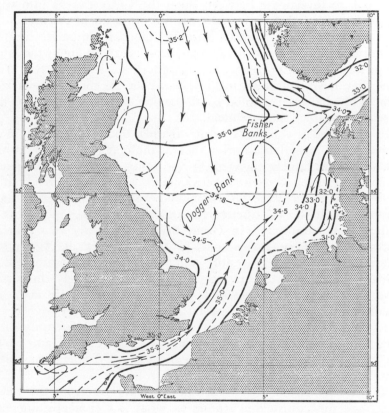

FIG. 6. The varying saltness (31·0‰ to 35·4‰) of the surface waters and the circulation typical of the North Sea in winter. From a chart kindly provided by Comd. J. R. Lumby of the Fisheries Laboratory, Lowestoft, and reproduced from Part I.

glance back again for a moment to see some of the circumstances which have given us such a notable increase in our knowledge of fish biology during the present century. The coming of steam-power and the larger and more efficient trawls led to some well-merited concern over the possible depletion of the stocks. The historic meeting of delegates from the European nations interested in fishing, called together in Stockholm by King Oscar II in 1899, led to the foundation of the International Council for the Exploration of the Sea, which came into being in 1901. The governments of all the countries represented agreed to appoint scientists and to equip research ships and laboratories to study the habits of the more important food-fish; they undertook to investigate between them the various areas into which they had divided the European Seas for purposes of research. The different nations work towards a unified plan of campaign and their naturalists meet every year to compare progress and plan for the future. Except for a temporary suspension of activities during the two World Wars, they have continued to the present day to show a remarkable example of what international co-operation can achieve when its aims are scientific rather than political.

In the earlier volume I wrote mainly about the work of the independent marine laboratories, such as those at Plymouth and Millport, which are largely engaged on researches concerning the general biological background to the fisheries. Here I shall say more about the investigations made by the government laboratories which are primarily concerned with the fish themselves and the problems more directly relating to the industry. In Great Britian there are two principal centres: the Fishery Laboratory of the Ministry of Agriculture, Fisheries and Food at Lowestoft, and the Marine Laboratory of the Scottish Home Department, Fisheries Division (formerly the Fishery Board for Scotland) at Aberdeen. They have both made many and splendid additions to the natural history of the open sea; rightly they have taken fishery investigations to include not only a study of the actual fish, but also of their environment, their planktonic and benthic food, and all the physical and chemical factors which may affect them.

At the back of all this work, and often forgotten by the general public, are the painstaking studies in what is technically known as taxonomy carried out in the great museums of the world; they are the essential researches into the true identity, classification and relationships of the myriads of species of fish and other animals dealt with by the naturalists. At South Kensington, behind the display galleries of the British Museum (Natural History) are labyrinths of laboratories: a hive of taxonomic scholarship.

Before the International Council was formed, interest in fishery research had already been developing in several countries. The outstanding pioneers abroad were C. G. J. Petersen, of Denmark, and Johan Hjort, of Norway; in this country they were T. W. Fulton in

Scotland, and Ernest W. L. Holt and Walter Garstang in England. Scotland was far ahead of England, for The Fishery Board for Scotland began its scientific investigations under Fulton[1] in 1882. The Government in England had no such scientific staff of its very own until 1908, a quarter of a century later; when the International Council began in 1902, the English Department commissioned the Marine Biological Association to carry out its share of the work. Actually the Association, which has always had its headquarters at its own famous Plymouth Laboratory, had already begun fishery investigations in the North Sea in 1892 when it appointed Ernest Holt to work on the fish landed at the Grimsby market; he made a brilliant start, initiating many new lines of enquiry, but, after only two years, the funds gave out and he went to Ireland to be Chief Inspector of Fisheries. However, with the Government support prompted by the birth of the International Council, the Association in 1902 established a new laboratory at Lowestoft under Walter Garstang and equipped it with a trawler which was rechristened the *Huxley*;[2] fishery research in England had at last come into its own and, six years later, the investigations were officially taken over by the Government—by the Board of Agriculture and Fisheries as it was then called. The greater part of our book will be concerned with the discoveries which have been won from the sea by these pioneer fishery naturalists of many countries and by those who have followed them to the present day.

The expression "won from the sea" is no exaggeration. The whole of the story I shall tell has been picked up fragment by fragment from an entirely hidden world and then put together like the pieces of a puzzle; and the picking up of the pieces has been by no means easy. Photographic and television cameras may help by giving us views of parts of the underwater world, and in the shallow water near the coast frogman equipment will enable us to see something of it for ourselves; but the greater part of the wide stretches of the sea which we must examine for our story can only be sampled by more indirect means. All the observations of the sea's temperature or saltness, at different depths as well as at different places, or of the composition of the plankton, or of the kind of animals on the sea-bed, have each to be sought for by sending down various pieces of equipment—thermometers, sampling bottles, nets or dredges—on wires or ropes dangling out of sight.

[1]Fulton's pioneer investigation of the current system of the North Sea by the use of drift bottles has been referred to in Part I (p. 15); in addition he made early studies on the fecundity, growth-rates and migrations of fish (1891, 1893).

[2]A fitting name, see p. 50.

The fishery naturalists are somewhat like marionette artists working blindfold; instead, however, of trying with puppets to play a story which they know, they are trying with gadgets to find out what kind of drama is being enacted on a stage they cannot see. The whole story I have to tell has gradually been unravelled by these very precarious means. Do we yet know which are its more important characters? The trouble is that it is really a complex of so many different plots linked together; the villain of one may be the hero of another. It is the working out of these hidden relationships that gives fishery research its peculiar fascination; but it is full of frustrations and disappointments.

The parts of the story we have secured have indeed often been gained against considerable odds. So often, when the naturalist has nearly succeeded in getting what he has been waiting for, the sea becomes lashed to fury as the gale rises. Can he use the nets just once more? Dare he risk the costly water-sampling bottles at one more position? No, the Captain knows better and has the final say; the ship must heave to or run for shelter. Two or three days of storm may pass before he can try again and then it may be too late; what he was looking for and had begun to find has gone—and it may now be a year or two before he can find it again. When it has all been told, we will return in the final chapter to say a little more about how the scientists and sailors have worked to give us our story.

Before I close this brief introduction I must mention one more outstanding event in the history of fishery research in our own islands: the setting up of the Development Commission by a special Act of Parliament in 1909. It was established to provide a body of Commissioners to recommend to the Treasury advances from a new Government Fund for the development of agriculture, rural industries and fisheries in Great Britain. At the end of the First World War the Commission appointed a committee of leading scientists interested in marine biology under the Chairmanship of the late Sir William Hardy[1] to advise on a comprehensive scheme of fisheries work; after a searching enquiry involving the examination of witnesses from all sides of the fishing industry, it recommended a considerable expansion of Government research and more support to the independent marine laboratories. It also recommended that a Scientific Advisory Committee on Fishery Research should be kept in being to meet from time to time to advise the Commission on the support to be given to different lines of enquiry. The vigorous growth of marine biology in Great Britain at both Government and independent laboratories is in

[1] The author regrets he cannot claim to be related to this great and far-seeing man.

large measure due to the splendid financial stimulus given by this Commission and their wisdom in basing the fishery investigations upon a broad foundation of fundamental research.

As I write this chapter (in 1956), Mr. E. H. E. Havelock, C.B., C.B.E., has just retired from the office of Secretary to the Development Commission; a special tribute should be paid to him in any history of our subject. He was Secretary of the famous 1919 Committee and ever since has served this great undertaking—but he has been far more than Secretary. With an amazing grasp of all that is going on in the different centres and with a sympathetic insight into the ways and feelings of scientists, he has helped forward research in his own special way. In the expenditure of public funds there must inevitably be all manner of regulations to safeguard against extravagance and waste. Those who have the drive and enthusiasm to do worthwhile research are just the men who are going to feel frustrated and discouraged if confined too closely within red-tape entanglements; the original creative scientist has much of the temperament of the artist. Havelock has been so outstanding because of his ability to combine his duties as a careful custodian with a real understanding of the researcher; he has devoted his life to helping scientists to give of their best by showing them how much they can do—with care and thought—within the official regulations and the resources available from time to time.

I must now delay no longer; having indicated the ground to be covered by this volume and linked it to the first, it only remains for me to outline its arrangement. It is convenient to consider the fish of the sea under two main headings according to their way of life: whether they are *pelagic* or *demersal* in habit. The pelagic fish are those like the herring, pilchard, mackerel or tunny, which spend much of their time in the upper layers of the water, feeding either upon the plankton or upon other smaller plankton-feeding fish; the demersal ones are those spending all or a greater part of their life close against the sea-bed, such as cod, haddock, plaice or skate, which feed mainly on the bottom-living animals. After a short chapter on fish in general, we shall begin with the pelagic species because, as just stated, they are associated more closely with the world of plankton which formed the subject of our previous volume; the herring and the herring fisheries will be treated first, to be followed by another chapter on the rest of the pelagic forms. We next go down to the sea-bed to explore its nature and fauna in preparation for several chapters devoted to the demersal fish and fisheries. Following this is a brief consideration of parasites and their place in marine life. Then, after a discussion of the over-fishing problem, we pass to the higher (zoologically speaking) vertebrates of the sea: to the turtles, to the whales and porpoises, to the walrus and to those strange stories in history of visitations to our islands of 'wild' fur-clad men in kayaks from the north. Lastly, having already dealt with man the fisher, we end by considering the way of life of the latest kind of mariners: the naturalists of the sea—the marine ecologists; and we take a brief look at the future.

CHAPTER 2

# ON FISH IN GENERAL

I N ORDER to have a good idea of fish as living animals and to appreci-
ate the differences between the various kinds we shall discuss, we must know something about their structure and how their bodies work. In this chapter I shall give a brief account of only the more important characters so as to save the general reader from continually having to refer to a text-book; later, if he wishes, he can go there for greater detail. The zoologist, who is familiar with the facts, is asked to pass on to the next chapter.

Fish, like all other animals with a jointed backbone (vertebrates), belong to that great division (phylum) of the animal kingdom called the Chordata; this name signifies that all its members have, at any rate at some time in their lives, a strong yet flexible rod (made up of cells of a rather special kind) called a notochord (Gk. *notos,* back; *chorde,* string), which extends down the length of the body and acts as a resilient skeleton. The name Chordata is zoologically preferable to the more usual and long-established one of Vertebrata because it enables us to include some creatures which are undoubtedly related to the vertebrates, yet are more primitive in that they have a notochord but no true 'backbone'. These include the curious sea-squirts or

*Plate 1.* TYPICAL PELAGIC FISH
1. Herring, *Clupea harengus* ($\times \frac{1}{3}$) Shetland. 2. Mackerel, *Scomber scombrus* ($\times \frac{1}{3}$) Shetland. 3. Garfish, *Belone belone* ($\times \frac{1}{6}$) North Shields. 4. Pilchard, *Sardina pilchardus,* ($\times \frac{1}{2}$) Mevagissey. 5. Thick-lipped grey mullet, *Mugil chelo,* ($\times \frac{1}{2}$) Plymouth. No. 5 was drawn from a living example in the Plymouth Aquarium and the others from freshly caught specimens.

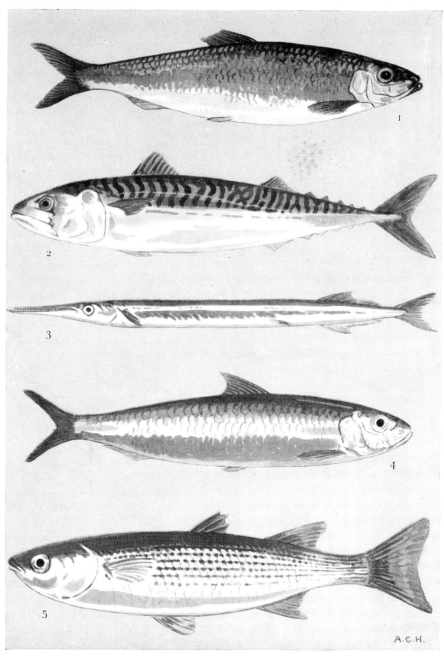

Plate 1

1

2

3

4

A.C.H.

*Plate 2*

ascidians (Tunicata), and the famous amphioxus or lancelet (*Branchio-stoma*) which we shall meet on the sea floor in a later chapter; the amphioxus has a notochord as its main supporting element throughout life, whereas the sea-squirts have one only as a transitory structure in their tadpole-like childhood. All the higher animals—from fish to mammals—start life with such a notochord, but then strengthen it with surrounding segments of cartilage (gristle) or bone to form the vertebral column or backbone; this, of course, is not just a single bone but a long series of connected vertebrae[1].

The most primitive fish-like animals are creatures which have never evolved jaws for biting, but have sucking mouths. These are the lampreys and hagfishes, belonging to the Class Cyclostomata (Gk. *kuklos*, a circle and *stoma, stomatos*, a mouth) so called because of the round mouth of the lamprey; they are mainly bottom-living creatures and will be dealt with later (p. 175). The true fish with jaws form the great Class Pisces (Latin, of course, for fishes) and this is divided into two main groups, those with skeletons of cartilage (the Chondrichthyes, Gk. *chondros*, gristle or cartilage and *ichthys*, fish) and those with bony skeletons (the Osteichthyes, *osteon*, bone). In this I follow the classification by that great authority on fish, the late Professor E. S. Goodrich[2]; for a study of fish anatomy his volume on *Cyclostomes and Fishes* (1909) in Lankester's *Treatise on Zoology* will remain an indispensable work for many years to come. The cartilaginous fish were once a much more varied and larger group than they are today; long ago three out of four subclasses became extinct, leaving us only the Elasmobranchii (*elasma, elasmos*, a thin plate; *branchia*, gills).[3]

[1]The development of these bony elements may constrict and, to a greater or less extent in different kinds, destroy and replace the original notochord.

[2]In its most recent expression it is to be found in his *Studies on the Structure and Development of Vertebrates* (1930).

[3]Because the bony fish, like all the higher vertebrates, begin life with a cartilaginous skeleton and then replace it by bone, it has usually been thought that the elasmobranchs have not advanced in evolution beyond an early cartilaginous stage; actually today we know that there were some much more primitive fish-like creatures—relatives of the cyclostomes but long since extinct—which had extensive

*Continued overleaf*

*Plate 2*. RARE AND UNUSUAL FISH IN BRITISH WATERS

1. Opah, *Lampris guttatus*, ($\times\frac{1}{10}$) Shetland, 1956. 2. Sea horse, *Hippocampus europaeus*, ($\times\frac{1}{2}$). 3. Red bandfish, *Cepola rubescens*, ($\times\frac{1}{3}$) Plymouth. 4. Rabbit-fish, *Chimaera monstrosa*, male ($\times\frac{1}{4}$) northern North Sea. Nos. 2 and 3 drawn from living examples in the aquaria of the London Zoological Society and the Plymouth laboratory respectively; No. 1 from a fresh specimen but kept for 24 hours in a deep freeze; and No. 4 from a freshly caught specimen.

F&F—C

Cartilage is a stiff glue-like substance having a bluish translucent appearance and is secreted by groups of separate cells which remain imprisoned within its matrix; it is fairly hard, yet can be cut with a knife, and, while it can withstand great pressure, it is apt to fracture if twisted. Bone, another organic substance (ossein), is much harder and stronger by being impregnated with phosphate and carbonate of calcium; it, too, is secreted by cells which remain imprisoned within it, but they keep connections with one another and with the blood supply of surrounding tissues by exceedingly fine canals running through the bone substance.

It is the long series of separate segments—bony or cartilaginous—linked together which gives the backbone of a fish the combined strength and flexibility of a chain. Its efficiency is much increased by the addition of spiny projections to each segment: usually above, and in the tail region below, and again at the sides, as ribs. These give extra support to the flesh and, acting as levers for the attachment of the muscles, play an important part in that beautiful locomotive action of the body which makes it 'swim like a fish'. Before, however, we come to their actual swimming, we must note some other general characters of fish in order to have a true picture of their form.

The shape of a fish is, of course, all-important in a fluid medium. While we see some remarkable exceptions in species which are specially adapted to unusual modes of life, as some in Plate 2 (p. 19), the typical form of the body is what we now generally call 'streamlined', as in most of the pelagic fish in Plate 1 (p. 18). The head end is usually more bluntly rounded than the hind end, which tends to taper gradually in section to the thin vane-like vertical tail. If we had not thought much about it, we might at first have imagined that a finely pointed front (like the exceptional gar-fish, also in Plate 1), to pierce and penetrate the water, would be better than a round and rather blunt one. However, the larger part of the resistance to be overcome in forcing an object through water is that due to the friction all over its surface; this is much greater if the surrounding water is thrown into turbulent eddies than if it flows smoothly past. The flow of water past bodies of different shape can be studied in tanks if the water-movements are made visible by suspended particles, as seen in the sketches in Fig. 7 opposite. In 7a a simple oblong gives, as might be expected, a big disturbance

armour-plating of bone, and so it is just possible that our cartilaginous fish may really be descended from a stock which once had bone but have since lost it. Without more fossils we cannot tell; among the true bony fish, however, we do see that the sturgeons have gone through just such a process; their skeletons are now mainly of cartilage with a few bony plates, but those of their ancestors were fully of bone.

on being forced through the water; so, however, and less expected, does quite a thin body, as 7*b*, whose front edge throws the water to right and left and produces numerous eddies down each side. In 7*c* with a slender pointed front we still notice something of such turbulence; whereas in 7*d*, which is the true streamline shape, we find the water passing over all its surface in smooth lines of flow which offer the very minimum of resistance. We now see how beautifully efficient is the form of a typical fish—the perfect adaptation brought about by long selection; those born with shapes tending to offer less resistance than others will rather more often win the race to capture a limited supply of food or to avoid becoming a meal for another.

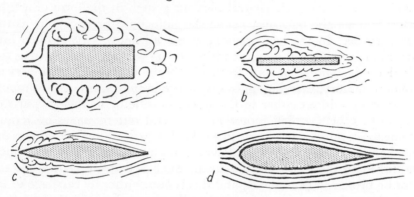

FIG. 7. Diagrams showing the relative disturbances in water caused by bodies of various shape moving through it towards the left: for further explanation see text.

Just as a torpedo or submarine has stabilizing fins, so has a fish. Apart from the vane-like tail (or caudal) fin, which, as we shall presently see, is really a propeller, there are other median fins (i.e. those in the mid-line of the body): the dorsal fin or fins on the back and the anal fin on the underside, behind the vent or anus. The anus, by the way, is never at the very end of the body, but always on the underside and in most species no more than half-way along it, (or, in a few, very much less); this post-anal extension of the body to form a tail region is typical of chordate animals as a whole. The dorsal fin may be long and continuous as in eels or more usually broken up into two or sometimes three separate fins: first, second and third dorsal; a few species, however, have only a single short one. The dorsal and anal fins act mainly as stabilizing vanes, particularly to prevent yawing. Most of what I shall say about fins is based upon the very interesting studies of the form and mechanisms of fins by Professor John Harris of Bristol; for a fuller treatment his excellent essay on the subject (1953) should be consulted.

In addition to those that are median, are the very important paired fins; primitively they were on the underside of the body—a pair of pectoral fins just behind the head and a second pair, the pelvic fins, further back but in front of the anus. These fins, of course, correspond to the paired fore and hind limbs of the later evolved terrestrial vertebrates. But before we discuss the function of these fins and their relation to swimming—and see them alter their positions in the course of evolution—we must first complete our outline sketch of the general form of a fish.

Unlike most invertebrate animals, such as worms or lobsters, which have their main nerve-chain running along the underside of the body, the chordates have their central nervous system in the form of a tube running along the back just above the notochord or backbone as the case may be. In the head region, as we all know, it is swollen into various lobes to form the brain; while down the body it is known as the spinal cord. Spreading out from the brain are the cranial nerves: some are sensory, carrying messages (nerve impulses) inwards to report changing conditions either in the world outside or in various parts of the body; others, called motor nerves, send out messages of action: signals to set muscles or glands to work. Likewise at intervals down the spinal cord stretch out the spinal nerves, both sensory and motor, which are linked to the brain via the cord. Such a delicate central system must be protected from shock, and this is done either by cartilage or by bony plates; in front a cranium or skull encases the brain as in a box, and down the back a series of curving buttresses, one from each side of every unit of the backbone, grow up and meet above to enclose the spinal cord within a sheltering tunnel of separate but usually closely placed arches which allow the spinal nerves to pass out between them.

Of special sense-organs, the fish have eyes of a typical vertebrate pattern, not unlike our own, and capable of being turned in different directions by a similar arrangement of muscles attached to the eyeballs; they differ, however, in their manner of focussing, moving the lens backwards and forwards instead of altering its curvature, and there is little, if any, iris adjustment. Some, if not all, at any rate of the higher bony fish, have well-developed colour-vision as is shown both by experiments on the behaviour of fish when presented with differently coloured models and by the frequent use of a wide range of colour-patterns in courtship display; compare, for example, the colours of the two sexes of the dragonet in Plate 3 (p. 34) and of the cuckoo wrasse in Plate 4 (p. 35).

Fish also have nostrils not unlike those of higher forms, ones which, in different kinds, open either in front of the mouth or up on the side

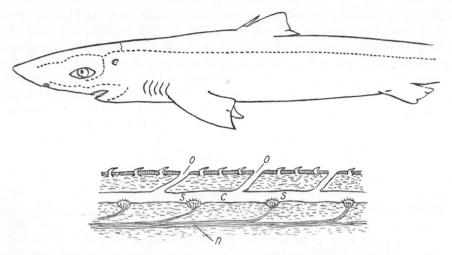

FIG. 8. *Above:* the lateral-line system of the piked dogfish (*Squalus*) shown in dotted line to represent the openings to the under-lying canal. *Below:* a diagram (redrawn from Goodrich, 1909) to show a small part of the canal in longitudinal section: *c*, main canal; *o*, openings to outside; *s*, sense organs; *n*, lateral-line nerve.

of the head. The sense of smell is, of course, just as important in water as it is in air, for the presence of food or enemies may be detected by the scent of very diffuse chemical traces. Some fish indeed hunt by scent more than by sight and have correspondingly larger smell-recording centres (olfactory lobes) in the brain. In addition to the organs of smell there are nerve-endings concerned with taste and these, in some fish, are not only, like ours, within the mouth, but on the out-side of the body as well; the whiting, for example, has been found to have taste-buds on its pectoral fins. What fun it would be if we could preserve our waist-line by tasting some of the delicacies of the table with just our fingers!

Without going into the finer details of structure, we must now consider some most remarkable sense-organs which are peculiar to fish (and the fish-like tadpole stages of frogs and other amphibia): the lateral line and associated organs. The main part of this system is usually clearly seen in both elasmobranch and bony fish as a line running along the middle of each side of the body from just behind the head to the tail; and over the head are similar lines which run in a fairly constant pattern as shown in Fig. 8 above. They are formed by series of separated groups of sensory cells arranged in these long rows. They are really in the outer layer of the skin, yet only in a most primitive and rare condition are they fully exposed on the surface; more often they are sunk in a groove for protection or, as is most usual, they are still more sheltered by the groove closing over to become a tunnel or tube which only connects with the outside water by a series of openings at intervals. Now these cells each have a little sensory hair-like process projecting into the water and each group of such cells is on a slightly raised cone; they form sense organs for detecting movements and vibrations in the water outside and are served by sensory branches of certain of the cranial nerves which run along beneath them.

We may not yet know all the functions of the lateral line system, but it has been conclusively shown by the experiments and observations of a number of physiologists that these organs do give nervous responses to changes of water flow down the sides of the fish, to jets of water projected against it and to disturbances in the water caused by vibrating objects such as glass rods etc. in its vicinity. Clearly they are organs of the utmost importance in an aquatic animal like a fish for registering the changes in its surrounding medium: vibrations or movements which may inform the animal of the presence of obstacles or the approach of enemies or prey; they may also perhaps act as speed-ometers for the fish by recording changes in the rate of water-flow past it. The patterns of the canals over the sides of the face may well be concerned with informing the fish of the exact position of small prey in front of it, for example, by recording the relative strength of the vibrations received on the two sides of the head from some swimming crustacean. These canals are greatly developed on the heads of plankton-feeding fish such as the herring.[1] In the bony fish, where the lateral line system is more highly developed than in the elasmobranchs, the canal is threaded through the overlapping scales down the sides of the body and the pores to the outside also pass through them; this is actually brought about, of course, by the scales being formed around the canal system as the young fish develops. In our first volume, in Plate 24, (p. 253) I figured the remarkable lateral line organs of the deep-water fish *Saccopharynx johnsoni* which stand out on stalks down either side of the body, most likely for the better detection of prey in the food-scarce regions of the abyss.

The sensory cells of the lateral line are similar to those in the semi-circular canal systems which, in the ears of fish and all higher verte-brates, act as organs of balance in giving a sense of orientation in the

[1]A remarkable method of detecting objects has recently been discovered by Dr. Lissmann in certain African fishes (*Gymnarchus*) which inhabit thick muddy rivers of the Gold Coast where eyes are of little use. These fish continually send out small electric impulses so that, when approaching any object, the electric field is altered and, in some way not understood, they become aware of it; they have indeed evolved a kind of radar to replace vision in a constantly foggy environment.

three dimensions of space. Indeed, there can be no doubt that our own ears, both as organs of hearing and equilibrium, have evolved, like those of the fish themselves, by the complete enclosure of these external sense-organs which were once concerned with detecting disturbances in the water surrounding our (and their) far-off aquatic ancestors. Our sense of orientation which enables us to adjust our equilibrium, is of course achieved by the sensory cells registering the flow of the fluid in the different semi-circular canals[1] as the body turns in various directions; as the curved canals turn, the fluid in them tends to lag behind and thus flow in relation to the moving sense cells. In the ears of fish there are also calcareous stone-like bodies, the otoliths; these, like some of the otocysts of invertebrate animals, by pressing against nerve-endings, give their owners information as to the direction of gravity. Further, the ears of fish, whilst not having a cochlea like ourselves and other mammals, have been shown to be sensitive to sound waves; they are, in fact, definite organs of hearing. Sound waves are, of course, nothing more than particular kinds of vibrations in either air or water; with us the vibrations in the air, having been picked up by a receiving ear-drum, have to be transmitted by a series of linked bones, to the capsule of the inner ear before we can sense them, like a fish, by detecting the vibrating fluid within.

Some of the bony fish like the carps and their relatives have a remarkable chain of bones, analogous to those of our ears but quite different in origin—the Weberian ossicles evolved from parts of vertebrae—connecting the air bladder, which will be described shortly (p. 29), to the inner ear; this is an amazing device for sound detection, for it is now known that such air-bladders act as sound amplifiers in a fluid medium; in the war microphones were towed in submerged hollow torpedo-like bodies for the better detection of submarines.

Space will only permit the very briefest reference to yet another set of sense-organs associated with the lateral line system: the sensory ampullae (of Lorenzini) found on the heads of elasmobranch fish in addition to the lateral line canals. They are little canals filled with jelly and provided with sensory cells. Their function is by no means certain; but there is some experimental (physiological) evidence to suggest that they are concerned with registering temperature changes in the water.[2] In such a slight introduction as this I have not been

[1]At right-angles to one another in the three planes of space.
[2]Since this was written R. W. Murray has described some experiments (again physiological ones with isolated ampullae and nerve fibres) which suggest that these ampullae may detect pressure changes due to approaching obstacles: *Nature, 179*, p. 106, 1957. There is as yet no evidence from behaviour studies with normal fish that either of these suggested functions is the true one.

able to quote the many authorities and experimenters concerned with the investigation of these various organs; for the most recent account, with references to all the important work, I would refer the reader to the excellent chapter on these (acoustico-lateralis) organs of the ear and lateral line systems written by Professor Otto Lowenstein for the second volume of the new book *The Physiology of Fishes* (edited M. E. Brown, 1957) to which I refer on p. 35. He, of course, has done so much of the pioneer experimental work on the labyrinth of the ear; I am most grateful to him for allowing me to read his chapter before publication.

The mouth of a fish opens, as we all know, either at the very front or, like a shark's, on the underside of the head. The gill-slits—an essential fish character[1]—are openings at each side leading from the back of the mouth cavity to the outside world; as their name implies, they are concerned with respiration. Water taken in by the mouth is forced out through these slits and its dissolved oxygen is taken up by the blood flowing in the fine and thin-walled gill-filaments or plates which line their sides. The heart, lying in a cavity below the gullet, pumps the blood forwards, up to the gills and so (after picking up the oxygen) onwards via the arteries to all parts of the body—and then back again by the veins to complete the circulation.

If a very active creature carried about bits of delicate apparatus in pockets like our own, such objects would soon be smashed to pieces. If, however, they were carried in closed internal pockets, entirely filled with fluid, they would then be cushioned by the liquid and carried in safety; they would be carried just as we may carry fragile glass tubes in our pocket if we first cork them up in a strong jar entirely filled with water. While it is not within the scope of this book to go into the intricacies of internal anatomy, I must just mention what we may call the main body cavity, or coelom (Gk. *koiloma*, a hollow), which serves this very purpose in all vertebrates and in some invertebrate animals as well.[2] It is a cavity, filled with fluid, surrounding the alimentary canal—i.e. between it and the main muscular body wall—and so protecting both the canal and its appendages like the liver and pancreas; the reproductive organs are also there, while, in a special similar pocket of its own, lies the heart. The drawings in Fig. 9, opposite, summarise in diagram form the general anatomical

[1]They are, indeed, a fundamental chordate character; all the higher terrestrial vertebrates which no longer breathe by gills have transitory gill-slits in their early stages of development.

[2]These are called by zoologists coelomate animals to distinguish them from animals without such cavities. Some animals, like insects and lobsters, have large blood spaces which are not true coeloms, but have similar functions.

features of the typical fish that we have so far discussed. Let us now consider how it swims.

Both cartilaginous and bony fish are beautifully adapted for swimming and, with the exception of some specialized types, both employ the same main method of propulsion. The bony fish, however, have in the course of evolution developed some notable advances in

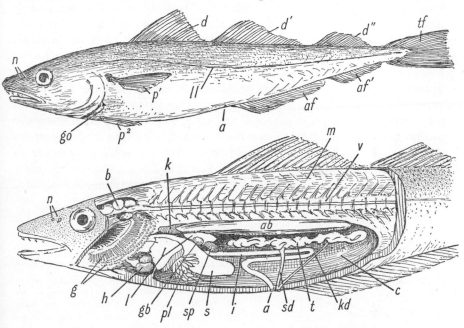

FIG. 9. The whiting (*Gadus merlangus*) as an example of a typical bony fish, with a sketch of a dissection from the left side to show the principal internal organs with the large left lobe of the liver cut away: *a*, anus; *ab*, air bladder; *af*, *af'*, anal fins; *b*, brain; *c*, coelom or main body cavity; *d*, *d'*, *d''*, dorsal fins; *g*, gills; *gb*, gall bladder; *go*, gill opening; *h*, heart; *i*, intestine; *k*, kidney; *kd*, kidney duct; *l*, liver; *ll*, lateral line; *m*, muscles; *n*, nasal openings; $p^1$, $p^2$, pectoral and pelvic fins; *pl*, pyloric caeca; *s*, stomach; *sd*, sperm duct; *sp*, spleen; *t*, testis; *tf*, tail fin; *v*, vertebrae.

their hydrostatic qualities which make them more efficient as compared with the elasmobranchs. But let us begin first with the propulsive mechanism. The main muscles of the body are divided into the vast number of segments from head to tail which are so familiar to us on our breakfast plates. The nerves issuing from the spinal cord pass out in a series exactly corresponding to their segmental muscles and control their working. Waves of contraction and expansion of these muscle-units pass down the body in such a way that those on one side are 'out of step' with those on the other; at one point the muscles on the right are contracted and those on the left relaxed, while further towards the tail they are just the opposite. Thus, in an elongated fish like an eel, the body is thrown into a series of sideways undulations which travel backwards. As the undulations pass along, the flanks of the fish press at an angle to the water right and left; this action, like that of the inclined blade of a propeller turning at right-angles to its axis, thrusts the water backwards and so drives the body, like the propeller, forwards. Now such a long sinuous kind of creature as an eel, or the red band-fish seen in Plate 2 (p. 19), is not typical of the form of a modern fish, but I have taken it to introduce the swimming action for two reasons. Firstly, because it is almost certainly the earlier type as seen in the long eel-like lampreys and hag-fish and the much more primitive amphioxus; and secondly, because the passing of the undulations down the body can be so readily seen and understood, as shown in the sketches in Fig. 10 below  We see similar undulations passing down the body of a swimming flat-fish, like a plaice or flounder, but here the body is turned over into the horizontal plane.

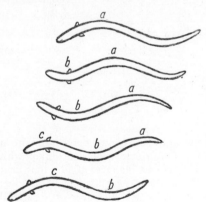

FIG. 10. A diagram showing the successive stages in the swimming of an eel-like fish: waves of curvature *a, b, c,* etc. pass down the body from head to tail and, by their backwardly directed inclined surfaces pressing against the water, drive the body forwards.

In the more typical modern fish the main part of the body, although curving slightly to right and left, is kept relatively straight and the tail region, with its vane-like vertical fin, is swept violently from side to side. The body is more rigid and the tail more flexible and the muscular contractions, while of the same kind as before, are more powerfully developed towards the tail end. The fish is now much more like a ship—like a submarine in fact—with its propeller at the stern; its propeller, however, is an oscillating one and not a rotary screw, but its effect, like the right and left movements of the body in the former example, is just the same. Nature, of course, has never yet produced a wheel or a rotary propeller as an actual part of an organism; the task of supplying a freely rotating, yet living, part with nourishment has proved too difficult for evolution. A comparison between a rotary screw and an oscillating propeller such as a fish's tail-region is shown in the diagram in Fig. 11 below.

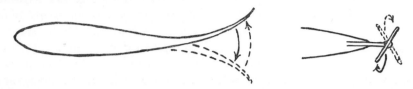

FIG. 11. A diagrammatic comparison of the tail of a fish (an oscillating propeller) and the screw of a ship (a rotary propeller); in both it is the inclined surfaces which press against the water and thrust the body forwards.

In the rotary screw, the blades on opposite sides are going in opposite directions, as regards right and left, as the shaft turns, and so any sideways thrust on the hull of a boat is cancelled out; a single-bladed oscillating propeller, however, like a single oar when skulling a boat from over the stern, will cause the boat to yaw a little from side to side. The size and weight of the boat in relation to that of the oar prevents this from being very marked. It is the same with the modern fish whose tail is relatively small compared with the bulk of the body which, being long and flat, is not easily pushed sideways—and the median fins help in this; further, the body is not rigid like a boat and the head region, as already noted, does flex slightly from side to side to compensate. Professor Sir James Gray, of Cambridge, has made a thorough experimental study of the mechanics of the swimming of fish, as indeed of nearly all forms of animal locomotion; in addition to his more detailed papers, he has brought together his conclusions in two general essays: in 'The Locomotion of Fish' in *Essays in Marine Biology* (1953a) and in the same year in his delightful Royal Institution Christmas Lectures *How Animals Move* (1953b) which being 'delivered to a juvenile audience' are excellent for those who want a simple non-technical account.

Now we must note an important difference between the modern bony fish and the cartilaginous elasmobranchs which affects their swimming; this is the presence of an air-bladder in most of the former and its absence in the others. This air-bladder—sometimes called the swim-bladder—is formed, in development, as a pouch separated off from the alimentary canal; in some fish it retains a connection with the gut, but in others this is lost. It is generally believed that the air-bladder was originally evolved as a lung to assist in breathing when in water of low oxygen-content; we know that this was so in the true lung-fish whose extinct relatives gave rise to the air-breathing amphibia and so to the conquest of the land and to the evolution of all the higher forms. That was, of course, in the far-off palaeozoic days of some three hundred million years ago. The lung-fish today are as much "living fossils" as the famous coelacanth; they are remnants of an equally ancient stock and are now only found in the fresh-water swamps and rivers of Africa, South America and Australia.

Once such an air-bladder came into existence, it could be used as a buoyancy chamber in addition to serving as a lung. While some of the fish with lungs developed the greater use of these organs for breathing air, others, having left the areas poor in oxygen (and so being able once again to breathe quite well with their gills) turned their lungs into hydrostatic organs with great effect.[1] The form of these air-bladders varies but most bony fish are provided with means of controlling their buoyancy; they have glands for the production of more gas, if required, and also either valves for its release or opening and closing vascular areas for its absorption back into the bloodstream, if there should be too much. Their air-bladders serve, in fact, like the trimming tanks of submarines.

The cartilaginous fish, or elasmobranchs (the sharks, dogfish, skates and rays), which have never evolved an air-bladder, have to move up and down in the water without such a desirable aid, and so we see certain special features in their design. The tail, with the backbone and its associated propulsive muscles, curves up towards the tip carrying the tail-fins above the line of progression, and the fin-lobe below the tip is more developed than that above; this has the effect, so beautifully demonstrated by Professor Harris (1936) in his models and experiments, of raising the tail as well as propelling the fish forwards. This keeps the front of the fish down and enables it to explore the bottom for food more easily; but to counter this tendency there are the paired fins (pectoral and pelvic) spread out on either side as planes to act as elevators to lift the fish when it wants to rise. The body is only slightly heavier than the water it displaces so it takes but a little force to raise it and the planes can be small; it is, in fact, more like an underwater aeroplane than a submarine. This principle of the raised tail and the arrangement of the fins in the elasmobranch fish are shown in the diagram in Fig. 12, opposite. The skates and rays have

---

[1]In all such phrases I am speaking metaphorically for simplicity; I mean, of course, that those with lungs which varied in the direction of more efficient hydro-static organs have been continually favoured by natural selection.

their paired fins enormously developed, and not only as great supporting surfaces like wings; they actually use them as swimming organs by
throwing them into horizontal undulations. These fish, however, we
shall discuss later in Chapter 9, (p. 181).

The bony fish, with their controllable buoyancy-chambers, have
greatly modified the form of their fins. The upturned and asymmetrical
tail of the elasmobranch type, which was also that of the primitive bony

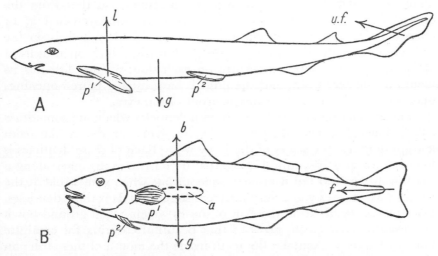

FIG. 12. A comparison of the hydrostatic qualities of an elasmobranch fish, such as
a dogfish or shark in A, and those of a teleost fish, such as a cod, in B. In each,
$g$, marks the centre of gravity. In A gravity is overcome by the lift $l$ of the paired
fins $p^1$ in front and by an upward and forward thrust $u.f.$ of the tail. In B the
buoyant force $b$ of the air-bladder $a$ counteracts gravity and the symmetrical tail
now gives an entirely forward thrust $f$.

fish, has become converted into one vertically symmetrical about the
mid-line of the fish. Actually if you look very carefully you will see the
tip of the backbone is still bent up towards the top of the tail as shown
in Fig. 13 overleaf—an interesting piece of evidence of past evolution;
and the lower lobe of the fin, now pointing straight backwards, is so
modified as to give every external appearance of full symmetry. The
paired fins are now used less as elevators and more as lateral stability
planes, or even as brakes; they tend in the course of evolution to move
up the sides of the body nearer the centre of gravity and pressure, so
as to avoid tilting the fish when braking. The pelvic fins also tend to
be shifted forwards and close to the pectorals or sometimes have even
moved in front of them, as in the cod and its relatives. Such a fin

arrangement is seen compared with that of the elasmobranch in Fig. 12.

Leaving the subject of swimming, we may now briefly note a few other characteristic differences between the two main categories of fish. The elasmobranchs show all their gill-clefts—typically five in number—emerging on either side of the back of the head; in contrast, the bony fish have their gills, with their separate clefts, all covered by a single large protecting flap, the gill-cover or operculum, so that from the outside we only see one opening. The two are compared in Fig. 14 opposite. The mouth of an elasmobranch, as already noted, is on the undersurface of the head, and so are the nostrils, which open in front of the mouth by a single aperture on each side; a bony fish has its mouth at the very front, and the nostrils have usually paired openings upon either side of the face just in front of the eyes.

The elasmobranchs are covered with denticles which are sometimes called 'placoid scales'; they are, however, ivory structures like teeth and quite unlike the scales of the bony fish. Each of these denticles is like a sharp spine pointing backwards; if you run your finger along a shark from head to tail it appears smooth but when you 'stroke it the wrong way' it gives you a very different sensation. It is these denticles, placed close together, on the skin of sharks which, when ground down and usually dyed green, gives us that beautiful covering for cigarette boxes—shagreen. Actually the teeth inside the mouth of these fish can be shown to be nothing more than just such denticles which are, however, often enlarged and altered in shape; they come to be there

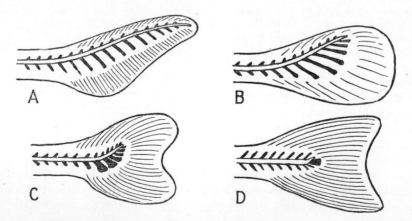

FIG. 13. Diagrams representing stages in the evolution of the symmetrical tail of a modern teleost (bony) fish, as shown in D, from the more primitive type similar to that of an elasmobranch fish, as shown in A. For further explanation see text.

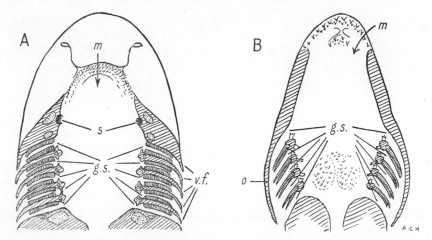

FIG. 14. Diagrammatic horizontal sections through the mouth *m* and gill slits *g.s.*, of, A, the dogfish, an elasmobranch and, B, the whiting, a teleost fish. Water enters by the mouth (and in most elasmobranchs also by the spiracle *s*) as the mouth cavity enlarges (in A by lowering floor and in B by pushing out sides); with the mouth closed and its cavity reduced (by the reverse process) the water is driven out between the gills which take up dissolved oxygen in respiration. Note the external valvular flaps *v.f.* (one to each gill slit) in A and the single opercular flap *o* in B.

because the outer skin is tucked into the mouth to form its lining in front. In fact the teeth of all higher vertebrates, ourselves included, have been evolved from the denticles, which once formed a protective covering over the bodies of our far-off early fishy ancestors. Who knows?—perhaps the frogman vogue and the craze for new underwater equipment will lead suppliers to provide our aquarists, in shark-infested waters, with skin-tight chain armour of plastic artificial teeth and we shall at one stroke, step (or slip) back some two or three hundred million years. In the bony fish the teeth in the mouth have become fixed to the jaw. In the elasmobranchs, however, they are still simply embedded in the gums, and in many they may be continually replaced, as they wear out, by new ones growing outwards in a fold of skin.

The scales of the modern bony fish, which appear to cover the outside of the body like overlapping slates on the roof of a house, are extremely thin plates of bony material,[1] quite different from denticles,

[1]It is material like bone, but too thin to have the bone cells actually enclosed within it as in typical bone. These scales first appear in evolutionary history in some of the ancient and extinct fossil fish as bone-like plates which developed underneath groups of denticles and, by fusing with them, formed composite scales; in the modern bony fish, however, all trace of the layer of denticles has been lost, leaving just the thin bone-like scales.

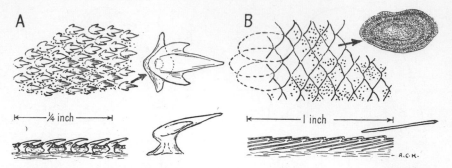

FIG. 15. A comparison between the denticles (placoid scales) of an elasmobranch (the dogfish), A, and the scales of a teleost fish (the cod) B; they are seen in surface view above and in section below, and one of each is shown enlarged.

and are not strictly on the outside of the body at all. They are covered by a thin layer of transparent skin which we do not realize is there till we look carefully with a lens; while they do overlap one another very like slates, each scale is really enclosed in a little pocket of tissue so that one scale does not rest upon the one next to it as slates do. Scales and denticles are compared above in Fig. 15.

Let us mention just one more character which distinguishes these two groups, before passing on to discuss the various examples in our waters. As a general rule the bony fish lay eggs which are fertilized by the male's sperm in the sea outside the body; in the sharks and rays fertilization is internal, and the males are provided with so-called 'claspers'—extensions of the pelvic fins which are not really used for clasping the female, as has often been supposed, but as intromittent organs. The male dogfish holds the female by coiling his body around her, as shown in Dr. Wilson's excellent photograph on Plate XV, (p. 178). In correlation with their internal fertilization most elasmobranchs are either viviparous or lay large yolky eggs enclosed in those familiar horny envelopes, known popularly as mermaid's purses when they are found washed up on the beach (See Fig. 84, p. 180).

In ending this brief sketch of fish in general it is seen that I have deliberately omitted any account of their internal mechanism: the

---

*Plate 3.* More Fish of Striking Appearance

1. John Dory, *Zeus faber*, ($\times \frac{1}{2}$). 2. Boar-fish, *Capros aper*, ($\times \frac{1}{2}$). 3. Reticulate dragonet, *Callionymus reticulatus*, ($\times \frac{1}{2}$) male in courtship display. 4. Common dragonet, *Callionymus lyra*, ($\times \frac{1}{2}$): *a*, male in courtship display; *b*, female. 5. Leopard-spotted goby, *Gobius forsteri*, ($\times \frac{1}{2}$): a new species only just described (see p. 212). All drawn from living specimens in the Plymouth Aquarium.

1

2

3

4a

4b

5

A.C.H.

*Plate 3*

1a

1b

2

3

A.C.H.

*Plate 4*

physiology of their digestion, excretion, osmotic regulation, reproduction, the working and influence of their ductless glands and so on. All this I have felt to lie outside the scope of our volume, which is concerned with the natural history of our animals in relation to their various habitats and fellow creatures in the sea. I must also add that I am myself no physiologist and had there been space for such treatment all I would have put in would have been very second-hand. Fortunately, there has recently been published a two-volume work, the first of its kind, which deals entirely with its title subject, *The Physiology of Fishes*, and fills a big gap in the literature; it is written by experts from all over the world and edited by Dr. Margaret Brown (1957)—now Mrs. G. C. Varley—who has done so much work herself on the growth of fish.

CHAPTER 3

# THE HERRING AND THE HERRING FISHERIES

THE herring *Clupea harengus,* must surely be our most plentiful fish. So important is it in the life of our seas that I give it pride of place and a chapter to itself; its near relatives, the sprat and pilchard, will be dealt with among the other pelagic fish (p. 83). We all know a herring by sight: a creature beautifully adapted for living in the upper water layers. Its blue-green back matches the colour of the depths when viewed from above and its silver flanks, seen from the side or below, mirror the varying lights and shades of the surrounding waters.[1] The herring is shown in Plates 1 and I (p. 18 and 50).

[1]In his recent book, referred to on p. 67, Dr. Hodgson (1957) tells of observations on an actual change in the colour of the back of the herring when moved from one background to another; when swimming in an oak tub they were a golden-brown colour, but when transferred to a zinc bath they became grey-green.

*Plate 4.* COLOURFUL FISH FROM THE ENGLISH CHANNEL
1. Cuckoo Wrasse, *Labrus ossifagus,* ($\times \frac{1}{2}$) male *a,* in bright courtship colours, and female *b.* 2. Comber, *Serranus cabrilla,* ($\times \frac{1}{2}$). 3. Red mullet, *Mullus surmuletus* ($\times \frac{1}{2}$). All drawn from living specimens in the Plymouth Aquarium.

When any fish gives rise to a considerable fishery, that fishery not only becomes a part of the sea's ecology but may well serve as a good starting point for our study of the fish itself. I believe this applies to the herring; only when we realise the magnitude of its fisheries will we appreciate its true position among the other inhabitants of our seas.

Just as the various fish may be separated into two categories according to their manner of living, so is the fishing industry itself divided into two main branches: the drift-net fisheries for pelagic fish and the trawl fisheries for demersal fish. The little steam or motor vessels which pour out of Yarmouth and Lowestoft nearly every day in the autumn, off to the herring grounds for the night, are not trawlers—in spite of what our leading newspapers often call them—they are drifters.[1] A trawler, as we know, drags a large bag-like net over the sea-bed; a drifter, on the other hand, does not steam forward as it fishes—it just drifts, with the tide and wind, pulling on the end of a long line of nets which it has laid in the water hanging from a row of floats. The drift-nets hang vertically like so many very large and deep tennis-nets placed end to end to form a continuous wall of netting stretching for one, two or occasionally nearly three miles from end to end. Each net is about 50 feet from top to bottom and some 50 yards in length. They are tied by their upper corners to ropes—the strops—coming down from the floats above; and are kept vertical by seizing ropes fastening their lower corners to the heavy cable or 'warp' which hangs below and weights them down. The top of each net, which is about six feet below the surface, is kept up by a line of small corks. When the drifter has 'shot' its 'fleet' of nets, steaming slowly down-wind in the process, she stops her engine as the last net goes overboard, hoists her mizzen sail and swings round to face up wind; she now just drifts, pulling all the time on the long warp and so keeping the nets in a straight line. Fig. 16, p. 38 shows a drifter fishing, and if you look on page 57 you will see the other end of its fleet of nets; imagine the drawing continued across all the pages in between and you will have an idea of the length of an ordinary fleet of herring nets—usually about 80 nets make up a 'fleet'. So the little drifter rides through the night like a seagull asleep; and in the darkness the herring, swimming up in dense shoals towards the surface, strike the nets. The meshes of the nets are just wide enough to allow an adult herring to go so far in, but no further; when it tries to wriggle backwards, it is held by the

---

[1]Similarly the vessels called trawlers in the caption below the excellent photograph forming Plate XX (p. 235) of the New Naturalist volume *Climate and the British Scene* are actually typical steam drifters; the picture was obviously included there to show the weather conditions and not the fishing craft.

threads of the mesh catching under its gill-covers and there it hangs till it and thousands more are drawn out of the water with the nets in the early morning.

Let us imagine for a moment that we are now aboard a drifter in the autumn herring-fishing, that it is two o'clock in the morning and we have just been roused up to haul the nets. We left Lowestoft yesterday afternoon, one of a fleet of such craft steaming out to the fishing grounds some thirty miles from the coast; they are trim little vessels, these drifters, each with a gaily painted funnel, a picturesque name such as *Silver Spray, Herring Queen* or *Violet and Rose* painted in gold letters on the bows, and the foremast lowered backwards to rest on the wheelhouse to reduce wind resistance. We 'shot' our nets just before dusk and have been lying all night, a fleet of close on five hundred vessels drifting with the tide. It is still quite dark and all around us are the twinkling lights of the other craft—not only Yarmouth and Lowestoft men, but a multitude of Scotsmen from Wick, Banff and Peterhead, visiting these ports for the fishery, and Dutchmen and Frenchmen too. I write of my impressions of more than twenty years ago; today the steam drifters are mostly being replaced by motor vessels which lack the sprightly funnels, and since the last war there has been a sad falling off in the number of drifters fishing, as I shall later explain.

We are now beginning to haul and we shall see how the fish have been caught in these very simple nets. I know of no sight in all industry to equal that of the hauling of the herring nets unless it be the running of molten metal in the foundry. The ship is rolling gently; and the fishing-lantern slung from the mast swings to and fro, so that all the shadows sway. One of the deck-hands winds in the warp on the steam capstan, and the rest of us are at work on the nets, hauling them in over a roller on the side of the ship. If the catch is a good one, the nets will come up laden with fish hanging in the meshes—a mass of glistening, quivering silver. If we are lucky, too, we may see the nets as they leave the water ablaze with green fire—the phosphorescence of the sea. Once aboard, each net is shaken so that the meshes are pulled open, and the herrings either fly upward or fall down from the net according to the way they are facing. There is the rich smell of sodden netting; and as each net is shaken, the air is filled with fluttering silver scales, glittering in the lamp-light, like a shower of tinsel. The deck is piled with fish, which from time to time are shovelled through circular openings to the holds below. They have indeed been caught in thousands; a good catch may be anything from 50 to 100 crans, and a cran is a volume measure of roughly a thousand fish

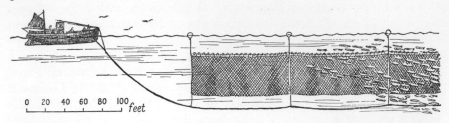

0 20 40 60 80 100 *feet*

FIG. 16. A sketch of a motor drifter lying drifting with her 'fleet' of nets which is continued on the opposite page and ends on p. 57 to give a true idea of its length.

(varying from nine to thirteen hundred according to their size). As soon as the nets are hauled—and it may take four or five hours of very hard work if there is a good catch[1]—we shall steam full speed for port to be in as early as possible for market. If our catch had been a poor one, we would have salted our herrings and remained out another night or even two nights. So the fishing has been going on all through the summer and autumn, since it started in June in Shetland. So, too, it has been going on, year after year, for centuries. There has been no real change in the actual method of fishing; old drawings of the sixteenth century show the Dutch using just these same kind of drift-nets and floats; steam and diesel engines now carry the drifters more quickly to and from the fishing grounds, but that is the only difference.

There are early records of herring being caught on the coasts of East Anglia long before the Norman Conquest. Swindon (1772) believes that the fishery at Yarmouth very probably began soon after the landing of Cerdic the Saxon in the year 495. In 647 it is stated that a church was built by Felix, Bishop of the East Angles, "and a godly man placed in it to pray for the health and success of the fishermen that came to fish at Yarmouth in the herring season". There is also evidence that Scotland exported salted fish to Holland in the 9th century, but whether it was herring is not certain, though most likely.[2] It was, however, not until the middle of the 12th century that the herring began to be important in history; then it was that the great Baltic fishery developed and built up the wealth and power of the Hanseatic merchants. The fishery was actually performed by the Danes, largely off the south coast of Sweden, which was then a part of Denmark; the curing and exporting, however, were monopolised by the merchants from the north German Hanseatic towns, who sent

[1]An exceptionally heavy catch of some 200 crans has been known to take up to twelve hours to haul.

[2]Taken from A. M. Samuel (1918).

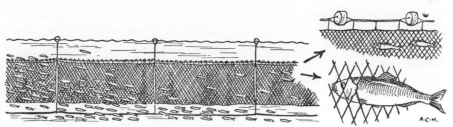

FIG. 16. *(continued)* with some details enlarged.

salted herring to nearly every country in Europe and secured in return almost the whole of their export trade.

For more than two hundred years the Hanseatic League was a dominant influence in northern Europe; it possessed great merchant fleets, sailing in armed convoys for protection against pirates, to carry herrings from the Baltic ports to many countries in exchange for wool, wine, timber, hardware and many other necessities of life. *Clupea harengus* was certainly a power in the land in those days; so he continued to be for a long period, although quite unexpectedly the scene changed. In the 15th century, somewhere between 1416 and 1425, a most extraordinary event occurred. The historians nearly all tell us that the herring suddenly migrated from the Baltic into the North Sea. That is really most unlikely, but certainly a major catastrophe occurred to the Baltic herring from which the stocks never recovered; the great shoals, which had poured wealth into the Hanseatic cities, dwindled in a few years to minor proportions. Just at this time the Dutch were developing their North Sea herring fisheries, which rose rapidly in importance as the Hanseatic fortunes waned.

It was natural at the time to think that a migration had taken place; recent research however, has shown that the Baltic herring of today is quite a different race from the southern North Sea stock, and presumably it was so five hundred years ago. It is a smaller fish with fewer segments (vertebrae) in its backbone; it becomes sexually mature when only two or three years old—that is a year earlier than the North Sea herring—and it does not live so long. What happened to reduce the stock we do not know; perhaps some submarine earthquake disturbance altered the sea-floor sufficiently to deflect the flow of currents from their previous course and so either upset the drift of larvae from the spawning grounds or affected their supply of planktonic food. It is not likely that overfishing could have produced so lasting an effect, as we shall presently see. From time to time in our own day we see similar changes taking place, but on a smaller scale.

The Cornish pilchard fishery which flourished in the last century dwindled to insignificance in this; the herring-shoals which gave rise to the winter fishing off Plymouth at the New Year, disappeared some fifteen years ago and have not returned. There are now signs of the Cornish pilchard stocks improving once again; but the stocks of Baltic herring have never regained their former glory.

Just as the Baltic fishery failed, and Europe looked with increasing urgency to Holland for their supply of herring, one of those happy coincidences of history occurred; a Dutchman called Beukels, or as sometimes written Beukelsen, invented a new method of pickling herring in brine, i.e. in a strong salt solution, instead of the earlier and cruder method of just packing them in dry salt. Herrings kept in barrels of brine now became a food which could be stored for many months and carried anywhere without harm. At that time the eating of meat was prohibited for two days every week and for forty days during Lent; the Dutch with their rapidly developing herring fleet sought to supply the urgent need of the whole of Christendom for fish. For nearly four hundred years, from the beginning of the 15th to the end of the 18th century, Holland was the leading fishery nation: her great fleet fished from Shetland down to East Anglia. Like the Hanseatic cities, she too built up a huge merchant fleet to trade her herring, so that in the 17th century it was said that four out of every five merchant ships were Dutch; it was her navy, built to protect her shipping, which under Van Tromp smashed the Spanish Fleet and made her for the time being mistress of the seas. It has been well said that the foundations of Amsterdam were built upon herring-bones.

Our history has been no less influenced by *C. harengus*. It was naturally galling to us to see the Dutch drawing this huge wealth from out of the waters close against our coasts. The Stuarts attempted two things to remedy this. Firstly they did everything they could to encourage our own fisheries; but in this they failed. Secondly they decided to make the Dutch pay tribute for fishing in our waters, and began to build up a navy to exact it; in this they paved the way for future success. It actually fell to Cromwell to enforce the policy of the Stuart Kings; it was of course in the war of 1652-54, which arose over the herring disputes, that the British finally wrested the mercantile supremacy from the Dutch.

The efforts at encouraging the British fisheries were not really successful until the beginning of the 19th century. It was only then that the great fleets of Scottish herring-luggers were built and the fishing towns of the north-east of Scotland (Wick, Buckie, Banff, Macduff, Fraserburgh, and many smaller ones) sprang into importance.

The story is well told in Neil Gunn's delightful novel *The Silver Darlings* (1941). Peterhead, another of the herring ports, had already been famous for its Greenland-whaling ships from the previous century. A fleet of more than a thousand sail, after fishing all the summer on the Scottish grounds, came south to work the early autumn fishery off the Yorkshire coast, and then passed on to the climax of the season—the East Anglian fishery of October and November. One of my earliest

FIG. 17. A sketch by the late Mr. Edward Dade showing the fleet of Scottish herring luggers sailing into Scarborough Bay at the end of the last century.

recollections is seeing the Scottish herring-fleet sailing into Scarborough Bay to land their catches—the sea filled with red-brown sails from the harbour to the horizon; that must have been about 1900 or '01, for very early in the century the old sailing luggers gave place to steam drifters. I, reproduce, here in Fig. 17 a drawing of the scene from the last century by that superb marine artist Ernest Dade. Today the steamers are fast being replaced by vessels powered by diesel motors. And another change is taking place: in the old days hundreds of Scottish lassies followed the fleets south to gut the herrings, bringing colour, song and laughter to the east coast ports; today they are being replaced by machines of almost incredible ingenuity—but these don't sing and, for all their miracles of mechanism, they are not such fun to watch.

The British herring fisheries reached their peak of production just before the first world war. The table on this page, which is taken from Dr. J. T. Jenkins' *The Sea Fisheries* (1920) shows the quantities of herrings landed by the different herring-fishing countries of Europe in the last year for which statistics were available before the 1914 war; it also shows their approximate relative values. Over a million tons of herring have been taken by the different nations out of our seas in one year. The greater part of our own herrings are not eaten fresh in this country, but are barrelled in brine for export. It is a great pity we do not eat more fresh herring; it is one of the cheapest of foods, with a very high protein value. Because so many of our herrings were then sent to Germany and Russia, our export trade has never regained the value it reached in the five years preceding 1914; we lost the greater part of these markets through the war and the Russian revolution.

HERRING-FISHERIES OF EUROPE BEFORE THE FIRST WORLD WAR

| | | | cwt. | £ |
|---|---|---|---|---|
| England | (1913)[1] | | 7,313,425 | 2,325,084 |
| Scotland | (1913) | | 4,449,323 | 2,087,754 |
| Ireland | (1913) | | 420,620 | 159,457 |
| France | (1911) | | 846,503 | 529,739 |
| Germany | (1913) | Fresh | 148,354 | 75,738 |
| ,, | ,, | Salted | 1,030,039 | 563,033 |
| Holland | (1911) | | 1,685,751 | 919,973 |
| Norway | (1912) | | 4,404,400 | 580,570 |
| Denmark | (1912) | | 845,295 | 140,051 |
| Sweden | (1912) | | 861,420 | 205,555 |
| Belgium | (1911) | | 13,000 | 5,000 |
| | Total: | | 22,018,130 | 7,591,954 |

It is not likely that we shall ever again export these large quantities of pickled herring to Europe; Russia and Germany have greatly increased their herring-fleets and are now largely supplying their own demands. New processes of freezing or desiccating herring may perhaps give us new markets in supplying food to the vast populations of Africa or Asia. For many years now we have not seen the huge fleets of some two thousand drifters which once worked from Yarmouth

[1] Of this total 2,488,183 cwt. (value £763,256) were landed by Scottish boats and men.

and Lowestoft in the autumns before 1914; the fishing is now controlled to meet demand, and I suppose that since the end of the last war the number of drifters in the East Anglian fishery has averaged only some four or five hundred.

Is all this enormous harvest being taken from one stock of fish? We have mentioned a succession of fisheries—off Shetland and the north-east of Scotland in summer, off the Yorkshire coast in early autumn, and then the great East Anglian concentration of October and November; further, there used to be the fishery in the Channel off Plymouth in December and January. It was natural that this succession of fishings along our coast should suggest that every year there is one vast movement of herring round Great Britain. It was Pennant, I believe, in his *British Zoology* of 1769, who first talked of the armies of herrings coming each year from the Arctic and dividing into two streams—one going down the coast of Norway and the other down the eastern side of Britain, to pass through the channel and back towards the Arctic to the west of us.[1] We know now that this cannot be so. A careful study of the herring from different localities tells us that we are dealing with a number of distinct geographical races. It is quite clear for instance that the very large herring on the coast of Norway are of quite a different stock from those of the southern North Sea; not only are they larger but they become sexually mature at a later age, at five to eight years old as compared with our herring which begin to breed at three and four years of age; the Norwegian fish live longer too—up to twenty years as compared to ours which rarely exceed eleven years. The separate race of smaller Baltic herring we have already mentioned. Among our own herring too, it seems there are a number of local races which can be distinguished, those which spawn in different places and at different times; there are summer, winter and spring spawners—groups of fish which, at one and the same season, are behaving very differently from one another on their respective parts of the coast.

There are so many of these local herring-fisheries round our islands that, if we are to give any account of them—and it is well that we should have some idea of their complexity—we must choose some system for their examination. Very briefly we will survey them season by season round the year. The information here given, and shown in

[1]Dr. Tucker has drawn my attention to an earlier reference which is nearer the truth than the arctic story of Pennant: R. Binnell (1758) writes in *A Description of the River Thames, etc.,* (London, Longman) on p. 226: "Their chief abode seems to be in the seas between the north of Scotland, Norway and Denmark, from whence they make annual excursions through the British Channel as far as the coast of Normandy."

the maps in Fig. 18 on the next page, is taken from that huge 'double folio' *Herring Atlas* compiled by my old friend Dr. William Hodgson, late of the Ministry of Agriculture and Fisheries, and published by the International Council for the Exploration of the Sea. For a more detailed account of the various herring races the reader should consult the papers by Dr. Henry Wood (1930, '36 and '37) for the Scottish area and Dr. Hodgson's Buckland Lectures (1934) for the southern North Sea.[1] In describing the condition of the fish in the different areas I shall use the same five terms as Dr. Hodgson employs in his Atlas: *immature* fish; *'full and filling'* fish, i.e. those which are fattening up ready for spawning, with their gonads well developed; *spawning* fish; *spent* fish, i.e. those which, having cast their spawn or milt, are in poor condition; and lastly the *recovering 'spents'*, those which are now improving in quality but cannot yet be classed as full and filling fish.

*January to March.* In Scotland there are several small fisheries at the beginning of the year. In the Minch, between the Outer Hebrides and the mainland, there is a fishery first for spent fish, then for recovering spents, and later on, in February and March, a stock of early spawning fish comes in. In the Firth of Forth area there is a fishery for full and filling fish in January extending to one for spawning fish in March.[2] In the Clyde area young immature herring are taken early in the year but in February and March larger spawning fish are caught south of Arran. In Ireland there are two fisheries for full and filling herring and later for spawners, one at the North (in the Buncrana and Burton Port area) and one in the south east; both are over by the end of February. In England, now that the Plymouth winter fishing is no longer profitable (as already mentioned), there is no herring fishing to speak of in this period—except that in some years a spring fishery for recovering spents may begin in March at Lowestoft.

*April and May.* This is a lean period of poor fisheries, mainly for recovering spents. The small fishery at Lowestoft does not always materialise. That in the Minch increases in May; in this month too there may begin a fishery for both recovering spents and immature fish at Lerwick in Shetland, at Peterhead and Fraserburgh, and off the Northumberland coast. In Ireland, too, they are catching recovering spents both in the north and south in May and sometimes in the south in April.

---

[1] And especially Dr. Hodgson's new book just published (1957) referred to on p. 67.

[2] This fishery has been failing during the last ten years and only a vestige of it remains today (Hodgson, 1957).

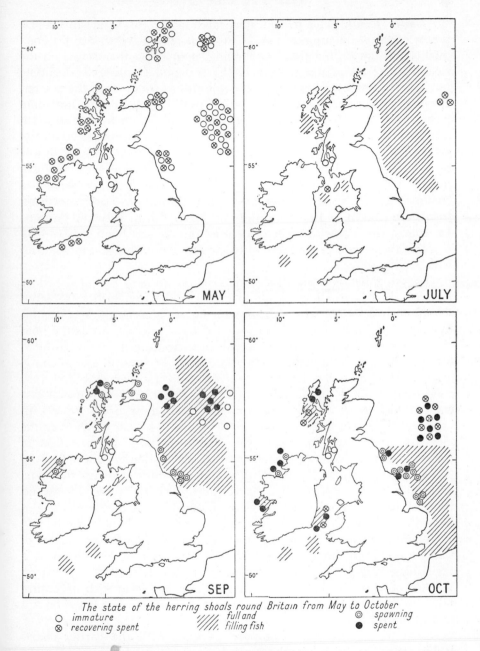

The state of the herring shoals round Britain from May to October

○ immature            ⁄⁄⁄⁄ full and        ◎ spawning
⊗ recovering spent    ⁄⁄. filling fish       ● spent

FIG. 18. Maps redrawn from Dr. Hodgson's *Herring Atlas* (with the addition of some more recent information from the *Annales Biologiques*) to show the distribution and state of the herring shoals round Britain during the summer and autumn.

*June to August.* This period, illustrated in the July chart in Fig. 18, is that of the great summer fishery in the northern North Sea for good quality full and filling fish: the herring, nourishing themselves on the rich crops of zooplankton, largely the copepod *Calanus,* are building up their reserves for spawning and for tiding them over the winter. Lerwick, Stronsay, Wick, Fraserburgh and Peterhead are the main ports. To join with the Scottish fleet come many boats from Yarmouth and Lowestoft. There is also a fishing for herring in similar condition and of exceptionally good quality at the west Scottish ports of Stornoway, Castlebay, Ullapool and Mallaig; in the Clyde area they are mainly young and immature. In England the drift-net fishery is confined to the North Shields area where immature and recovering spents are caught in June, and full and filling fish in July and August. In August the Yorkshire fishery centred on Whitby begins; here ring nets like those used in the Firth of Clyde have recently been introduced with great success.

The ring net is somewhat similar to the purse-seine net used in Norway, but is smaller. A shoal of fish is located either by echo-sounding or a feeling wire (a wire which gives a tremor when it is hit by the passing fish) and then surrounded by a net cast out as the boat circles round. Herring do not spend all their time near the surface; for a good part of the daytime they are near the bottom and a knowledge of this habit has led in recent years to another new and very considerable development: that of fishing for them with special fast trawls which skim over the bottom and have their head ropes kept very high by extra floats or underwater kites. The Germans were the pioneers in this and for many years have operated a large fleet of herring trawlers, working particularly on the Fladen grounds. During July and August some of the Hull companies also take up this type of fishing in the North Sea; and more recently some Fleetwood trawlers have worked the new gear off the west of Scotland, as also have Cardiff and Milford Haven boats to the south of Ireland.

There is only a little fishing from Ireland itself in the early part of this period, both north and south. We must not forget, however, a flourishing ring-net and drift-net fishery in the Irish Sea, centred on the Isle of Man: beginning actually in May and June with immature fish, it extends through July and August into September for good full and filling fish.

*September to December.* Compare October with the earlier charts in Fig. 18. The fishery in the north is over, although a few spawning and spent fish may be landed in September at Fraserburgh and Peterhead. In Scotland there is little fishing for the rest of the year, except in the Clyde area (famous for its 'Loch Fyne' herring, of such excellent quality), and a small fishery for spents and recovering spents in the Minch. The fishing off the Yorkshire coast is in full swing during September, with landings at Whitby, Scarborough and Grimsby; but by the end of this month all the drifters are concentrated at Yarmouth and Lowestoft ready for the great October and November fishery for the immense shoals of fine quality full and filling herring which are flooding the East Anglian grounds preparatory to spawning in the Channel. This is the climax of the year; there is no more important herring fishery in the world. It is unique in another respect; it appears to be the only herring fishery which is influenced by the moon. But, before we make a digression to discuss this lunar effect, let us briefly round off our review of the year. When I first wrote this chapter I said that this intense fishing effort in the southern North Sea is practically over by the beginning of December and that just a few boats may continue working at the entrance to the Channel, for the first ten days of the month. This is still true as regards drifters, but in the last few years there has been an amazing development of trawling for the herring when they are actually spawning on the Channel bed or being carried as weak spent fish in the current up the Belgian coast. Some two hundred trawlers, mostly continental and working in pairs with huge fast trawls of a new type, are sweeping up the herring in appalling quantities—partly for meal and oil. Will the stocks stand it? There are signs in the failure of the East Anglian fishery in the last two years—1955 and 1956—which suggest that they will not; but we shall return to this later (p. 66). In Ireland there is a fishery to the north throughout this period and to the south-east from October to December.

From this rapid survey of the seasons round our coasts it is clear that we are dealing with a number of different stocks of fish; but how many? We shall not really be sure until we have more results from the new tagging experiments which will be described at the very end of the chapter. The stocks off the west of Scotland, in the Irish Sea, and off the western end of the Channel are surely distinct from those off our eastern shores. And here in the North Sea we can distinguish spring spawning groups from autumn and winter spawning fish; but the former—apart from those to the north of Orkney and Shetland and the very different Norwegian fish—are confined to a small stock off the Firth of Forth. What of the huge mass of North Sea autumn and winter spawning herring? Recently Dr. D. H. Cushing (1956) has stressed the view that there are two main stocks of these fish. One stock, called the Bank herring, he believes, circulates round the North Sea with the main current drift. He supposes that they feed in the northern area to the east of Shetland, Orkney and the Moray Firth, drift south to spawn between the Fladen and the Dogger Banks from July to September and, as spent fish, are carried in the great swirl towards the Skagerrak which they reach after Christmas; subsequently they move with the northerly current up the more eastern side of the North Sea and so across to their northern feeding grounds again. The others, called the Downs herring, he believes, feed during the summer off our east coast rather to the south of the grounds of the Bank herring, although they may go as far north as Fraserburgh; then in the autumn they come down to the East Anglia grounds and pass into the eastern end of the Channel to spawn in December and January. From there they drift as spent fish up the coast of Holland in February and then make their way north in spring across the Dogger Bank to the more northern feeding grounds again. We shall later see that the early results of the tagging experiments do perhaps lend some support to this idea of two main stocks, although it is by no means accepted by all the herring experts; Dr. Hodgson, I know, is sceptical.

Let us now return to the 'Herring Moon'. For generations the East Anglian fishermen have spoken of the autumn full moon by such a name; they did so, however, not as farmers speak of 'the Harvest Moon' as helping them by giving a good light for continued working, but because they believed that the herring are caught in greater numbers at and around the full moon during this fishery. The late Mr. R. E. Savage and Dr. W. C. Hodgson (1934) of the Fisheries Laboratory at Lowestoft made a special study of the subject, and conclusively proved that the belief was indeed correct. It was found that the dates of full moon in the autumn have a profound bearing upon the nature of the fishery. If there is a full moon towards the end of October or at the beginning of November, then the fishery is likely to be a comparatively short one, building up to a climax of highest catches in the days around this 'herring moon'. In years when there is a full moon in the middle of the month, there is a much longer fishing season with two lesser peaks in the yield; one around the full moon in mid-October and another at that in mid-November.

It appears that at this season there is some special shoaling excitement around the full moon, leading to the fish swimming more often, or in greater numbers, up into the nets; no doubt it is part of a courtship behaviour, for these great shoals are, as we have already said, collecting preparatory to spawning in the Channel. It is something no doubt analogous to the nuptial excitement and swimming up to the surface of the swarms of palolo worms in the tropics, only for them it takes place at the last quarter of the October-November moon in the

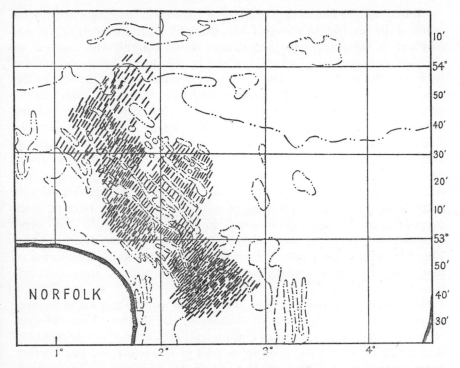

FIG. 19. A chart taken from Graham (1931) showing all the herring drifters fishing on the night of October 18, 1930. "Each stroke of the pen", he writes, "represents one boat and her nets, roughly to scale and approximately the correct number of boats are recorded. As regards position of fishing the chart is somewhat speculative." Note that a degree of latitude (60 miles) provides a scale.

Pacific species (*Leodice viridis*) and at the third quarter of the June-July moon in the West Indian species (*L. fucata*). It is very surprising that this well-marked lunar behaviour of the southern North Sea herring does not appear to have its counterpart among the shoals preparing for spawning in other seasons and waters round our coasts. On the contrary, in Scottish waters fishermen believe that their catches are poorer on bright moonlight nights. Perhaps the behaviour of the herring is actually the same, but in the clearer Scottish waters the fish are better able to see the nets on moonlight nights and so avoid them; whereas in the shallow southern North Sea waters, where there is so much sediment stirred up by the tidal currents running over the many sand-banks, the fish may be unable to see the nets even on the brightest moonlight nights.

While we are discussing matters of behaviour, mention should be made of the interesting views of Mr. Michael Graham (1931). Fig. 19, overleaf, is taken from his paper, and shows roughly the position of the drift-nets on one particular night in the autumn fishery; we see how exceedingly close together are these parallel walls of netting as the whole fleet of vessels drift together with the wind and tide. As he points out, the shoals of herring must be making sudden upward sweeps towards the surface and down again instead of steadily swimming forward in the upper layers; this must be so because it frequently happens that one line of nets may be full of fish while those on either side catch comparatively few. Graham suggests that the fish are really caught because they are indulging in frantic antics of excitement—rushing to the surface and down again as part of their prenuptial sexual behaviour—and so dash blindly into the nets; or sometimes, perhaps, these sudden stampedes may be due to panic, when the whole shoal takes fright and careers headlong this way and that. There is much work yet to be done in the study of fish behaviour.

Now that we have seen the great shoals assembling for spawning we may begin to follow the life-history of the herring from the egg. Nearly all the other sea-fish of commercial importance lay eggs which float freely in the water, drifting as part of the plankton; the herring is an exception and deposits its spawn in masses on the sea-bed, particularly on a gravel bottom, thickly plastering stones, shells and even the backs of crabs with it. As soon as the eggs are laid, they sink and stick to whatever they touch—as you will find if you squeeze a freshly caught ripe herring so that the eggs fall to the bottom of a bucket of sea-water. In the summer when the fish are feeding they are perhaps in smaller shoals, but now it seems that these combine together as the spawning time approaches. Some shoals are said to be eight or nine miles in length and two or three in breadth.

Our great T. H. Huxley, who took a keen interest in all fishery matters and for a time held the post of Fishery Inspector, made the following estimate of the density of a shoal in a special lecture on the herring delivered at the National Fishery Exhibition at Norwich in 1881:[1] "In these shoals the fish are closely packed, like a flock of sheep straying slowly along a pasture, and it is probably quite safe to assume that there is at least one fish for every cubic foot of water occupied by the shoal. If this be so, every square mile of such a shoal, supposing it to be three fathoms deep, must contain more than 500,000,000

[1]Published in *The Scientific Memoirs of T. H. Huxley*, Vol. 4; it is full of points of interest to the student of the herring today.

*Plate I.* A composite photograph, derived from two, of herring (*Clupea harengus*) swimming in the aquarium of the Scottish Marine Fisheries Laboratory at Aberdeen. (*D. P. Sharman*)

*Plate II. (above) a.* A steam-drifter leaving Lowestoft for the herring grounds; note wireless equipment for talking to home port and other drifters; diesel engines are now largely replacing steam. (*The Times*). (*below*) *b.* A drift-net being hauled in, showing how the herring are caught and held in the meshes by their gill covers. (*Ford Jenkins*)

herrings". Each herring lays at least 10,000 eggs. It will readily be seen that the quantities of spawn produced by a shoal will be enormous. The spawning grounds are an attraction to many bottom-living fish, especially haddock, which collect to gorge themselves with this rich food. 'Spawny haddocks', as they are called, are well known to fisher-men trawling off the Yorkshire coast in August and September. Trawlers are sometimes accused of depleting the stocks of herring by their activities and sometimes they do haul up masses of spawn which pile up in heaps on the deck; it is likely, however, that the bottom-feeding fish caught by the trawlers would, if they had remained, have done more damage to the spawn than did the trawl. If such spawn brought up is shovelled back into the sea, it will sink again and most likely hatch out unharmed.

The position and dates of the main herring spawning grounds in the North Sea are shown in Fig. 20 overleaf; these are inferred either from the capture of the "spawny haddocks" just referred to or from the capture of herrings which are just about to spawn, or again, from the presence of newly-hatched larvae in the plankton. It is remarkable that, although repeated attempts have been made by naturalists using all manner of dredges, grabs and underwater cameras, they have never, until quite recently, succeeded in charting a patch of spawn and only very rarely in getting samples of the eggs at all. The very first voyage I made on the *George Bligh,* the Research Vessel of the Fisheries Laboratory at Lowestoft, when I joined the staff in the summer of 1921, was to go with Mr. Michael Graham—now Director of Fisheries Research[1]—in an attempt to find and chart the herring spawn known to exist somewhere near the Farne Islands off the Northumberland coast. We grabbed and dredged everywhere in vain. It gives me much satisfaction that the first naturalist to make a proper survey of a patch of herring spawn should be one of my old pupils from Oxford, Mr. George Bolster, who has now succeeded, where his Director and old Professor failed some 35 years ago. Mr. Graham has recently told me how it occurred. When Mr. Bolster was carrying out herring tagging in the region where the Channel opens into the North Sea, someone noticed that there were herring eggs in the meshes of the trawl. On completion of the tagging Mr. Bolster turned to chart the eggs, making grab hauls over the grounds consisting of gravel and stones, and showed that there was a patch only about 300 yds. wide at the most. His success in finding such a narrow strip may be ascribed to his having previously echo-sounded[2] herring shoals in the same area and found them to have the same narrow and elongate shape. The patch of

[1] Just retired.   [2] See foot-note on p. 63.

F&F—E

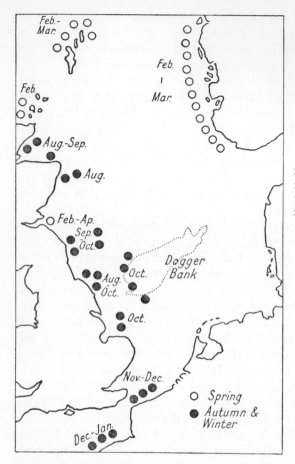

FIG. 20. The principal spawning grounds of the herring in the North Sea and Channel from Hodgson (1957).

eggs extended for 3 miles in the direction of the main tidal stream, and was 6 miles south-west of the Sandettie light vessel. In Plate III (p. 66) I reproduce a photograph taken in the laboratory of some of these eggs still alive and clinging to the stones which were brought up in the grab and carefully brought ashore without disturbance.[1]

When at Lowestoft in 1923, and specially interested in the herring, I was brought a jam-jar full of spawn which had been scraped up from

[1]Since this was printed I have just heard of the detailed survey of a patch of herring spawn off the Ayrshire coast made by the Scottish Fishery naturalists using underwater cameras and grabs; it was approximately 350 yards square—a continuous blanket of spawn varying from two eggs thick at the edge to seven or eight eggs thick at the centre  It was estimated that it was spawned by some eight or nine million fish, and it was considered that there must be several other such patches of spawn in the vicinity.

the deck of a trawler as it had fallen from the net two or three days previously. I could scarcely believe that the eggs could still be alive; but on the off-chance I put it into an aquarium. In a few days' time I was surprised and delighted to see little fish developing within almost every egg; each became a distinct creature curved round a mass of yolk within an outer transparent sphere. Their eyes began to show black, and in about ten days' time the first little herrings began to hatch. We could see them wriggling and turning round within the egg and then suddenly breaking out. Plate III also shows some photographs taken by my friend the late Dr. Donald Hutchinson on this very occasion, when he made a ciné film of their actual hatching. First would come the head, and then by a desperate struggle or two, the whole little fish would free itself: a tiny transparent fellow only about a quarter of an inch long. Below its body it carries a supply of food in a small bag; this is the unfinished remnant of the yolk from the egg which will help it through the early days of its strange new life.

All too soon the supply of yolk is used up and the baby herring must fend for itself; it is now swimming up from the bottom and beginning to feed on the tiny plants of the plankton—those diatoms and flagellates which are of convenient shape and size to go into its tiny mouth. As it gradually grows in length, it changes its diet from a vegetarian one to one consisting almost entirely of the very small crustacea, nauplii and the later young stages of copepods.[1] For a period of a month or so, in the North Sea, it now appears to be almost entirely dependent upon one species of these little crustacea, the copepod *Pseudocalanus elongatus*. Most of the other common copepods, *Calanus, Temora,* and *Centropages* are probably too large to be tackled; these and the other plankton animals mentioned below are illustrated in the sketch in Fig. 24 (p. 62) and described and figured more fully in Part I. *Pseudocalanus* is a very common species in the North Sea but its numbers tend to fluctuate considerably from year to year. Here no doubt we see our herring passing through one of the critical periods of his life. If there is a shortage of *Pseudocalanus* and other small copepods one year, there may be a heavy mortality among the baby herring, and this may deplete the stocks of adult fish in later years. Just as deadly may be an unusual number of enemies. At a time when the spawn is hatching there may be swarms of planktonic predators such as the comb-jellies (ctenophores) *Pleurobrachia*—or 'sea gooseberries', as the fishermen call them—which may eat as many as five young herring at a time, or the transparent arrow-worms *Sagitta* which may

[1]Dr. Marie Lebour (1921) records the young herring off Plymouth feeding upon larval gastropods (sea snails).

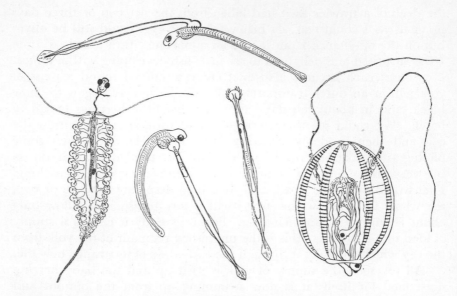

FIG. 21. Planktonic animals which are important predators of the very young herring: the worm *Tomopteris* swallowing one (*left*); two arrow-worms, *Sagitta*, in the act of capturing them and another with one being digested (*centre*); and a ctenophore, *Pleurobrachia*, with many in its gullet. Drawings made by Dr. Lebour at Plymouth and reproduced from her paper (1923) with her kind permission.

swallow young herrings almost their own size. In Fig. 21 above I reproduce again Dr. Marie Lebour's striking drawings of these happenings, which I showed in Volume I, together with another of her drawings of the planktonic worm *Tomopteris* also devouring a herring.

All the time the little herrings, those which survive the many perils, are growing as they are carried along by the currents; they are long and slender—almost worm-like—as shown in Fig. 97 on p. 220.[1] Carried with them may be numerous other young fish, but the only ones likely to be mistaken for them are the young sand-eels (Fig. 93, p. 209); the baby herring, however, can readily be distinguished by the greater length of their gut, which extends almost to the tail. At about $1\frac{1}{4}$ inches, they begin to take the larger copepods such as *Temora* and before long, at about $1\frac{3}{4}$ inches, they rapidly undergo a remarkable change. The body increases in depth from one which had been thin and eel-like, to one approaching the proportions of an adult herring in miniature; and while this metamorphosis is taking place, it becomes covered for the first time with a coat of tiny silver scales.

[1]We also see one in the photograph in Plate XI of Part I (p. 140).

The little fish now collect together in shoals, and tend to come in towards the coast into shallow water, and (if possible) to enter some large estuary like that of the Thames or the Wash. Here, together with the young of its close relative the sprat, *Clupea sprattus*, they are caught and marketed as whitebait. In the old days the whitebait used to be thought, following Yarrell, to be a distinct species—a small member of the genus *Clupea*: 'C. alba';—but now we know that this was an error. The specimens so named by Yarrell were fortunately deposited in the British Museum where they can be seen to be undoubted herring. In the Thames estuary enormous shoals of whitebait are fished by the so-called stow-nets, which are huge conical nets lowered below anchored vessels and streamed out with the ebb and flow of the strong tides. The composition of the catch varies at different times of the year; but it is said to be nearly always a mixture ranging from up to 90% herring at one season to almost 90% of sprat at another. While in the whitebait stage, the herrings feed largely upon the estuarine copepod *Eurytemora hirundoides* which occurs in very large numbers at the mouth of the Thames, but they also eat larval shrimps and prawns and various species of mysids. They are in fact beginning to eat almost as wide a range of food as do the adults, as we shall presently see.

After a sojourn of some six months or so in the estuaries and coastal regions, the herrings appear to scatter over the North Sea. They do not join the main shoals until they become sexually mature for the first time, and this, curiously enough, occurs in different individuals from the ages of three to five years. A few fish come into the main spawning shoals at 3 to 3½ years; most come in at 4 to 4½, but a few postpone their joining up till they are 5 years old. Until recently we knew little of the herring between its 'whitebait' life and its joining the main shoals, as there was no fishing for these small fish. Now, however, very large quantities of young herring, mostly 2 year-olds, are being caught east and south-east of the Dogger Bank by continental trawlers using specially fast trawls; they are being swept up, not for human consumption, but for meal for feeding poultry and other live stock. The quantity taken in 1954 reached the high figure of 100,000 tons (Hodgson 1956). An enormous nursery ground has been discovered and is being ruthlessly exploited; the possible effect of this upon the stocks of herring will be considered later (p. 66).

I have said that the young herrings do not join the main shoals until they are three or four years old. How do we know this? Very fortunately, the herring carries on every scale a little register of its age. If we take off a scale and look at it with a lens we shall see on it a number of rings, one inside the other, as shown below in Fig. 22. These are formed yearly like the rings seen when a tree-trunk is sawn across. There must in the life of a herring, as in the tree, be some round of events affecting its growth: something like the burst of activity each spring following the rising of the sap and the opening of the leaves. By studying the feeding of the herring throughout the year we see what this is. They live for the most part on the small animals of the plankton, and we see their habits adjusted to the yearly round of events in the planktonic world. They feed hard to take advantage of the rich production of animal life in the summer months,

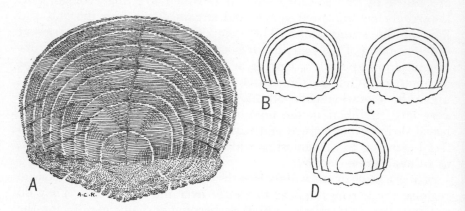

FIG. 22. Herring scales. A, a sketch of a scale from an eight year old fish, showing eight winter rings (× 8). B, C and D, diagrams to show the relative size of the innermost zone of scales of herring hatched in summer, autumn and winter respectively.

and so build up a reserve of food in the form of oils and fats to carry them through the lean period of the winter when their food is very scarce and they hardly feed at all. That is why the herring is such a valuable article of food.

This yearly wave of feeding is reflected in the herring's rate of growth. They grow more rapidly in the spring and summer, and then more slowly again through the autumn to a period in the winter when, for the time being, they stop growing altogether. Their scales, as we should expect, grow in proportion to their body; each winter, therefore, the scales stop growing, and this leaves its mark. When growth is resumed in the spring there is formed on each scale what we may call a winter ring; this is, in fact, the part which was the edge of the scale during the winter. Thus, we see that a scale has three, four, five, six or more winter rings, separated by wider zones indicating growth

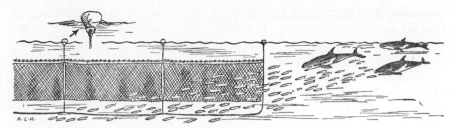

FIG. 16 (*continued from p. 39*). The end of a line of driftnets; to gain a true idea of the length of the line imagine the drawing continuing across all the pages between this and page 38 where its other end is shown.

during the intervening summers. As the herring get older their growth slows down so that the zones between the rings become narrower and narrower, and scales become with age increasingly difficult to read.

Not only do the scales tell us the age of the herring, but it is believed by herring-experts that they may also tell us at what season of the year they were spawned. If you look at a collection of scales from many different fisheries round our coasts you will be struck by the fact that the innermost zone—i.e. the central 'bulls-eye' area *within* the first winter ring—varies very much in size, as shown in Fig. 22 opposite. Fish with the largest inner zones to their scales are thought to be those which were spawned in the summer. Having spent the autumn and winter as larvae drifting in the plankton, they would begin to lay down their scales in the spring and so have all the summer to grow before forming their first winter ring—actually a year and a half after hatching from the egg. Those with the smallest inner zones are supposed to be those fish which were spawned in the winter or early spring, and so did not begin to form their scales until the summer feeding season was half over—when they had less time for growth before their first winter came. Then medium-sized inner zones, of course, are considered to be those of fish spawned in the autumn. I have given what appears to be an obvious explanation with expressions of some caution because of a very strange state of affairs that has been reported by Dr. Hodgson and some other workers. It appears that sometimes herring, with scales indicating (by the above criteria) that they were summer-spawned fish, are found swimming in the same shoals as winter-spawning fish; and, moreover, that their gonads appear to be ripening to spawn *in winter* with the fellows of their adopted shoal. If these different kinds of scales really indicate the season when the fish were spawned, and if it is true that a summer-spawned fish can change its habits and spawn in the winter if it gets in company with winter-spawning fish, then there is something very unusual in such behaviour and its control. Moreover, if this is true, it makes one want to re-consider what one means by separate local races of winter-spawning and summer-spawning fish.

There is much more yet to be found out about the herring. I have elsewhere (1951) urged the importance of establishing an institute equipped with large breeding pools, perhaps connected to the sea by lock-gates, for the special study of herring races. It is quite time something was known of the genetics of the different races of this fish which is so important commercially to so many different nations. We do not yet know if such differences as the form of scales or the number of segments (vertebrae) in the backbone, etc. are really inherited, or whether they may just be due to the influence of changes in the environment. It is known that if some other species of fish are allowed to grow up in aquaria of different degrees of temperature and saltness, they may come to have a larger or smaller number of vertebrae. We should be able artificially to fertilize the eggs of different races of herring; and, by crossing different stocks, learn very much more about the relative share of inheritance and environment in determining the form of the different kinds of herring known to us.[1]

The reading of scales plays an important part in modern fisheries research. By studying those taken from a large number of fish caught at the same time, we can see that a shoal is made up of fish of different ages—there will be some three years old, some four, five, six and seven, and a few even older. It is found that the proportions occupied by fish of different ages vary from year to year. The fish born in one particular year may have been so successful in avoiding or overcoming the perils of early life, that, when they come into the adult shoals, they may for several succeeding years greatly outnumber those born in other years. It was this fact, discovered by Einar Lea, the great Norwegian pioneer in herring research, which first proved that the rings on the scales of the herring were indeed annual rings. He happened by chance to observe one of the most remarkable events ever recorded in the natural history of the herring; so important is it for our understanding of the lives of sea-fish in general, that it will repay us to examine it rather closely.

Working on the hypothesis that the rings were annual ones, Lea began in 1907 to analyse the age-composition of the Norwegian herring-catches. To save words let us look at a diagrammatic representation

---

[1] Work on this has now begun and such a cross-fertilization of different stocks of herring has been accomplished by Mr. J. Blaxter (1953) of the Scottish Fishery Department.

of his results as shown in Fig. 23 (p. 60). He analysed the age-composition of the shoals of herring every year from 1907 to 1923 and worked out how many per cent. in each year were four-year-olds, how many five-year-olds and so on; these percentages he expressed and compared in graphical form as black columns of appropriate heights for each of the age-groups from 3 to 21 years old. We have already noted that Norwegian herring live to be much older than ours and that they also become mature and enter the main shoals later than ours—at ages from 5 to 9 years old. In each year, the age-groups are arranged in order from left to right. In 1907 we see that there were rather similar proportions of fish of ages from 4 to 8, but in the next year, 1908, there was a considerably greater proportion of four-year-olds, i.e. fish spawned in 1904. In the next year (1909) the five-year-old fish—i.e. the same year-class, of those spawned in 1904—were still more prominent because more of them had become mature at 5 years old; in 1910 the six-year-old fish, i.e. again the 1904 year-class, were found to be nearly 80% of the stock. For some extraordinary reason the fish spawned in 1904 had been overwhelmingly successful compared to those spawned in normal years; we see them, in fact, dominating all the other year classes unto 1918 when they were 14 years old. The results of this analysis, which was made on the supposition that the rings on the scales indicated age, could only make sense if, in fact, this hypothesis were correct; the fish of the successful 1904 year-class must have been adding one extra ring to their scales each year—no other explanation is possible.

Apart from proving the annual nature of the rings, this unusually successful year-class shows, in very striking fashion, how the stocks of fish may fluctuate and how the fate of any year-class or brood, whether prolific or poor, is most likely bound up with conditions, favourable or unfavourable for survival, in very early life. We have already considered some of the hazards the young fry must face, either in the shortage of the right planktonic food, or in an unusual abundance of predatory enemies. This type of fluctuation in the strength of different year-classes we meet in many kinds of fish.

In our own herring-shoals in the great autumn East Anglian fishery there are similar, but not so striking, good and poor year-classes which show up year after year for a number of successive fisheries. An exceptionally high proportion of five-year-old fish one year will most likely mean a big proportion of six-year-old fish the next year. The older fish are bigger and more valuable than the younger ones. Now, by studying the age-composition of the shoals from year to year, Dr. Hodgson (1934) of the Lowestoft Laboratory

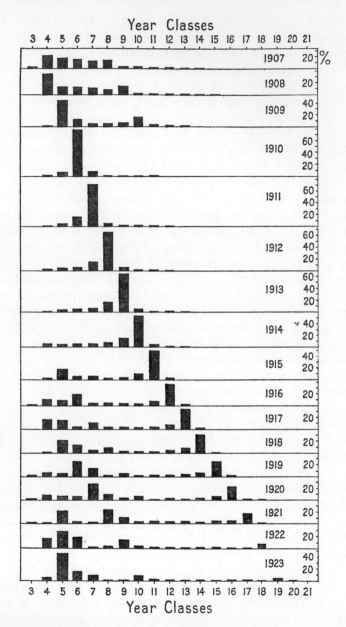

FIG. 23. Histograms representing the percentage year-class composition of the Norwegian herring shoals from 1907 to 1923 as analysed by Dr. Lea. For explanation and significance see text.

has found it possible to forecast the expected quality of the fish—i.e. the relative proportion of large and small fish—in the coming season's fishery: a great boon to the merchant to know the type of fish he will have to deal with in the largest numbers.

It will be well, at this point, to say a little more about the feeding of the adult herring, if only to dispel a commonly believed error. If you examine its gills you will see that the divisions between the openings, i.e. the arches which actually bear the gills, are provided on their inner side with a fringe of stiff processes like the teeth of a comb; these are known as the gill-rakers and serve to prevent small plankton animals taken into the mouth from being carried out again by the stream of water flooding through the gills. It has been commonly supposed that the herring feeds by just swimming forward with its mouth wide open so that the plankton that goes in is automatically strained from the water by the gill-rakers—much as the food of a plankton-feeding whale is caught by the vast sieve of fibres on the baleen or whalebone plates in its mouth. But this is not so. It can be shown that the herring actually selects the organisms it prefers from the mass of different species in the plankton. If samples of plankton are taken at the same time as herring are caught, and the contents of the herring's stomachs examined and compared with those of the tow-net, it will be found that there are some interesting differences according to particular circumstances. If the copepod *Calanus* is plentiful in the plankton it will be found that the herring has been taking this and little else. If *Calanus* is scarce then the herring will take a number of other plankton organisms such as *Sagitta* and the pteropod *Limacina* roughly in the proportion in which they occur in the plankton; these are often plentiful in the plankton, too, when *Calanus* is abundant, but they are then ignored. Herring in an aquarium can be seen to snap at individual specks of food as a swallow catches the tiny insects in the air. Early in the year, in March and April, the North Sea herring is feeding very largely on young sand-eels; and often at this season you will find the stomach of the herring crammed full of them, lying neatly side by side like sardines in a tin.

My first bit of research, after graduating and joining the Ministry of Agriculture and Fisheries as Assistant Naturalist at their Fisheries Laboratory at Lowestoft, was to investigate the food of the herring at all ages and at all seasons of the year. From such a study (1924) I tried to make out the main food-chains between the herring and the different members of the planktonic community; the diagram in Fig. 24, (p. 62), which summarises these relationships, is based on this study and on the researches of a number of other plankton workers—

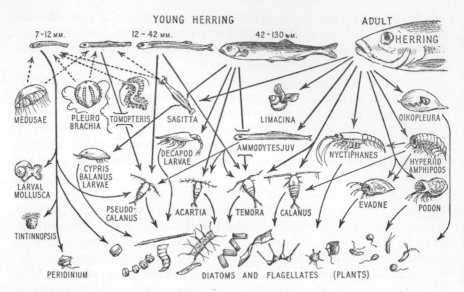

FIG. 24. A sketch showing the feeding relationships between the herring of different ages and the members of the plankton, redrawn from the author's original diagram (1924); the broken lines show some of the food links between different members of the plankton community derived from the work of other authors, notably Lebour (1922-23). The arrows point in the direction of predation.

particularly Dr. Marie Lebour (1922-23) who at Plymouth has made such extensive observations on the feeding of different plankton animals. The diagram also shows the planktonic predators which in turn feed upon the tiny herring fry.

The late Mr. R. E. Savage (1931, 1937), continuing the investigations, showed how much the proportions of the different items of food may change from year to year and also how the landings of herring in the Shields fishery fluctuate in different years in relation to the quality of planktonic food available. Mr. R. S. Wimpenny (1950) has further shown how the varying richness of the copepods in oil in different years is reflected in the quality of the herrings caught.

I have already dealt with the movements of the herring in relation to the plankton in the last chapter of the earlier volume. There I also referred to the interesting hypothesis, put forward by Dr. K. M. Rae concerning the times of the beginnings of the different fisheries down the east coast, which are apt to vary from year to year; he suggests that the arrival of the different shoals from north to south, as the season advances from summer to winter, may be linked with variations in the Atlantic inflow from the north; and we saw some evidence which appears to support it. The hope that the little plankton indicator might become a regular guide to fishermen in helping them to locate waters which are more profitable for fishing has not yet materialized; while on an average, in the summer fishery, it yields good results and a number of skippers have used it with great effect, it is not sufficiently reliable to be generally taken up. In recent years, however, science has given the fisherman something much more useful: the echo-sounder which will tell him when he is passing over the shoals of fish he cannot see.[1]

While the echo-sounder is being extensively used in detecting cod and other large fish swimming a little way from the bottom, it is of even greater importance in showing the presence of shoals of pelagic fish such as herring, sprat and pilchard. Some claim that it is possible by the nature of the trace on the recording paper to distinguish whether the shoal in question is that of one species or another by its shape or strength of outline; others are sceptical of such fine interpretation. In practical fishing, however, there is little doubt because one usually knows, in any particular area, which kind of pelagic fish it is likely to be. A typical appearance of an echo trace of a large herring shoal is shown in Fig. 25, (p. 64). The great pioneer in echo-sounding in the herring fisheries has been Skipper Ronald Balls who, by its use, has not only made most interesting observations on the movement and behaviour of the shoals (1946 and 1952) but has shown how it is possible to more than double one's catch. In the summer North Shields fishery he tells us that his average catch for 399 shots in the years without an echo-sounder was $11\frac{1}{2}$ crans, whereas for 69 shots since using the sounder to locate the shoals he caught an average of $25\frac{1}{2}$ crans.

Skipper Balls, who is a keen naturalist, was also a pioneer in using our plankton indicator and gave us a great deal of help in our experiments. I look back with very happy memories to the many talks on natural history I have had with him in the wheel-house of his *Violet and Rose* as we steamed out looking for signs of herring. There are many signs which may indicate to the experienced skipper whether one place is a more likely one for herring than another. Apart from the more obvious, such as congregations of birds, diving gannets, the presence of small whales and a certain oiliness of the surface, there are various

[1]The echo-sounder was described in Part I, p. 235. Briefly, sound impulses, given out from below the ship, are echoed back from the bottom of the sea and the time taken for their return accurately indicates the depth; second by second they are electrically recorded on a moving chart which automatically traces a section of the sea giving surface and bottom—and in addition makes a mark as echoes also come back from shoals of fish in between.

subtle distinctions in the colour and appearance of the water which are thought to be propitious by one skipper or another, and these they usually find very difficult to define; most, but not all, agree that the presence of a curious whiteness of the water is a good omen. I have already referred in our earlier volume to the very interesting observations of Skipper Balls on the occurrence of 'white water'; it is probable that the tiny organisms (coccolithophores) causing this whiteness are not themselves of any consequence to the herring, but rather indicators of water having other favourable qualities.

We have dealt with the food of the herring, but what of the other side of the picture—what are the animals, apart from man, which in turn feed upon it? There must be a great many. We have mentioned the destruction of its spawn by haddock and of its larvae by planktonic predators; but what are the principal enemies of the adult herring? Fin-whales, lesser rorquals, killer-whales and porpoises often follow the shoals in the North Sea; and sea-gulls and gannets levy a considerable toll; but perhaps the greatest herring-eater is the codfish. The herring, as we have already said, does not spend all its time in the upper layers—it goes down towards the bottom in the daytime, and here it is attacked by the cod. One may frequently find the remains of half-a-dozen herring in the stomach of a single cod, and there are records of up to twelve being found in a very large one. There are many other fish which are its predators. The late Dr. G. A. Steven (1930) records that the spur-dog "feeds almost entirely on herring while in Plymouth waters" and the same author (1932) shows, as recorded on p. 187,

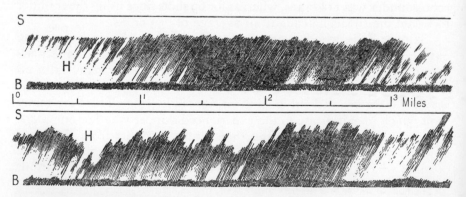

FIG. 25. Copies of two echo-sounding records of shoals of herring made in the southern North Sea near the entrance to the English Channel. S represents the sea surface, B the bottom and H the shoal of herring. The depth of water in each is 18 fathoms (i.e. 108 feet). From charts kindly lent by Dr. Cushing.

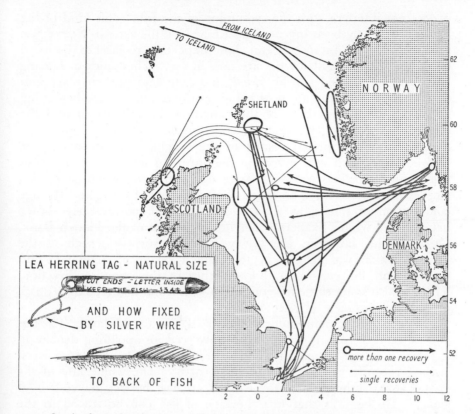

FIG. 26. A chart showing some of the more interesting movements of herring as revealed by tagging experiments. The arrows are drawn from the point of tagging to that of recapture. Inset is a sketch of the Lea herring tag.

that the thornback ray also feeds "mainly on herring", with once again "sometimes as many as six in one stomach." I was surprised to learn that a ray could catch such an agile swimmer.

There is much more that might be said about the natural history of this fish; but space is limited and we must now end our discussion, except for just two more points. After many failures, new and successful methods have recently been found of tagging herring to find out where they go. In the past the tags or little labels attached have either damaged the fish (which are very delicate and take poorly to handling) or have easily been pulled off and lost. Now a small and very light plastic tube, no more than $1\frac{1}{2}$ inch in length, but containing instructions for returning the fish, is attached by silver wire just in front of the dorsal fin; this has neutral buoyancy and is so slender that it does not interfere with the swimming of the fish. This kind of tag has only recently been invented by Einar Lea, the veteran Norwegian investigator, who, in 1907 began those important researches discussed on p. 59. Other similar types are now in use. Thousands of herring have been so labelled and liberated, and note kept of their place and date of tagging; many are now being returned, and we are beginning at last to learn something of the extent of the migrations and the connections between stocks in different areas. Fig. 26 (p. 65) shows a chart of the principal results of the tagging experiments up to October 1957, and very revealing they are. In some cases they confirm connections between stocks from different areas which have been suspected for some time, on account of similarity of scales and the age composition of shoals, as for example the link now clearly shown between the winter Skagerrak herring and those of the Fladen Bank. Other results, however, are giving us great surprises, such as the herring which was tagged in the Minch (West of Scotland) and recaught off the east coast, and another in the opposite direction. There is also some evidence coming in of fish marked on the Scottish grounds being taken off East Anglia.

My concluding point unfortunately strikes a note of alarm. The last two autumn seasons 1955 and 1956 have seen an appalling decline in the landings at Yarmouth and Lowestoft. As Dr. Hodgson says, writing recently in *The New Scientist* (1956): "The whole fate of the East Anglian fishery, once the world's greatest herring harvest, is at stake." He believes that this shortage of fish can be traced to the terrific new onslaught being made on the stock by the trawlers, both for the young fish east of the Dogger (p. 55) and for the adults at the eastern end of the Channel in December (p. 47). Other herring experts, however, are not at present agreed as to the cause. Some suggest that the massacre of very young herring east of the Dogger cannot be the cause of our shortage because, they say, it is our older fish which are failing to turn up and not the young, which are still coming in reason-

---

*Plate III.* (*above*) *a.* Herring spawn clinging to a stone brought up in a grab from the Sandettie spawning grounds at the eastern end of English Channel, obtained by the Ministry of Fisheries research vessel, *Sir Lancelot.* Note the little black eyes of the developing fish within the eggs; also attached to the stone are fern-like growths which are really animal in nature: hydroids (p. 95). (*R. Elms*) (*below*) *b, c, d* and *e.* Photographs from a film of the birth of a herring taken by the late Dr. Donald Hutchinson of eggs hatched out by the author in 1923 in the Ministry of Fisheries Laboratory at Lowestoft. Note the little yolk-sac, a reserve of food, carried by each baby fish; in *e,* the fry are compared in size to a pin's head put into the little aquarium for the purpose.

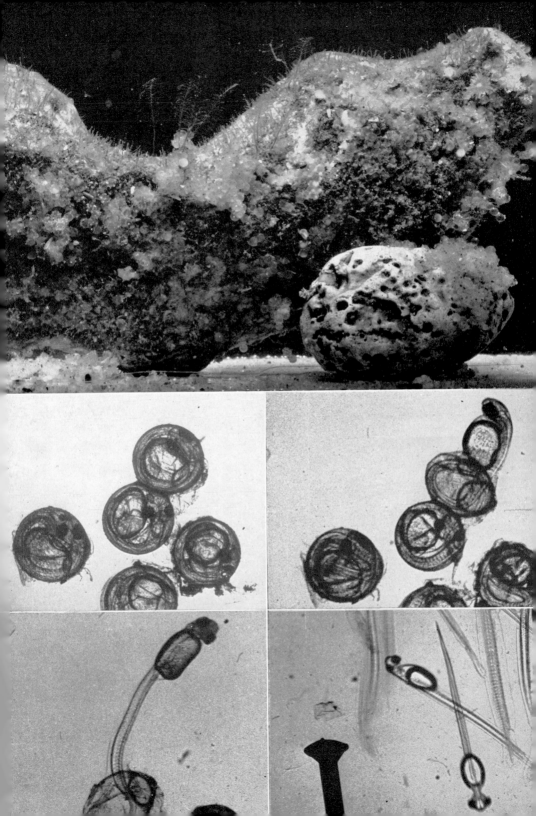

*Plate IV.* (*above*) *a.* A basking shark (*Cetorhinus maximus*) feeding on plankton and cruising slowly near the surface with its dorsal fin showing above the water, photographed by Dr. J. H. Fraser from the deck of the Scottish Fishery Research Ship *Explorer.* Note the extent of the gill slits and the width of the head region, together indicating the great filtering capacity of its plankton-catching apparatus. (*below left*) *b.* A view looking into the mouth of a basking shark to show the comb-like gill rakers which serve as a plankton sieve along the edge of each gill slit; the fish is on its back hanging by its *lower* jaw and the lower ends of the first gill bars have broken away from the inverted floor of the mouth: a breakage which actually shows the gill rakers (both right and left) more clearly than would otherwise be possible. (*below right*) *c.* A basking shark harpooned for its oil drawn up at a shark-fishing station on the island of Soay in the Hebrides. *b* and *c* are photographs taken by Dr. G. H. Paker, of the British Museum (Natural History)

able numbers; others point out that the heavy trawling in the Channel is actually taking no more fish from the stock than used to be taken in the East Anglian drift-net fishery in the old days when some two thousand vessels took part. Further, there are certain changes in the stock which lead some to believe that there are at work natural causes which are more powerful than man's efforts. It is unfortunate that we must leave the problem in such an unsatisfactory position as to its solution. We cannot help wondering if we may not be at the beginning of some great change like that which affected the Baltic herring stock in the fifteenth century and broke up the Hanseatic League.

I must now add a postscript to this chapter, written as it goes finally to press, to call attention to the excellent book *The Herring and Its Fishery* which Dr. Hodgson has just published (1957). Had it appeared a little earlier I should have made frequent reference to it, for it is filled with so many interesting facts about the natural history of the herring and the ups and downs of its fisheries. In his last chapter on the causes of the present decline of the East Anglian fishery, he presents his case with great clarity and force; only time will show if he is right. He ends his book with the following words: "We know that the herring stock of the Southern North Sea has been capable of feeding a large part of Europe's human population for hundreds of years, but it has yet to be proved that it can, in addition, also feed Europe's livestock". But surely the livestock are for consumption in Europe, so that the herring may still be feeding its people if now in the form of pork or poultry which they seem to prefer. There must, however, be sufficient adult herring spared to keep up the stock, so perhaps those who prefer them may still be able to buy a few fresh herrings and Yarmouth bloaters as a luxury food, which by their fragrance and flavour they richly deserve to be. In Dickens's day the oyster was a poor man's food; our grandchildren may rightly come to rate the herring above the trout.

# CHAPTER 4

# OTHER PELAGIC FISH

THERE are more kinds of surface-living fish in the tropical and subtropical waters than there are in those of higher latitudes. It is in warmer seas than ours that the larger members of the mackerel family (Scombridae)—the tunnies, bonitoes and albacores—abound, likewise *Coryphaena,* the sailors' 'dolphin',[1] and shoals of flying-fish (Exocoetidae) and the smaller lantern-fish (Myctophidae) upon which these larger fishes prey. The opah or moon-fish (*Lampris*), the larger sun-fish (*Mola*)[2] and the sword-fishes (Xiphiidae) are also typical of milder conditions. The northern boundary of these subtropical waters is usually taken to be a line at the sea surface having a mean annual temperature of 12°C.; this isotherm, as such lines are called, luckily skirts the south-western tip of Ireland and the entrance to the English Channel, so that from time to time in summer some of these exciting exotics stray into our area.

We must take our fish of many different families in some order; before, however, we embark upon any review, I must emphasise that, in a book of this character, we cannot hope to find a full account of all our different species. I shall not attempt to give detailed descriptions of anatomy, but rather to discuss the more interesting features in the natural history of the more important kinds—especially in relation to the life of the sea as a whole—and to give only a brief mention of the other species likely to be met with. For a more detailed and systematic study of our marine fishes the reader is referred to the classical two volumes of Francis Day: *The Fishes of Great Britain and Ireland* (1880-1884), or to J. T. Jenkins's *The Fishes of the British Isles* (1925); there is also the more recent *The Sea Angler's Fishes* of M. Kennedy (1954).

We will begin with the cartilaginous elasmobranchs and in doing so we at once meet one of the largest fishes of the world: the great

[1] Not to be confused with the true dolphin which is, of course, a small toothed whale (p. 289).
[2] = *Orthagoriscus.*

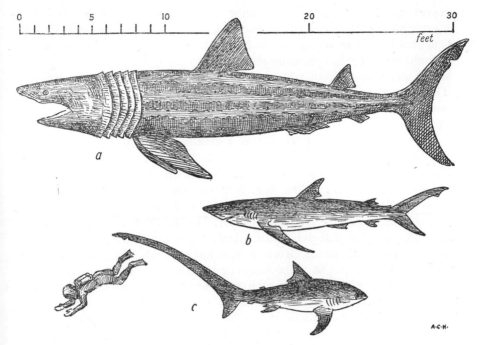

FIG. 27. Sketches of three of the largest pelagic sharks which visit British waters drawn to scale with a frog-man for comparison: *a*, the basking shark, *Cetorhinus maximus*; *b*, the blue shark *Prionace glauca*; and *c*, the thresher *Alopias vulpes*.

basking shark, *Cetorhinus maximus*; in size it is second only to its close relative, the whale-shark *Rhineodon typus*, which, however, is confined to warmer waters. Basking sharks have been recorded off Norway of up to 40 feet or more, but, there do not appear to be authentic records of British fish reaching over 30 feet. Nine fish caught in a west of Scotland fishery in 1947 and measured in great detail (Harrison Matthews and Parker, 1950) had total lengths ranging from $20\frac{1}{2}$ to $24\frac{1}{2}$ feet with an average of $23\frac{1}{4}$ feet. It is surprising that such huge fish should be so much creatures of mystery: they turn up every year in large numbers off the western coasts of Ireland and Scotland in early summer and leave in the autumn, but where do they go for the rest of the year? No one seems to have ever seen them in spring migrating from some definite quarter to our coasts or away from them in any particular direction in the autumn: suddenly one day in April or May they are here, cruising this way and that against our coasts; and then equally abruptly, in late September or October, they are gone.

Quite recently Parker and Boeseman (1954) have published a

report upon a few stragglers caught in winter in the North Sea. It is most unlikely that the main body of basking sharks from the west coast could winter in the North Sea without being noticed; nevertheless, the few which were caught revealed a most unexpected condition which helps to explain why they are not seen on the west in winter. This, however, must wait till we have described how these animals feed. It is in that hidden rest of the year that they breed, and it is not even known for certain whether they lay eggs or are viviparous, though the latter is strongly suspected from a detailed study of the reproductive organs recently published by Dr. L. Harrison Matthews (1950).[1] The specimens discussed by Parker and Boeseman throw no light on the question of breeding. The best information we have about this remarkable fish is to be found in the paper by Matthews to which I have just referred and one by him and Dr. H. W. Parker (also 1950). In Fig. 27 (p. 69) is a sketch made partly from the excellent drawing in their paper and partly from a specimen in the British Museum; for scale I have put in a six-foot frog-man as he would appear beside it. A terrifying creature for such a frog-man to encounter? Not a bit of it—the basking shark is one of the most harmless creatures in the sea; like the huge whalebone whales it is a plankton feeder, and the only damage it may do is to accidentally upset a small boat with the swish of its great tail, if it is suddenly frightened.

It is only when feeding, and when the plankton happens to be high up in the water, that they cruise along slowly, their great triangular dorsal fin showing above the water and sometimes also the tip of their tail; when on migration they most likely swim well below the surface. It is the large fin looking (in miniature) like the sail of a small fishing-boat, that gives them the name of 'sail-fish' on the west of Scotland. They are dark grey, and very often have longitudinal streaks of lightish grey along the sides and lighter grey to white on the underside. In addition to the huge fins we note the enormous gill-

[1]Dr. Denys Tucker has drawn my attention to a statement by Pennant (1776) in his *British Zoology*, Vol. 3, p. 104: "They are viviparous, a young one about a foot in length being found in the belly of a fish of this kind."

---

*Plate V.* (*above*) *a.* A composite print of two remarkable photographs of flying fish (*Cypselurus californicus*) taken at night by electronic flash by Dr. H. Edgerton, of the Massachusetts Institute of Technology; one fish is in full flight and the other just leaving the surface. Note the wash from the propeller strokes of the tail as the fish gains speed for flight. (*below*) *b.* Another of Dr. Edgerton's photographs showing the track left by the vibrating tail of a flying fish taking off; an effect only seen on a very calm surface. These are *not* the British species, but closely related.

clefts that seem to go from the very bottom of the throat to the top of its head; in fact the front pair do all but meet at the top and bottom, where there is little more than six inches between the openings on either side; between the tops and bottoms of the last pair of slits there is more space—about 16 inches. Along both the inner sides of all the gill-openings is a line of gill-rakers—long slender processes placed like the teeth of a comb—spaced at about 32 to the inch; when the gill-clefts are wide open these are erected by a special band of muscle, so that the two rows interlock to form a most efficient sieve covering the exit.

The basking shark feeds not like the herring but like the whalebone whale; it cruises along with its mouth wide open and the water streams through the greatly expanded gill-slits, while the contained plankton is strained out of it just as if by a large tow-net. That is why the basking shark, when feeding, cruises at a speed of only some two knots—a higher speed would give less efficient filtering as it would push a mass of water in front of it, just as happens if a tow-net is towed too fast. Matthews and Parker estimate that the volume of water filtered must be at least 2215 cubic metres—over two thousand tons—of water an hour. In Plate IVa, p. 67, I reproduce an excellent photograph, taken by Dr. J. H. Fraser of the Scottish Fishery Laboratory, looking down from the research vessel at a basking shark cruising and feeding just below the surface, with its gill-clefts expanded to give maximum filtration. The food consists of whatever plankton may happen to be in the water; but no doubt these sharks tend to collect in regions where the plankton is rich in *Calanus,* which abounds in the waters to the west and north of Scotland. It is when *Calanus* is especially abundant in the Clyde sea area that one sees the large dorsal fins of these 'sail-fish' dotting the surface of the Kilbrennan Sound between Arran and Kintyre, or sometimes far up Loch Fyne. In the summer of 1952 we counted 43 of them between the Paddy Rocks and Tarbert when coming down the loch in the Millport research vessel *Calanus*. This is the largest number I have seen together, but to see a dozen or so is quite a common sight. Now to return to the surprising condition shown by the few winter-caught specimens which I mentioned earlier: they had lost their gill-rakers! There can be no

---

*Plate VI.* (*above*) *a.* A tunny (*Thunnus thynnus*) breaking surface photographed by the author from a trawler fishing for herring on the Fladen Grounds in the northern North Sea; it is circling the ship picking up the herring which have dropped from the trawl in hauling. Note how the first dorsal fin is almost completely retracted into its slot (see p. 82). (*below*) *b.* A tunny caught by rod and line from a drifter off Scarborough. (*Victor Hey*)

doubt now "that the basking shark loses its rakers in October and November (in north-western European waters) and undergoes a resting, non-feeding, demersal stage during which a new set of rakers is developed; their new rakers are fully developed by February" (Parker and Boeseman, *loc. cit*). Now we know why we don't see them in winter; after feeding all summer in the plankton-rich waters near our coasts they sink to winter in deep water and there replace their frayed and worn out 'net' by a brand new one ready for the fresh outburst of plankton in the spring. At several places on the west of Scotland the basking sharks are hunted and harpooned for their liver-oil, (as in Plate IV c) and off the west of Ireland, as vividly depicted in Flanerty's film, "Men of Aran".

It is remarkable that these huge creatures, which normally cruise at such a slow speed and weigh up to four tons, are capable at times of accelerating to a speed which will enable them to leap completely clear of the water. This performance has often been recorded, but as often doubted as probably being due to a confusion of identity, perhaps with a thresher-shark or a dolphin. However, recently Matthews and Parker (1951) have published an excellent firsthand account of this leaping from Captain Harry Thomson of Portessie, Banffshire, who has had many years' experience in commercial basking-shark fisheries, and we can no longer doubt that it actually occurs. I quote the following extract:

"During June, 1948, whilst hunting in the Loch Brolum-Shiant Islands area I recorded the following incident. The weather was fine with bright sunshine and a light southerly wind and excellent visibility. I was in the wheelhouse 'conning' the catching vessel and leaning out of the open side window conversing with a member of the crew who was leaning against the wheelhouse structure with his back towards me so that we were both facing in the same direction. Suddenly, at no more than 30 yards range a huge shark (i.e. 25 ft. to 29 ft. class) leapt into the air, the entire fish being clearly outlined against the sky. Whilst in mid air the shark gave a pronounced twist or wriggle of his entire rear portion from the dorsal fin tailwards whereupon he fell back upon his flank into the sea with a resounding smack and splash. He disappeared in a shower of spray and foam."

Captain Thomson later says that of the many basking sharks he has seen leaping clear of the surface not one has done so in shallow water, but all have been outside the 40 fathom line; consequently he very reasonably believes that the fish must start his 'take-off' from a very considerable depth.

Another large shark which is said to break the surface in a similar spectacular fashion is the thresher (*Alopias vulpes*) which not infrequently comes into our waters from further south; it cannot be mistaken for any other fish on account of the extraordinary length of the tail, which, as also shown in Fig. 27, is as long as all the rest of the fish. It feeds on smaller fish and is called the thresher because—so it is said—it swims round and round a shoal of pilchard or mackerel at great speed in ever smaller circles threshing up the water with this peculiar tail and frightening them into a close huddle at the centre: a conveniently concentrated meal. Its total length to the tip of its long tail rarely exceeds 15 feet.

Also of a good size is the great blue shark *Prionace glauca*[1] which visits our water from warmer seas, particularly off the south coast in summer; the really big specimens, however, which are said to grow to 25 feet, hardly ever come into our area. Small specimens may sometimes be seen on calm sunny days swimming lazily near the surface, with the tips of their tail and dorsal fins showing like those of a basking shark. It is also shown in Fig. 27. In the last few years it has given much sport to 'big-game' anglers fishing from motor boats off the Cornish coast and it is sometimes caught entangled in pilchard drift-nets in the same area. Tucker and Newnham (1957) have for the first time recorded this species breeding in British waters: "On July 24th, 1956, some ten miles south of Looe, a gravid Blue Shark was caught which subsequently gave live birth in the boat to 22 young; three more remained undelivered, making a total of 25 for the litter, which included at least 12 males and 11 females." Two were measured: a male of 13¾ inches and a female of 15 inches.

Two other sharks may be mentioned here: the porbeagle and the mako. The former, *Lamna nasus*, is fairly common off the west coast, particularly off Ireland where it may give good sport on rod and line; it reaches a length of 9 feet. On the side of the tail there is an extra little horizontal keel. While it often swims up to the surface and may, like the blue shark, get entangled in drift-nets, it really frequents the bottom just as much, and sometimes plays havoc with fishermen's lines set for bottom-living fish. It feeds on all kinds of fish. The inclusion here of the mako or mackerel shark, *Isurus oxyrinchus*, is a surprise for which I am indebted to Dr. Denys Tucker who has kindly given me the following new information. On August 25th, 1955, a shark was caught off Looe which was at first thought to be a record

[1] =*Carcharias glaucus*, Day.

Porbeagle (352 lbs., 8 ft. 7 ins.) but which later turned out to be a mako, and another, proved by the examination of the jaws, came from the same area in the following June. In all, he says, the Shark Angling Club of Great Britain claims a dozen specimens since 1951 and he thinks "we may in future also expect to encounter the mako *Isurus tigris* Atwood now that supposed porbeagles are being more carefully scrutinised." He also tells me that there is clear evidence that the

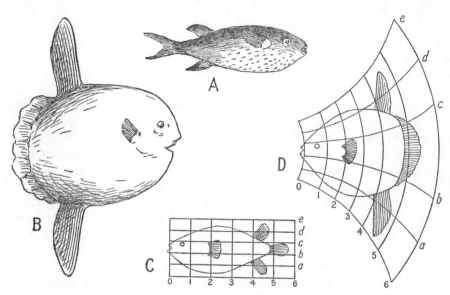

FIG. 28. The globe-fish, *Lagocephalus lagocephalus*, A, and the sun-fish, *Mola mola*, B, drawn from specimens in the British Museum (Natural History). C and D show the hypothetical derivation of the form of *Mola* from that of the related *Diodon* (C) by the principle of transformations, redrawn from D'Arcy Thompson (1942).

mako has been here before, for its teeth are figured as those of the porbeagle by Couch in his *A History of the Fishes of the British Islands* of 1877. The tope *Eugaleus galeus*[1] is another shark which gives great sport to the sea-angler, but this is more definitely a bottom-living form and will be referred to among the demersal fish.

Now we must pass on to the bony fish, and begin by briefly referring to some of the more interesting exotics mentioned at the beginning of the chapter. The great sun-fish (sometimes also called the moon-fish) *Mola* ( =*Orthagoriscus*) *mola* occurs all over the warmer Atlantic Ocean and in summer is not infrequently seen off the west coast of Ireland; indeed Jenkins (1936) writes that at times it was so abundant that the

[1] =*Galeus vulgaris*, Day.

Aran Islanders are said to have fished for it by harpoon. It is less common off the west of Scotland and only rarely enters the North Sea. It is a huge creature, almost circular in side view, as seen in Fig. 28 opposite, and may reach a size of 9 feet across from head to tail, if such terms may be used for so strangely fashioned a fish. Its reduced tail apparently takes little part in swimming and acts more as a rudder; the main propulsion appears to be by the side to side oscillation of the large dorsal and anal fins, which are said to cause, as might be expected, the animal to yaw somewhat from side to side as it advances. One might never suspect, at first, that it is closely related to the tropical porcupine-fish, *Diodon*; yet such is the case. The late Sir D'Arcy Thompson, in his great book *Growth and Form* showed by his remarkable principle of transformations how the relative proportions of the parts of one may be changed into those of the other by applying a simple mathematical formula as can be seen in our sketch (Fig. 28) redrawn from his book. Whatever the meaning of such a transformation may be, perhaps in terms of modified growth rates, it clearly confirms an already established relationship. *Diodon* never strays so far from the tropics as to reach our shores but another closely allied fish, the globe-fish *Lagocephalus lagocephalus*[1] very occasionally may do so. Like *Diodon*, it has the power of suddenly inflating itself with water to swell out like a football covered with spines to frighten off its enemies. It never reaches a length of more than 22 inches.

Another wanderer from warmer waters, coming right into the North Sea and occasionally being taken off the Yorkshire coast, is the most brilliantly coloured of all our fishes, the opah or moon-fish, *Lampris guttatus* (which has in turn also been called the sun-fish). Specimens in our waters are rarely more than 3 feet in length, but it is said to reach twice that and the specimen I was lucky enough to draw at Lerwick, Shetland, this summer (1956)—shown in Plate 2 (p. 19)— measured nearly 4 feet. Its colours are iridescent. The reds, greens, blues and purples of its body change with one's point of view; then all over the lower part of this lustrous multi-coloured background are flecks of white, and the whole gay livery is heightened by the addition of fins and tail of the most vivid scarlet. I have never seen it alive, but I once saw a quite freshly-caught specimen brought in by a fishing boat at Scarborough; and the one I painted at Lerwick, which had been caught in a seine net the day before, had been kept in cold storage for me. While the opah is characteristically a warm-water form, in summer it may go far north and has been taken off the coasts of Iceland and northern Norway. It must be a much faster swimming fish than

[1] = *Tetrodon lagocephalus*, Day.

one might think from its shape, for Orkin (1950) records that it feeds largely on oceanic squid, as many as 50 of their beaks having been taken from a single stomach. Its mouth, on opening, is pushed forward to a remarkable extent, somewhat like that of the John Dory (p. 207) only more so, because the maxilliary bones are free; this movement and sudden enlargement of the mouth cavity must have a powerful suction effect and so greatly assist in the capture of prey.

In the same group of fish as the opah is one of the rarest and most extraordinary fish in the sea: the oar-fish *Regalecus glesne,* which is world-wide in distribution; although so different in form it is placed with the opah because it has the same type of unusual jaw mechanism. Günther, in his *Study of Fishes* (1880) says not more than sixteen specimens are recorded as having been captured in British waters between 1759 and 1878; yet I believe it has been taken as often in our waters as anywhere else in the world, except perhaps off Japan. One was stranded near Anstruther, Firth of Forth, in June 1952, (Rae and Wilson, 1953); although mutilated, the part remaining measured 11½ feet. It is the largest of the so-called ribbon-fish and it must, if a good-sized specimen, be one of the most exciting fishes to meet, for it looks almost like one's idea of the mythical sea-serpent (Fig. 29 opposite). According to Günther specimens up to 20 feet in length have been recorded; they are flat and ribbon-like and swim with serpentine undulations. The sides of the body, i.e. the surface of the 'ribbon', are about 1 foot in depth and glistening silver in colour; along its entire length is a continuous dorsal fin of brilliant scarlet which at the front, at the top of the head, is enlarged into an amazing crest or mane. The paired fins, too, are scarlet and the pelvic ones are drawn out into the exceedingly long oar-like structures which give the fish its name, but it has no anal fin. It has sometimes been called the "king of the herrings" from the erroneous idea that it accompanies herring shoals. Related to this species is the deal-fish, *Trachypterus arcticus,* with its curious up-pointing tail, also shown in Fig. 29; one or two may be taken every few years off the North of Scotland, but 1954 gave a record of 15 specimens (Rae and Wilson, 1956).

Very rarely, as recorded by Day and by Jenkins, a few flying-fish, *Exocoetus volitans,* have been seen as stragglers in the western English Channel, or in the southern Irish Sea, so luckily we can just claim them for our book. I say 'luckily' because it enables me to include the remarkable photographs of flying fish in flight[1], taken by Dr. H. E. Edgerton of the Massachusetts Institute of Technology, which are shown in Plate V (p. 70). Before discussing their flight, however, let

[1] Actually not the British species, but the closely related *Cypselurus californicus.*

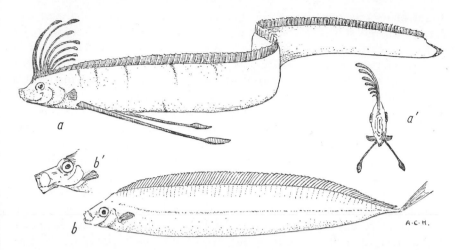

FIG. 29. *a*: the oar-fish, *Regalecus glesne*, in side view and *a'* seen from in front, drawn from a 13 foot specimen caught off Flamborough Head and now in the Tring Museum. *b*: the deal-fish, *Trachypterus arcticus*, showing the curiously upturned tail and, in *b'*, the remarkable protrusible mouth, drawn from a 6 foot specimen in the Department of Natural History, University of Aberdeen.

me refer to two relations of theirs which are not at all uncommon in our waters: the garfish and the skipper.

The garfish *Belone belone*,[1] appears to accompany shoals of mackerel, for it is often taken with them in the drift-nets, sometimes in dozens in the western Channel, and in odd ones and twos when mackerel are being caught along with herring in drift-nets in the North Sea. The specimen drawn in Plate 1 had been landed in this way at North Shields. It is another quite unmistakable fish, combining a long slender body—blue-green above and silver below—with long finely pointed jaws. Specimens are said to have been recorded nearly three feet long, but half that length is the more normal size. It is quite good eating and an interesting fish to have at table on account of its striking and unusual turquoise-green bones. Closely related to the garfish, and like it in general form, is *Scomberesox saurus*; it is called the skipper on account of its habit of leaping into the air and often skimming along the surface for quite long distances, apparently on the very tips of its pectoral fins, propelling itself with the violent oscillation of the lower lobe of the tail fin. No doubt it is doing this for the same reason that flying fishes fly—to escape through the surface from predators down below; it shows us quite clearly how the powers of

[1]=*B.vulgaris*, Day.

flight of its relatives have been evolved. The flight of the flying fish
has now been shown to be achieved by attaining a high initial speed
before it leaps out into the air, accelerated by the powerful strokes of
the lower part of the tail after the body has left the water, to enable
it to soar into the air supported on its outspread pectoral fins. This
is beautifully shown in Dr. Edgerton's photographs in Plate V. The
flight is continued as a long glide without any actual flapping of the
pectorals which may, however, passively 'flutter' in the breeze; on
reaching the surface the flight may sometimes be at once renewed by
rapid strokes of the tail before the rest of the body has been immersed.
A form such as *Scomberesox* would develop flight of this kind if natural
selection continually favoured larger and larger pectorals to keep it
longer out of harm's way when chased by fish like *Coryphaena*.

On a recent voyage of the R.R.S. *Discovery*, when lowering
lights over the side to catch squid, we found, particularly in the Bay
of Biscay area, that on some nights large numbers of *Scomberesox* were
also attracted and kept continually crossing and recrossing the patch
of light. They are said to prey upon pilchards and follow their shoals
as the garfish follows the mackerel; incidentally, it is exceedingly
doubtful that the garfish can actually feed on the mackerel, which
must be a much faster swimmer and is usually larger. *Scomberesox* is
not so often taken in our waters as is the garfish.

Now we come to the Scombridae, the family which, in addition to
its larger members of the warmer seas, includes our common mackerel,
*Scomber scombrus* (Plates 1 and VII, p. 18 and here. Next to the herring
the mackerel is commercially the most important of our pelagic fish.
It occurs in large shoals and is caught, as the herring is, in drift-nets
when it is in its plankton-feeding phase of spring and early summer.
The best account of its biology is in the papers of the late Dr. G. A.
Steven (1948-1952), upon which this brief sketch is largely based. Most
mackerel-fishing takes place from English ports; and by far the most
notable centre is Newlyn, in Cornwall, where from a third to over
half of the English catch is landed. Just before the last war the landings
for all England were some 140,000 cwt. valued at about £80,000.

Let us follow the typical movements of the mackerel throughout
the year, beginning with a curious phase which sets in at the end of
October, when they leave the surface-waters and become densely
concentrated in a number of very localised positions, particularly in
little hollows or troughs on the sea-bottom. Towards the end of December the fish, still keeping on the bottom, begin to spread outwards
from these dense concentrations over the surrounding areas of the
sea-bed. At this time they are feeding upon various animals living on

*Plate VII.* (*above*) *a.* A shoal of mackerel (*Scomber scombrus*) swimming in the Plymouth Aquarium (*Douglas Wilson*). (*below*) *b.* A comparison between the rare "scribbled" variety and the more typical form of the common mackerel : the fish are both gutted as they have come from the market. (*N. T. Nicoll*)

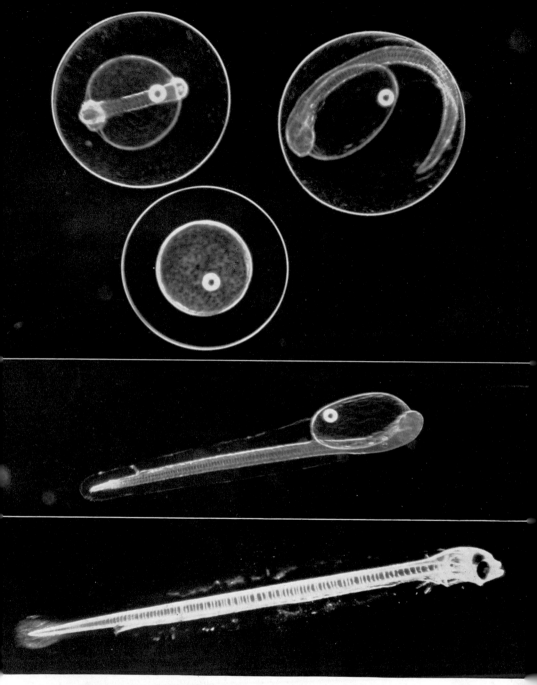

*Plate VIII.* (*top*) *a.* The planktonic floating eggs of the pilchard (*Sardina pilchardus*) in three stages of development; note the embryo fish curled round its yolk-sac which contains an oil globule. (x27) (*middle*) *b.* A baby pilchard just after hatching, it drifts upside down at this stage because the yolk-sac, with its oil globule, is more buoyant. (x25) (*bottom*) *c.* A later stage with yolk-sac completely absorbed; it now swims right-way up. (x22)

(*Douglas Wilson*)

or near the bottom such as shrimps, mysids, amphipods, polychaete worms and small fish, but not taking so much food as they do later in their pelagic phase. Towards the end of January or in early February, this new period begins; they now form shoals swimming up towards the surface, and start on their migrations, slowly moving towards the spawning areas, which they reach in April. In the area south of Ireland and west of the English Channel which has been called the Celtic Sea, are the great mackerel spawning-grounds towards which the shoals converge from the west of Ireland, the Irish Sea, the English Channel and the coasts of western France; here enormous concentrations of mackerel collect to spawn over the deeper water towards the edge of the continental shelf. Cruises made with the Plymouth research ship have charted the distribution of the floating eggs and shown them to be spawned in a wide crescentic band just inside the 100 fathom line some hundred miles to the west of the Scilly Islands (Corbin, 1947).

After spawning, these vast shoals of mackerel return very slowly back towards the land. The period of spawning is a most protracted one, reaching its height in April but extending into June; this is due partly to the eggs of some fish ripening earlier than others and also because all the eggs in one ovary ripen not together, but successively over a long period. They begin to spawn far out to the west, and continue as they move back again. During this pelagic phase from March to June the mackerel are feeding voraciously on the animal plankton, particularly the copepods *Calanus* and *Anomalocera*; they feed like the herring, by selective acts of capture. Interesting observations showing this were made by Commander G. C. Damant R.N. (1921) while hanging below a ship in a diver's suit during salvage operations; he saw them distinctly snapping at individual copepods one after the other. The plankton animals, in the shadow of the ship, showed up in dark silhouette against the brighter sunlit waters beyond, and so the fish collected under the hull to take advantage of this unusual condition. It is during this plankton-feeding period that the mackerel are the object of the drift-net fishery centred on Newlyn; here a number of the steam-drifters come to take part from Yarmouth and Lowestoft before going off to join in the great summer herring-fishing in the northern North Sea. They usually fish with nets of a larger mesh than for herring, and sometimes with a longer fleet of nets—stretching for a full three miles.

From June to July a change in the behaviour of the mackerel occurs; they disperse into quite small shoals to frequent the inshore waters, and change their diet from plankton to small fish—particularly the young of herring, sprat and sand-eels—which are swarming in the shallower bays along the coasts. Drift-net fishing is over; they must now be caught by baited hook and line. This lasts through the autumn until late October, when they disappear from the surface-waters, and begin to collect on the sea-bed for that November phase of compact concentration with which we began.

Little is known of the mackerel in the first two years of its life. By repeated surveys with tow-nets the developing eggs, and then the young larvae, can be shown to be carried by the currents towards the Channel and Irish Sea till they reach the coastal areas. After that very little is seen of them until they join in the main shoals, as two-year old fish, having become sexually mature and reached a length of nearly a foot; occasionally, however, young mackerel are taken against the coast in seine nets used for capturing sprat. Dr. Steven records that very large numbers entered Newlyn harbour in early August 1937; he caught 273 and found them to range in size from 3¼ to 6½ inches. At the end of the same month he caught 84 more which then ranged from 5½ to 7½ inches.

The movements of the mackerel in the North Sea have not yet been so fully worked out, but it is clear that they follow the same general sequence of changing phases; here, however, the great concentration of shoals for spawning is over the deep water off the Norwegian coast. At first sight it appears that their habit is quite different from that of those in the west, for they migrate in *towards* the coast to spawn whereas those in the west do the opposite. Actually their behaviour is only different if we judge it in relation to the coast, not if we judge it in regard to depth of water; to the west they spawn over deep water, over the 100-fathom line, and to find similar deep water in the North Sea they have to move over towards the Norwegian coast instead of away from it.

All the Scombridae are beautifully coloured for concealment in the upper sunlit layers of the sea—blue or blue-green above and silvery white below—but the common mackerel has that characteristic darker ripple pattern on its back. Two varieties are occasionally met with: *punctatus,* the dotted mackerel, in which the typical ripple-marks are replaced by small round black spots all over the upper surface, and *scriptus,* the scribbled mackerel, with a much smaller and finer ripple pattern, as seen in Plate VII, (p. 78). These variations of the common mackerel should not be confused with another species *Pneumatophorus colias,* the Spanish mackerel, which occasionally turns up off the south coast from warmer seas. It is similar in size, but has a more regular ripple marking above the lateral line, combined with spots below it; and it can most readily be distinguished by its area of much larger scales in front of and below the pectoral fins. The so-called horse-mackerel (p. 83) is not a real mackerel at all.

The great tunny *Thunnus thynnus*, which is the only large member of the family to be common in our waters, has a back of dark ocean blue. Whether the tunny have only recently developed the habit of coming into the North Sea after the herring is not certain: but it seems that it was not until the late twenties that the herring-fishermen reported them in numbers, and only then began the annual gathering of big-game fishermen at Scarborough and Whitby to test their skill at battling with rod and line from yacht or motor boat for these large and powerful fish. They appear to be particularly attracted to the area by the quantities of herring which are dropped from the fishing nets as they are hauled on board; and so they circle round the drifters off the Yorkshire coast or round the herring-trawlers working on the Fladen grounds.

The real home of the tunny is the Atlantic to the west of Spain and Portugal and in the Mediterranean;[1] it is known to spawn near the Azores, near Gibraltar, and between Sicily and Sardinia. While many of the fish appear to remain in these latitudes throughout the year, quite a number migrate northwards after spawning in early July and spend August to October in the waters to the west and north of Britain, in the North Sea, and off the coast of Norway. They come into the North Sea from round the north of Scotland sometimes in shoals of twenty or more; at the end of October they return south by the same route. The Italian zoologist Marsino Sella has given us much information on these migrations by studying the various kinds of hooks used by the fishermen of different nations, for the fish are sometimes found to be carrying a hook of the type used in quite another locality. In this way many migrations have been established between the Atlantic and different parts of the Mediterranean as well as some between these areas and Norway. In Norway they harpoon the tunny, and a Norwegian harpoon has been taken from the flesh of one caught near Tunis. Dr. F. S. Russell (1934a), who accompanied Sir Edward Peel on a two month's tunny-fishing cruise on his yacht *St. George*, made a special study of these visitors to the North Sea; thirty-two specimens, which he measured during August and September, 1933, ranged in length from 232 to 271 cms. (7½ to nearly 9 feet). He has also written a short but excellent account of the general biology of the fish (1934b).

[1]The tunny on the American side of the Atlantic, called the tuna, used to be considered a distinct species, *T. secundo-dorsalis*, on account of certain small differences in the size and position of the fins; most modern authorities however, regard the American and European tunnies (and indeed the Pacific ones) as only geographical races of the same species, i.e. sub-species.

Perhaps no fish is more beautifully steamlined for speed than the tunny; its fins—median, paired and tail—are all crescent-shaped like the swept-back wings of high-speed aircraft. The first dorsal fin can be suddenly erected for stability or flicked back, like a folding fan, into a groove in the back into which it fits exactly so as to offer no resistance. On Plate VI (p. 71) is a snapshot I was lucky enough to get from the deck of a herring-trawler as a large tunny broke the surface, and showed its first dorsal fin just emerging from its groove. The other photograph on the same plate is of a tunny caught off Scarborough and shows the dorsal fin completely hidden; note also the series of little finlets, so characteristic of the mackerel family, behind the dorsal and anal fins. The pelvic and the long pectoral fins can also be folded back against the side of the body, and here again there are hollows into which they exactly fit so as to produce not the slightest interference with the flow of water over the surface of the torpedo-like body. The tunny has red flesh and is unique among fish in having a body temperature some three or four degrees above that of the surrounding water; this is no doubt due to its combination of large size with very high activity.

Several other members of the Scombridae, allied to the tunny, very occasionally stray into our waters; these are the albacore *Germo alalunga* (see Tucker, 1955), the bonito *Auxis rochei*, the smaller bonito *Katsuwonus pelamis*, the marbled tunny *Euthynnus alliteratus* and the short-finned tunny *Sarda sarda*. Examples of the three last species were taken in Scottish waters in 1951 (Rae and Wilson, 1952).

While it is nothing like as common as the tunny, another very large exotic fish, which not infrequently visits our waters in summer, is the swordfish *Xiphias gladius* shown in Fig. 30 (p. 84); most often met with off the south-west, it has occasionally been found off the coasts of East Anglia but then only in a weak and dying condition. It owes its name to the enormous 'beak' or rostrum which extends forwards from the upper jaw in a truly swordlike fashion. How and for what function this structure came to be evolved we have really no idea. The swordfish does not appear to feed upon very large fish, and it can hardly use its sword to spear smaller prey, which would be caught

---

*Plate 5*. COLOURFUL FISH FROM THE NORTH
1. Blue-throat, *Scorpaena dactyloptera*, ($\times\frac{1}{2}$) Moray Firth. 2. Norway 'haddock' or bergylt, *Sebastes marinus*, ($\times\frac{1}{2}$) northern specimen landed at Aberdeen. 3. Torsk or tusk, *Brosme brosme*, ($\times\frac{1}{4}$) see note on colour on p. 000. 4. Ballan wrasse, *Labrus bergylta*, ($\times\frac{1}{3}$), a species which varies much in colour and pattern; see another example on *Plate 16*. All drawn from dead but freshly caught specimens.

1

2

3

4

A.C.H.

*Plate 5*

1a
1b
1c
2a
2b
2c
3

*Plate 6*

as on a skewer and so be very difficult to remove; and there does not appear to be any evidence of the sword being used for fighting by rival males. Specimens taken in our waters rarely if ever exceed 10 feet in length; in its native seas however, it may grow to nearly 20 feet and is one of the largest bony fish in existence. Allied to the sword-fish is the sailfish *Istiophorus americanus,* which has a shorter and more slender sword but a very large and long dorsal fin which gives it its name. This species, which is much fished for with rod and line off the American coasts, had never been recorded in our waters until August 1928, when the large individual, just over 7 feet in length, which is also shown in Fig. 30, was captured in the Yealm estuary, South Devon (Norman, 1929).

The horse-mackerel, *Trachurus trachurus,*[1] as already remarked, is not one of the real mackerel family at all, although it has the not dissimilar habits of spending part of its time on the bottom and part feeding on small fish up near the surface; it may be found either solitary or in shoals sometimes of considerable size. It is one of the Carangidae and is widely distributed in our seas. When freshly caught it may have a most brilliant iridescent sheen on the upper part of its body, as shown in Plate 15 (p. 210); a characteristic feature is the band of large plate-like scales along the lateral line.

Now we must mention the rest of the Clupeidae, having already devoted a whole chapter to the most distinguished member, *Clupea harengus.* Very closely related to the herring, but smaller, is the sprat *C. sprattus.* We have already mentioned that the young of both herring and sprat often swim together in estuaries or bays along the coast and are together given the name of whitebait. The sprat, indeed, is like a herring that never grows up; it rarely reaches more than 6½ inches in length and usually remains a shallow-water coastal fish. We can hardly regard it as a fish of the 'open sea'. It gives rise to a number of small fisheries round the coast, in England specially round the south-east: Lowestoft, Kessingland, Southwold, Aldeburgh, Brightlingsea,

[1] =*Caranx trachurus,* Day.

---

*Plate 6.* FLOWER-ANIMALS (ANTHOZOA) FROM THE SEA-FLOOR
1. Dahlia anemones (*Tealia felina, var lophoteusis,* (×½), two colour varieties fully expanded (*a* and *c*) and another retracted (*b*). 2. Plumose anemones, *Metridium senile* (×½), orange and white varieties; note very small individuals being budded off from the base of specimen *a* by process known as laceration (see p. 107). 3. An unusual orange centred variety of the stony coral, *Dendrophyllia cornigera* (×½) dredged from the edge of the continental shelf to the west of the English Channel. All drawn from living specimens, Nos. 1 and 2 in the aquarium of the Millport Marine Station (Isle of Cumbrae) and No. 3 in the Plymouth Laboratory.

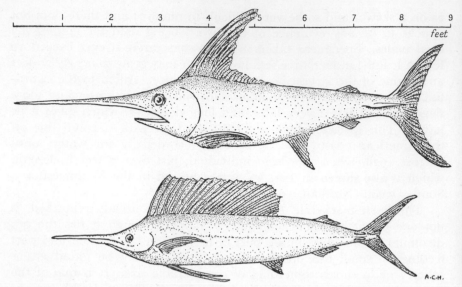

FIG. 30. *Above*, a swordfish, *Xiphius gladius*, taken off Brighton in July, 1931, and a sailfish *Istiophorous americanus* caught in the Yealm estuary, South Devon (the only record for Britain) in August, 1928. Drawn from casts in the British Museum (Natural History).

Southend, Deal, Folkestone, Hythe and Hastings. In Scotland sprats are caught from Dundee and in the Firth of Forth. The fishery is never large, varying from 50,000 to 100,000 cwts. a year for the whole country. Fishing is usually by drift-nets; but 'stow-nets', each like a very large tow-net or stationary trawl lowered below an anchored boat, are used in tidal channels where there is a very strong flow of water. Brightlingsea is justly famous for its delicious smoked and toasted sprats—home-smoked over burning oak chippings in little wooden kilns at the bottom of the cottage gardens. Sometimes larger sprats may be taken up to 20 miles off the coast in herring-nets, especially off the Tyne and Tees.

The pilchard, *Sardina pilchardus*[1] (Plate 1. p. 18) is really a subtropical fish and its range only just comes into our waters. Members of the genus *Sardina* throughout the world are closely confined to coastal waters lying between the isotherms of 12° and 20° C. It is only off our southern shores that large shoals of pilchard normally appear in British waters; it was thought that they were confined to the coasts of Cornwall and southern Ireland, but recently there is evidence of large shoals coming far up the English Channel. Just before the last

[1]=*Clupea pilchardus*, Day.

war French trawlers made big catches of pilchards from grounds between Dungeness and Beachy Head during the months of June and July and many of the landed fish were found to be spawning. Since the war the Ministry of Fisheries research trawler *Sir Lancelot* has made a number of cruises surveying the Channel for pilchard eggs and at the same time using the echo-sounder to record shoals of pelagic fish. The full results are not yet published but Cushing (1952) gives a chart of a 1949 cruise in which large patches of eggs were found off the coasts of Brittany and Normandy and a few even through the Straits of Dover into the North Sea.[1] In the same regions as the eggs, were, in many cases, found strong echo-traces of fish which, while not certainly, were most likely pilchard. In 1952 a large shoal of pilchard appeared off the coast of East Anglia to the great surprise of the herring fishermen. Dr. Hodgson in his recent book tells of the trouble pilchards may cause if they mix with the herring, because they are not easily shaken out of the driftnets; this causes the herring men to waste a lot of time in cleaning the nets before putting to sea again.

The spawning season of the pilchard is a protracted one, like that of the mackerel, and extends over the same period of time from April to July; the main centre of the spawning is off the South coast of Cornwall (Corbin, 1947). The pilchard and sprat, it should be noted, lay a floating egg like the mackerel and not one that sinks to the bottom as does that of the herring. Plate VIII, (p. 79), shows photographs of living pilchard eggs and young. Like the herring and sprat, the pilchard is a plankton-feeder, but is adapted to feed on smaller organisms; in addition to copepods and other small crustacea it takes quite a quantity of diatoms, particularly in spring and autumn, and also peridinians. Dr. Hickling, who has made a special study of the Cornish pilchard (1945), says that its year may be divided into three periods. In the first period, from April to July, feeding is vigorous; but since this is also the breeding period, most of the food goes to nourish the ripening gonads rather than to growth or fat-storage. The second period, from August to October, is the main period of growth and laying down of reserves of fat. In the third phase, from November to March, feeding is at a standstill, growth ceases and the reserve is called upon.

The pilchard fishery off Cornwall has been an important one for many generations; the fish are mainly exported to Italy. As previously mentioned, it seems that there was some reduction in the numbers of fish coming into the coastal waters in the early part of this century; more recently, however, the larger shoals seem to be returning.

[1]Since this was written Dr. Cushing has now published a fuller account: "The Number of Pilchards in the Channel" *Fish. Invest.*, 21, No. 3, 1957.

Dr. A. E. J. Went, in his history of the Irish pilchard fishery (1946), has shown how, for sometimes quite long periods, these fish have forsaken the Irish coast only to return again in great numbers; after being very scarce in this century up to 1935, they came in small shoals up to 1939, then were very abundant for the next four years and have since fallen off to smaller shoals again. Experiments in locating shoals by echo-sounding carried out by Dr. Hodgson and Mr. Richardson (1949) of the Lowestoft Laboratory have shown that some of the shoals off the Cornish coast in recent years have been of great size.

The shads, which are members of the herring family must be briefly mentioned: *Alosa alosa* the allis shad and *A. finta*[1] the twaite shad. Both these fish enter rivers to spawn; they are very like herring in size and shape but have more yellow on their sides, and either species may, or may not, have a row of black round marks along the body as seen in Fig. 31 opposite. They are sometimes taken in drift-nets with herring. Usually they are solitary when out in the open sea, but collect into shoals before coming in to spawn. There are stories of both species being attracted by music, and the Germans are said to hang little bells to their shad-nets which ring under water and 'not only attract the fish, but keep them lost in admiration as the nets are drawn in'.[2]

The anchovy *Engraulis encrasicholus* is, of course, also a clupeid but, like the sprat, it can hardly be classed as a fish of the open sea; it swims in shoals, spending most of its time in estuaries or shallow bays. It is a more slender fish than the sprat and grows to a length of 8 ins. It is very local in its distribution, and has been taken at many points round our coasts; from Wick in the north to the Wash, and the Essex coast in the east, and off the coasts of Cornwall, and Wales in the west. A great centre for the anchovy in the North Sea was that part of the Zuider Zee which was drained and reclaimed as rich agricultural land some twenty years ago; its shoals of anchovy are said to have moved into the estuaries of the Elbe.

The lantern-fish (Myctophidae) of the open ocean to the west have already been dealt with in our earlier volume along with the pelagic fish of greater depths.

The grey mullets: *Mugil chelo* (the thick-lipped) and *M. capito* (the thin-lipped grey mullet) should be included in this chapter for they are surface-frequenting fish; they are both very similar in appearance, the former species being shown in Plate 1 (p. 18). They migrate to our coasts from more southern waters in summer and to that extent are

[1] =*A. fallax* (Lac.).
[2] I am quoting from W. J. Gordon's *Our Country's Fishes*. (1902).

fish of the open sea; but once here tend to live in shallow water against the coast and often go up rivers in shoals with the tides. Another truly coastal fish of pelagic habit should just be mentioned: the very small so-called 'transparent goby' *Aphia minuta* which is sometimes taken in large shoals in shallow waters with a sandy bottom, particularly on the west coast.

The salmon *Salmo salar* is as much a fish of the sea as of the rivers. It is out of place here to take up any room in describing its journeys and breedings in fresh-water; however, since it spends so long in the

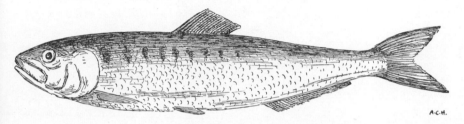

FIG. 31.   The allis shad, *Alosa alosa* ($\times \frac{1}{2}$).

sea and certainly does nearly all—if not quite all—of its feeding as an adult there, we should surely bring it into our picture.   But how very little do we know of its habits and movements in the sea!   It is true that there are definite drift or fixed-net fisheries for it at various points along the coast, for example, off Robin Hood's Bay and Filey in Yorkshire and at many places round Scotland; but these are capturing the fish that are just moving along the coast preparatory to entering the rivers. This tells us little that we do not know from river observations.   Occasionally fishermen far out to sea may catch a salmon by trawl, line or drift-net, but this is a comparatively rare event as will be seen from the chart in Fig. 32. This figure, from that recently published by Balmain and Shearer (1956) with some later additions, shows the positions of all such captures which have been reported between 1888 and 1956; as the authors say, however, these must certainly represent only a fraction of those which have been caught.   It is likely that the salmon spends the greater part of its time either in mid-water or up towards the surface, feeding upon the euphausiacean shrimp-like crustaceans which occur in immense swarms and make vertical migrations up towards the surface at night and down into deeper water by day.   The red colouring of the salmon's flesh is thought to be derived from the carotenoid and allied pigments found in the crustaceans of their diet.   We actually have very little

FIG. 32. Showing all the records of salmon taken at sea between 1888 and 1956, redrawn, with a few later additions, from the chart by Balmain and Shearer (1956); inset are those in the small shaded rectangle on the east coast of Scotland.

information regarding their food, although there are records of them taking euphausiacean and amphipod crustaceans herring as well as sand-eels and other small fish.[1] Of 108 salmon taken at sea recorded by Balmain and Shearer no fewer than 23 were found in shark stomachs (species not given) and often several together; these instances, the authors remark, suggest that salmon retain their shoaling habit in the sea. When fast mid-water trawls are developed we may perhaps catch more salmon in the open sea and the gap in our knowledge of

[1]Mr. Peter David of the National Institute of Oceanography tells me that he thinks the colour and pattern of the salmon-flies made by anglers may have been evolved by trial and error so that the more successful ones selected are those which happen more closely to resemble marine planktonic animals such as euphausiaceans or small squids. Observations on the feeding of salmon at sea are given by F. Day (1880-84), R. J. Tosh (1895, '96) and K. A. Pyefinch (1952).

their life there may be filled in; on the other hand it may well be that, as suggested by W. J. M. Menzies (1949), the main feeding grounds of our salmon lie much further away to the north-west, perhaps in arctic waters where these shrimp-like crustacea are particularly abundant and form the food of the northern whales.

The results of tagging experiments tell us very little about any regular migrations of the salmon in the sea, although there are some notable journeys recorded. Fish which have been marked when caught in coastal nets in the sea, are as a rule, as we might expect, caught again in rivers or sea-nets which are close at hand, but occasionally there are exceptions as in the following examples. Menzies (1949) records salmon tagged at Fascadale on the west of Scotland being re-caught as far away as the Moray Firth, Montrose and the Tay on the east, and Conway, North Wales and the Liffey at Dublin in the south; he also mentions a fish marked in Scottish waters being caught in Norway and several Norwegian fish being caught in Scotland. Salmon tagged by Went (1951) on the west of Ireland have travelled to the Moray Firth, to the west of Scotland and to North Wales. Menzies (loc. cit.) gives some idea of the speeds attained by salmon over long distances. In Scotland, he says, the usual range is 17 to 23 miles a day, but exceptional fish have travelled at speeds of 28, 33 and 35 miles a day covering distances of 250, 300 and 240 miles respectively. Norwegian fish, migrating along the north coast of Europe, showed speeds of 24 to 40 miles a day and one completed a 680-mile journey at an average of 62 miles a day. Now, since this chapter was originally written, Menzies and Shearer (1957) have announced the remarkable migration of a salmon which was tagged at Loch na Croic on the Blackwater River, Ross-shire, in November 1955 and recaptured in the following October in Eqaluq Fjord on the south-west coast of Greenland: a journey of over 1,700 miles. This record gives the first direct evidence supporting the suggestion made by Menzies, which we referred to above, that the salmon may go far to the north-west for feeding.

The sea-trout (Salmo trutta), as Jenkins (1925) says, "is less marine in its habits than the salmon, remaining for the most part in the vicinity of the coast." This is well brought out by a chart given by Balmain and Shearer (loc. cit.) showing all the reported captures of sea trout at sea from 1914 to 1954. Another fish of the salmon family which breeds in fresh water and spends part of its life in the sea is the houting (Coregonus oxyrhynchus); it occurs in the southern North Sea mainly off the Dutch and German coasts and is only rarely taken in English rivers. The smelt, Osmerus eperlanus, which is still more of a coastal and estuarine fish, can hardly be called a fish of the open sea.

A chapter on the pelagic fish of our seas should not close without mention of the remarkable little "*Leptocephalus brevirostris*" which was once thought to be a distinct species but is now known to be the young of our common freshwater eel *Anguilla anguilla=A. vulgaris*.  In the ocean to the west of the British Isles—indeed to the west of all Europe—may be found this little creature of glass-like transparency; it is the shape and size of a willow-leaf and as flat.  The life-story of the eel is now so well known that it will scarcely bear repeating; yet I must give it in brief outline because I would like to make a point regarding it which I do not believe has been made before[1].  It had for long been known that the fully grown male and females migrate down the rivers and pass into the sea.  Such old fish have never been seen coming into the rivers again; but instead baby eels, known as elvers, slender little creatures about two inches long, enter the rivers from the sea in vast numbers in the spring and gradually grow into the familiar eels of our rivers and canals.  In the year 1896 the Italian naturalists Grassi and Calandruccio kept the little 'Leptocephalus brevirostris' (which passes from the Atlantic into the Mediterranean) in an aquarium at Messina and for the first time saw it turn into the common elver.

I will only very briefly recapitulate the story of the magnificent work of that great Danish oceanographer, the late Professor Johannes Schmidt.  It was in 1904, when he was fishing for cod-fry to the west of the Faeroes, that he first caught specimens of *Leptocephalus*.  He thereupon decided to hunt further out to the west till he should find the source of the supply of these frail little fish—in fact the breeding ground of the freshwater eels.  In a series of expeditions in the ships *Thor, Margreth* and *Dana* he surveyed the North Atlantic with large tow-nets.  As he went further and further west he found smaller and smaller *Leptocephalus*.  Eventually he found the smallest at a point some 600 miles south-east of Bermuda—over the deep water of the Sargasso Sea.  Thither our mature 'freshwater' eels, after spending some five to seven years in our rivers, canals, and backwaters, set out in old age upon this fantastic adventure: a pilgrimage to lay their floating eggs some thousand fathoms deep in the ocean at a point more than 2,000 miles away.  From the eggs laid there the little transparent larvae hatch out, to drift in their millions in the great circulation of the ocean—growing as they drift—and eventually to approach the coasts of Europe.  Here they undergo a striking metamorphosis: by becoming narrower, rounder, and pigmented they change into the little black elvers.  These now have a strong instinct to enter fresh

[1]For the full story see Johannes Schmidt (1922) and L. Bertin (1956).

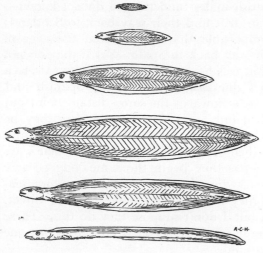

FIG. 33. Stages in the development of the common eel, from the young '*Leptocephalus*' larva to the elver, drawn natural size from specimens in the British Museum.

water and to swim against the current, and so they pass up into our rivers. This remarkable development is shown in Fig. 33.

The little elvers enter the rivers of Europe all along its coasts from the north of Norway to the south of Spain and in the Mediterranean. They have all been spawned in the same place and their distribution on the coasts of Europe must surely depend on chance ocean drift. When fully grown and adult, back they go to this one far-away spot in the Sargasso Sea. It has always seemed a great mystery how these eels can find their way back to this single small area in the ocean so far away; how can they navigate through all the directional changes in the flow of the great ocean circulation? Do they swim near the surface or in mid-water? or do they follow the ups and downs of a particular course over the ocean floor? Only one adult eel has been taken in the open Atlantic, that found by the Prince of Monaco in the stomach of a sperm whale near the Azores (Vaillant, 1898); this is no doubt due to the lack of fishing with proper gear at the right depth[1]. The adult eels are seen leaving the rivers for the sea, and their eggs and newly-hatched fry are found in only one spot in the world: we cannot doubt that they make the journey.

Many have marvelled as to how the hazards of this migration can be overcome; but as far as I know one aspect of these difficulties seems to have been overlooked. It seems too much to suppose that the larvae from the eggs of (say) Scottish eels—even supposing that Scottish

[1] Adults have been taken 20 miles south of the Devon and Cornish coasts (see Bertin, 1956).

females are fertilized by Scottish males (and this we do not know)—should by the chance of ocean drift find their way back to Scotland; similarly it seems equally impossible that larvae from the eggs of Spanish eels should find their way back to Spain. Yet if they do not do this, how can Scottish adult eels have the instinct to navigate to a point lying some 2,000 miles due *south-west*, whereas Spanish and Mediterranean eels must navigate towards the same distant point but on a course *west-by-south*? Not only that, but how—unless they be distinct stocks, which seems impossible—do the North Sea eels and the Mediterranean eels have their separate instincts to find their ways out of their respective seas *before* they begin the same long oceanic navigation that other eels make directly they leave the western sea-board? The varying courses they would have to take, if going direct, are shown in Fig. 34 below, but I don't suppose they do this. These indeed are problems to ponder over. Perhaps only those from just one area return to the spawing ground.

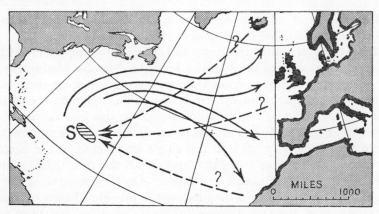

FIG. 34. The continuous arrows show the drift of the eel larvae from the spawning ground S towards the coasts of Europe and North Africa, and the blacked-in coasts are those into whose rivers the young elvers go. The broken line arrows show the bearings which the adult eels must take if they should all swim back to the spawning grounds by the most direct routes—a most unlikely event.

By way of an appendix to this chapter on pelagic fish we may mention certain "hangers-on". The remarkable remora (*Remora remora*)[1] or sucking fish has the dorsal fin on top of the head modified to form a most effective sucker by which it attaches itself to large fish, especially sharks, and sometimes to turtles and to whales. The remora is of world-wide distribution in the warmer seas and only rarely comes into

[1] = *Echeneis remora*, Day.

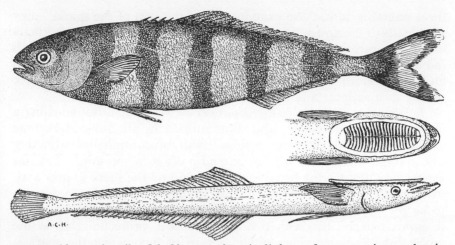

FIG. 35. Above, the pilot fish *Naucrates ductor* ($\times \frac{1}{2}$) drawn from a specimen taken in a driftnet off Lewis in the Outer Hebrides and, below, the sucking-fish *Remora remora* (also $\times \frac{1}{2}$) drawn from a specimen in the Oxford University Museum, with inset a view of the sucker on the head from above.

our waters; when it does it is most usually found attached to the great blue shark. Our specimens are usually not more than five inches in length, but in their normal habitat they may grow to nearly two feet. They are not parasites: they appear to be merely cadging a lift. In Plate XXVI (p. 259) is seen a splendid photograph taken by Dr. Wilson in the aquarium at Miami, Florida, showing one remora already attached to a hawksbill turtle and another just about to attach itself. In Fig. 35 above I give a sketch of a British specimen to show the details of the sucker. J. R. Norman in his excellent *A History of Fishes* (1931) writes:

> "Feeding as they do on other fish, the Remoras are in the habit of attaching themselves to Sharks, Whales, Porpoises, Turtles, and even occasionally to ships, and in this way they are not only protected from their enemies, but are carried without effort to fresh feeding grounds. Once among a shoal of fish they soon detach themselves, dart off and swim actively about in pursuit of prey, seeking a fresh anchorage when their appetite has been satisfied".

The lamprey *Petromyzon marinus*, which will be referred to in one of the chapters on demersal fish (p. 175) is often found attached to the huge basking sharks. Matthews and Parker in the paper (1950) already quoted say that practically every shark captured had one or more of them adhering to it. "An examination of the skin of the sharks" they say "leads to the conclusion that the armouring of closely-set denticles forms a protection too hard for the lamprey to penetrate with its radula. The sucker leaves a mark but this is entirely superficial and no open wounds were found . . . The lamprey thus uses the shark merely as a support and means of transport . . . "

Lastly there is the pilot-fish *Naucrates ductor*, a small fish reaching a length of about 10 inches and distinguished by its broad dark blue vertical bands. It has the curious habit of continually swimming below large sharks and whales, and also often below ships. Popular legend says that having better eyesight, it guides the shark to prey and, in return, gains some scraps from the resulting meal. There appears to be no sound observation in support of the first part of this story; it appears likely, however, that pilot-fish seek protection below the larger fish, and sometimes obtain scraps of food when the shark is tearing its prey to pieces. They may well follow ships, as sea-gulls do, to pick up the scraps thrown overboard. In some of the old natural histories it was suggested that these pilot-fish have some means, such as a dorsal fin-ray, for attaching themselves like 'straphangers' to the larger fish they accompany; there is, however, no evidence for this. They are not common in our waters, but have been met with from time to time along the south coast; individuals, or even a small shoal, may accompany sailing ships right into harbour, as has occurred at Plymouth and Falmouth. Occasionally odd ones may also be caught in the mackerel nets off Cornwall, and more rarely in herring nets up the coast of Scotland; my drawing in Fig. 35 p. 93, is of a specimen taken in a drift-net off Lewis in the Outer Hebrides.

CHAPTER 5

# BENTHOS—THE LIFE ON
# THE OCEAN FLOOR

BEFORE we can understand the natural history of the bottom-living fish we must know something of the sea-bed over which they swim and of the other less familiar creatures which live there with them. All these other forms of life, referred to collectively as the *benthos* (Gk., depth of the sea), are vitally important to the fish either as their prey or as voracious competitors for limited supplies of food. It is not, however, just their relations with the fish that make these benthic animals interesting to the naturalist; in themselves they present a world of life rivalling that of the plankton in its wealth of surprising adaptations.

Many people imagine that the bottom of the sea is covered with seaweeds, but, as we have already seen, (p. 5), they will only grow in shallow water near the coast where sufficient light can reach them. Yet if we put down a dredge or trawl in certain parts of the North Sea we may bring up from the bottom tufts and tufts of fern-like growths, as if our net had been dragged through some woodland glade. Indeed, so fern-like are these objects, that a new industry developed in Germany between the two wars to collect them, dry them, and dye them a bright green, for use in hanging baskets to decorate our restaurants and cinemas.[1] It was only the zoologists who knew that they were really dead animals. If we take one of these alive, fresh from the dredge, and put it in a bowl of sea-water, and then, after a few minutes, examine it with a lens, we shall see something even more beautiful than the frond of a fern; along each little branch are what might be rows of tiny flowers, only from time to time their 'petals' move like fingers. If we look more closely we will see that in the centre of each 'flower' is a tiny mouth. Each spray is a colony of little animals which, having budded off one from another like our freshwater *Hydra*, have remained connected like the branching stems of a plant; they are hydroids (marine relations of *Hydra*) and each little flower-like head is an individual polyp with a ring of tentacles reaching out to capture food from the water about them. How plant-like they are will be seen in Plate III (p. 66) where all the growths on the stone to which the herring spawn is attached are hydroids; the species gathered for the trade belong to the genus *Sertularia* (Fig. 36 p. 96).

Many of these hydroid colonies bud off the little medusae—the tiny jelly-fish—so characteristic of the plankton round our islands; these, being male or female, represent the sexual phase and, floating in the moving waters, spread the species far and wide. Both polyps and medusae, like other members of the great phylum Coelenterata (Gk., *koilos*, hollow; *enteron*, bowel or gut) are armed with numerous small stinging devices—the nematocysts; these, which were described in detail in our earlier volume (p. 93) paralyse their prey and also drove sufficiently unpleasant to discourage larger would-be predators

[1]Hancock, Drinnan and Harris (1956) now report the start of a similar 'white-weed fishery' in the Thames estuary in recent years.

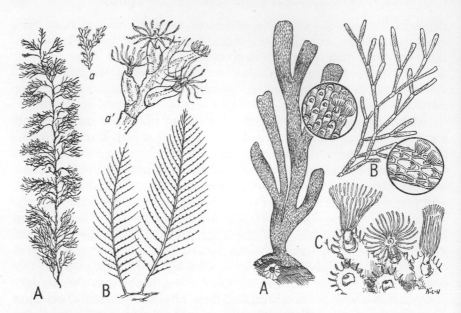

FIG. 36. (*left*) Examples of hydroids: A, a spray of *Sertularia argentea*, the 'white weed' of commerce ($\times \frac{1}{2}$), with small portions magnified to different degrees a and a'; B, two sprays of *Nemertesia (Antennularia) antennina* ($\times \frac{1}{2}$).

FIG. 37. (*right*) Examples of polyzoans: A, a spray of *Flustra* and, B, of *Salicornaria;* natural size, but each with a portion enlarged and C, a greatly enlarged portion of *Flustrella* showing some zooids with tentacles expanded.

from taking a meal. The medusae of some hydroids (as also explained in Part I) are not set free, but remain attached to the parent colony and are often reduced to mere egg-bearing sacs. This is so in the genus *Sertularia* just mentioned, and here we can see a good reason for it. Hydroids cannot grow on sand or mud, but *Sertularia* frequently lives on patches of stony bottom surrounded by wide tracts of such unfavourable ground; if the medusae were set free, the majority would carry the eggs to areas where they could never grow. Thus the eggs of those medusae which failed to be liberated would tend to survive and give rise to future generations more often than those which floated away; genetic variations in this direction would thus continually be selected and the free-swimming medusae be eliminated from the race.

Why do these creatures resemble plants, and make up what we might call miniature forests of animal life? It is because, just as plants spread out their branches and leaves to catch as much sunlight as they can, these animals depend upon food falling from above or swimming round them; they stretch out their tentacles to catch either the dead or dying material continually sinking from the teeming plankton community in the waters overhead or the little animals actually alive in the plankton about them.

If the hydroids look like ferns, there are other coelenterates which are much more flower-like and indeed are called the Anthozoa (Gk., *anthos*, a flower; *zoon*, an animal). The sea-anemones, such as the beautiful and well-named Dahlia anemones (*Tealia*) seen in Plate 6 (p. 83), are typical examples; there are many species on the sea-bed, and a wide variety may usually be found at low tide on a rocky coast. The beautiful monograph by Professor T. A. Stephenson (1928, '35) should be consulted for a full account of them. There are other flower-animals, however, which form branching colonies like the hydroids only much larger; these are the gorgonians or soft corals such as the brilliant orange-red *Eunicella* from the English Channel (Plate 7, p. 98) On some of the deeper rocky bottoms to the west of Scotland are many more kinds of gorgonians and other allied but more delicate forms of a different group (the antipatharians); they appear almost as if gathered in some orchard as the white, rose and salmon-coloured tentacles of the polyps of the various species spread out like miniature fruit blossoms covering branching stems perhaps several feet in length. Recently a very striking and unusual yellow and orange variety of a stony coral (*Dendrophyllia cornigera*) has been dredged up from the edge of the continental shelf to the west of the English Channel by the new Plymouth Research Ship *Sarsia*; I show it in Plate 6 (p. 83), looking almost like some exotic daisy. Why should all these animals be coloured as brilliantly as any flower?

Bright colours in nature are usually a form of advertisement. The flowering plants on land, of course, advertise their nectar to attract insects to bring about their pollination; their fruits and berries are gaudy signs, generally red or yellow, announcing food and drink to birds who in return will scatter their seeds. We might expect the flower-animals of the sea to carry their colours for some good reason. Among land-animals, bright colours are usually developed for one of two reasons: either to attract or stimulate the opposite sex or to give notice of some unpleasant quality. Examples of the latter function are found in some animals which protect themselves with stings or poison glands, as seen in the yellow and black bandings of wasps and venomous snakes, or in the scarlet of the fire-bellied toad; their distinctive markings have been evolved along with the stings or poison so that vertebrate animals, which are able to profit by experience, may soon learn to leave them alone. Such colours are called warning colours. Since we know that fish can distinguish different colours

(p. 22), we might well suppose that the brilliant hues of the stinging sea-anemones and coral polyps are danger signals reminding hungry fish from past experience that they are not good to eat; there are, however, some formidable difficulties in the way of accepting such a view. These difficulties have been pointed out particularly by Professor Stephenson who, in addition to being the great authority on the sea-anemones, is such a keen observer and recorder of colour and pattern in marine animals. His powers in this respect are seen in the exquisite paintings which illustrate his monograph already referred to and also his delightful "King Penguin" book *Seashore Life and Pattern* (1944). In a later paper (1947) he gives special attention to the colours of sea-anemones and writes as follows:

> "The situation is complicated by the fact that conspicuous individuals (e.g. blazing white and orange) and inconspicuous ones (e.g. an intricate mosaic pattern of browns) of one and the same species occur under identical circumstances in the same pool; and these may be accompanied by pure white and bright pink forms, again belonging to the same species.
>
> Has this coloration any value in the anemone's life? This question cannot be answered with any finality until far more field observations and experiments have been carried out than have yet been made. There are indications, however, which make functional explanations seem rather unsatisfying or which suggest that, even if the explanation is partly functional, it is partly to be sought elsewhere. The co-existence in the same pool of individuals exhibiting 'warning' and 'protective' types of coloration has just been mentioned, and it must be remembered that some at least of the animals which eat anemones possess such limited powers of vision that there is no question of their being able to see the patterns as we do".

Presently (in the next chapter, p. 128) we shall refer to this problem again when we discuss the brilliant colours of the sea-slugs; and we shall note how colour effects are modified as we go deeper in the water owing to the rapid absorption of the red and yellow rays.

There are other little animals which bud off from one another to

---

*Plate 7.* A SEA-FAN, A HONEYCOMB 'CORAL' AND A SEA-PEN
1. A sea-fan (a gorgonian soft coral), *Eunicella verrucosa: a,* whole colony ($\times \frac{1}{2}$) and *b,* small part enlarged. 2. Ross or honeycomb 'coral' (a polyzoan), *Lepralia foliacea: a,* whole colony ($\times \frac{1}{2}$) and *b,* part enlarged. (c.f. Fig. 37C, p. 96, for a higher magnification of a polyzoan). 3. A sea-pen, *Pennatula phosphorea: a,* whole colony ($\times \frac{1}{2}$) and *b,* part enlarged. All drawn from living specimens at Plymouth.

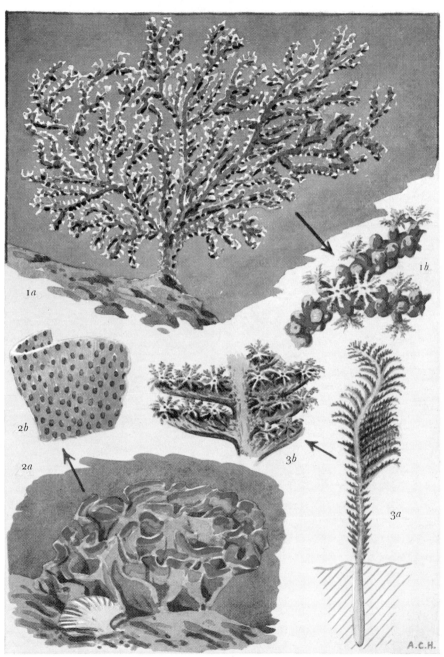

*Plate* 7

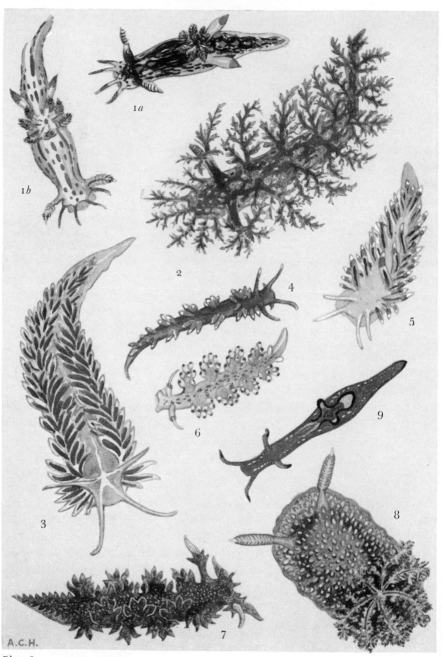

A.C.H.

*Plate 8*

form plant-like colonies looking at first sight rather like hydroids, but they are really very different. These are colonies of Polyzoa (Gk. *poly*, many), sometimes called the Bryozoa or moss-animals (Gk. *bryon*, a lichen, moss or seaweed); while each little individual bears a crown of tentacles like a hydroid polyp, it is a much more complex creature and its tentacles do not seize their prey, but, by the action of cilia (as I shall explain in a moment) create a little whirlpool in the water to draw tiny specks of planktonic food down to the mouth. If the polyzoan individuals are small, the colonies they build by repeated budding may be of quite a considerable size. Some form little branching fern-like sprays, others spread out in thin sheets like lichens encrusting the surface of a rock, and some there are which produce flat fronds like those of a seaweed, as the sea-mat *Flustra* (Fig. 37, p. 96); yet others, with a skeleton of lime, may build impressive coral-like growths such as the beautiful orange-coloured 'ross' or honeycomb coral, *Lepralia* (shown in Plate 7, p. 98) which may grow to be a foot or more across.

For those who are not zoologists, and who have not read the earlier volume, I must digress for a moment about cilia, for they play such an important part in the lives of so many marine creatures. Cilia are tiny (indeed microscopic) hair-like processes which project into the water in large numbers from the surfaces of these animals and by their rhythmic beating make the water flow in a particular direction. Very small animals like the ciliate protozoa or the flatworms use them for locomotion and propel themselves by driving the surrounding water backwards; many larger animals use cilia extensively for creating water currents for collecting food and driving it towards the mouth, or for bringing fresh supplies of dissolved oxygen to the gills for respiration. We shall see examples of some remarkable ciliary mechanisms.

On a rocky bottom we get a wonderful profusion of sponges, hydroids, sea-anemones, gorgonians, ascidians or sea-squirts (to be mentioned later) encrusting and branching polyzoa, together with hosts of roving worms, crustaceans, molluscs, starfish, brittle-stars and sea-urchins. Quite recently G. R. Forster (1954), equipped with a self-contained diving apparatus, has begun to give us a survey of all this life on the rocky regions of the sea-bottom off the Devon coast; he has

---

*Plate 8.* SEA SLUGS AND A YOUNG SEA-HARE
1 and 1a. *Polycera quadrilineata* (Müller) (×3). 2. *Dendronotus frondosus* (Ascanius) (×2). 3. *Coryphella lineata* (Lovén) (×1½). 4. *Coryphella pedata* (Montagu) (×3½). 5. *Eubranchus tricola* Forbes (×1½). 6. *Doto coronata* (Gmélin) (×4). 7. *Lomanotus genei* (Vérany) (×2½). 8. *Acanthodoris pilosa* (Müller) (×1½). 9. *Aplysia punctata* (Cuvier) very young 'sea-hare' (×3½). All drawn from living specimens in the Plymouth Laboratory except No. 6 which was drawn at Cullercoats.

provided us with a wonderful picture of it by accurately recording, foot by foot, all the animals he has seen while making traverses along lines of rock surface and descending into gulleys. But we need not wait till we have diving equipment to see much of this life for ourselves; it is very simple to use a dredge from quite a small boat and so bring up samples of the benthos for examination. In the opening chapter of the first volume I briefly told of the beginnings of the exploration of the sea-floor with the naturalist's dredge; let me now describe its use.

A small rectangular dredge of the kind shown in Fig. 38, which is suitable for use with a rowing- or motor-boat, may be purchased from the Marine Biological Association at the Plymouth Laboratory. If it is only a foot or eighteen inches across it can be used on a hemp rope, and hauled in by hand by two people without much difficulty. It should be kept on the bottom for only about five or ten minutes at a time as it very quickly fills up; several short hauls are better than one long one. On coming up the dredge should be emptied out into a shallow bath, and the more interesting specimens sorted out into glass jars or bowls full of sea-water so that they may be seen to advantage. Bottom-living animals will not live for long in an aquarium unless it can be kept cool and aerated;[1] and the animals must not be over-crowded.

The pleasures of looking at the spoils gathered by a dredge are every bit as great as those of examining a plankton sample; the range of different animal groups represented is as wide and their size is usually so much bigger that you can see the exciting novelties more readily. There is no need to search with a lens, at any rate at first. If you are exploring a reasonably good ground you will be astonished at the wealth of life brought up by so small a device in so short a time. Members from all the major groups of invertebrate animals may be there. But which members will they be? On a new ground it is the uncertainty as to what is coming up that makes dredging such a fascinating pursuit. It is indeed a naturalist's lucky dip: pulling from the hidden world a bag full of zoological treasures. Sponges, hydroids, anemones, polyzoans, worms, sea-slugs, ascidians, sea-spiders (pycnogons) and spider-crabs, starfish and brittlestars—all these, and more, may be in just one haul; and on each new ground there will be a different assortment of species. Dredging will continue to give endless delight.

When you have seen the larger animals, pick up a single stone which has come up in the bag and examine it carefully, perhaps now using

[1]Small and inexpensive electric aeration pumps may be obtained from many aquarium dealers.

a lens. It is a world in itself. Here are all sorts of organisms covering its surface: flat encrusting sponges, moss-like hydroids and polyzoa, little tube-forming worms, barnacles and spreading gelatinous ascidians (colonial sea-squirts); long slender bristle-worms wriggle from one piece of shelter to another, and stuck like a limpet to its underside may be one of those primitive molluscs *Chiton*, with a line of plates down its back, looking almost like a wood-louse. At the very bottom of the bag, by turning it inside out, you are sure to find a host of small crustaceans; shrimps, amphipods, mysids, cumaceans and the like.

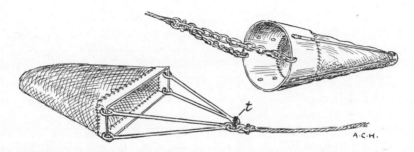

FIG. 38. *Left:* the naturalist's dredge, note that the arms of one side are tied to the shackle ring by twine at *t* as a safety device—if the dredge gets caught on a rock the twine will break before the rope will and so allow the dredge to swing clear and be saved. *Right:* the conical or bucket dredge.

Popular imagination is apt to picture the world under the sea as everywhere like a glorious fairyland of these strange plant-like forms which I have just been describing; and in some places this life is indeed very rich, as on the north and west of Scotland. The greater part of the sea-floor round our islands, however, is gravel, sand or mud with a very different kind of animal life, one living for the most part down below its surface. A rocky bottom only occurs extensively where mountain ranges dip below the sea to form great submerged reefs or where strong currents sweep away the deposits of sand or mud which would other-wise settle on the exposed surfaces. Off any rocky coast we can usually find some areas of hard ground on which to dredge; if we cannot, the sand and gravel may bring forth an equally rich, but quite different, fauna. If you are dredging on a sand or muddy bottom it is well to take a sieve with you and then you can wash away small parts of the deposit at a time to leave the animals behind as if washing for gold; the amount of life which may come out of just a bucket-full of sand, seems at first almost unbelievable. The photographs in Plates X and XI (pp. 115 and 130) show all the animals actually found below just one square foot of sand and gravel respectively.

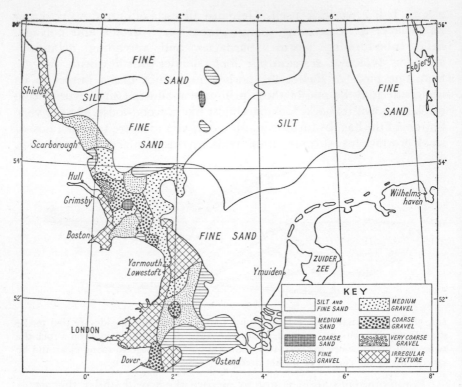

FIG. 39. Map showing the distribution of the main types of sea-bottom over the southern North Sea, redrawn (with some detail omitted) from Borley (1923). See Fig. 6 (p. 13) for position of the Dogger Bank.

We find a similar contrast between the benthos on a floor of rock and that on sand, or mud, to that between the animals on corresponding kinds of seashore. Indeed the faunas on rock and sand below the sea have certain general similarities to those of like habitat between the tides; there is, of course, the important difference that the benthic animals do not have to contend with the pounding action of the waves or the twice daily exposure to the atmosphere.

It is not surprising that the continental shelf, which has been largely formed by the action of the sea wearing away the rock of the land, should for its greater part be covered either by sand or mud. The broken rock fragments are, of course, gradually reduced to sand by these same forces; the mud is formed from the still finer particles of material carried out from the coast by the rivers and surface erosion, and mixed with detritus—the tiny organic fragments formed by the breakdown of sea-weeds and dead animals. All these deposits derived from the land are appropriately termed *terrigenous* in contrast to the *pelagic* deposits which cover the floor of the great oceans in the depths beyond the edge of the shelf. The name 'pelagic' is given to these deep oceanic oozes because in the main they are formed from the skeletons of tiny planktonic animals which once lived up near the surface; such are the globigerina, radiolarian, diatom and pteropod oozes, which have been accumulating for millions of years (see p. 141).

The first survey of the different kinds of terrigenous deposits *with* their animal life was made by Dr. E. J. Allen in the Plymouth area at the end of last century (1899). He used a small naturalist's dredge, as shown in Fig. 38 (p. 101), for collecting the animals, and the same instrument, but lined with a canvas bag inside the netting, for bringing up samples of the various gravels and sands they lived in. By using a set of standard sieves he classified these deposits into a series of grades ranging from those composed of large fragments to those of finest silt. Some ten years later Mr. J. O. Borley,[1] of the Board of Agriculture and Fisheries (as it was then) conducted an extensive survey of the different kinds of deposits over the whole of the North Sea using the bucket-like conical dredge which is also shown in Fig. 38; this digs further in than the ordinary dredge and so it scooped up better samples of the 'soil' in which he was principally interested. He used Allen's classification of grades, with an additional one (Ia in the table below). It is worth while looking at his results, because, as we shall see presently, these different grades of soil have a profound bearing on the types of animal life to be found in the different places. Fig. 39 opposite, shows a map of the North Sea giving the main areas of the various deposits as he found them; the grades are explained in the accompanying table:

*Table showing Allen's grading of terrigenous deposits*

| Grade I | | large fragments | — | over 15 mm. diameter | |
|---|---|---|---|---|---|
| ,, | Ia | very coarse gravel | — | 10–15 | ,, | ,, |
| ,, | II | coarse gravel | — | 5–10 | ,, | ,, |
| ,, | III | medium gravel | — | 2·5–5 | ,, | ,, |
| ,, | IV | fine gravel | — | 1·5–2·5 | ,, | ,, |
| ,, | V | coarse sand | — | 1–1·5 | ,, | ,, |
| ,, | VI | medium sand | — | 0·5–1 | ,, | ,, |
| ,, | VII | fine sand | — | 0·15–0·5 | ,, | ,, |
| ,, | VIII | silt | — | separated by special settling apparatus | |

[1]The first World War greatly delayed the publication of his results (Borley, 1923).

We can now see what great areas of the sea-bed are covered by gravel, sand and silt respectively.

Up to this time all the work done on the benthic animals had been of a purely qualitative kind—listing the various species brought up in the dredge from different places, and noting which were common and which rare. In 1911 that great Danish pioneer in marine research C. G. J. Petersen published the first account of a new method he had devised for giving quantitative estimates of the actual numbers of animals contained within definite volumes of sand or mud. Hitherto

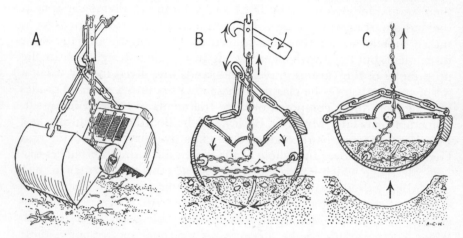

FIG. 40. Petersen's quantitative bottom-sampling grab: A, open and about to strike the bottom; B, closing to bite out its sample; and C, closed and carrying the sample to the surface.

the dredge had merely dipped into the bottom and brought up a sample of the type of 'earth' and some of the animals found with it; we had little idea of how dense the populations were, or indeed, if they were being properly sampled at all—for most of the animals burrow well down below the soil-surface. Petersen invented a 'grab' like that employed today by certain types of dredgers for lifting gravel. Its working will best be understood by reference to Fig. 40. It is lowered to the bottom on a steel cable, with its 'jaws' held wide open by supporting links slung from a hook on a counter-weighted lever. When the jaws strike, they bite deeply into the sand or mud; and at the same time the links supporting them are automatically released, so that they are now free to close. When the main cable, which is fastened to a chain passing round a system of pulleys on the inside, is pulled up, it first of all draws the jaws together; this encloses all the sand or mud between them as in a box and so brings it up to the surface with all the animals living in it. The size of the jaws are carefully made so that they 'grab' a definite area of the sea-floor, such as 1/10th or 1/5th of a square metre. This marked a great advance in the study of the ecology of the sea-bed; it was now possible to move about in a research ship grabbing similar quantities of deposit from different places and, after passing them through an appropriate series of sieves, to estimate the populations of the various kinds of animals found per square metre on each kind of ground.[1] We can now report, with much more assurance than we could before, that one area—at present—is so much richer (say) in plaice-food than another and so on; the 'at present' is important, however, for the populations of benthic animals may change with varying conditions, and sometimes change quickly. On the other hand we must realize that our collecting instruments are not yet perfect and some animals may be missed. The late Dr. G. A. Steven (1930) tells us that the curious worm-like animal *Sipunculus* has never been taken by any device in the waters off Plymouth, yet it is frequently found there, but only in the stomachs of the common dogfish (*Scyliorhinus canicula*). He reminds us of "the relative inefficiency of every type of gear compared with fishes as collectors."

Petersen's brilliant work revolutionized the study of the bottom-living fauna and enabled us to relate it much more closely to fish life and to fishery problems. We will, however, leave a consideration of the results of these benthic surveys to the next chapter; we must first say a little more about the natural history of the animals concerned. We have seen how there is a continual rain of organic particles settling to the bottom from the teeming planktonic world above—dead and dying organisms as well as faecal matter. They sink to form a rich layer of detritus covering the top of the sand or mud; in very shallow waters there will also be a copious flora of diatoms, flagellates and other simple plants. Here, too, is a microfauna of many kinds of protozoa; and there are hosts of bacteria breaking down the remains of the dead. It is all a great source of food for the larger bottom-living animals. Mr. O. D. Hunt (1925), when at the Plymouth Laboratory, made a splendid study of the feeding habits of the benthos, and grouped its members into three categories: (1) *suspension feeders* taking plankton and the scattered organic matter before it settles down, (2) *deposit feeders* living either on the detritus layer on the surface of the bottom or on the organic material mixed in with the bottom soil, and

[1]Since Petersen's day other devices for scooping up a smaller sample of the sea-bed with its contained animals have been invented which may give still more accurate results, e.g. Holme (1949, '53).

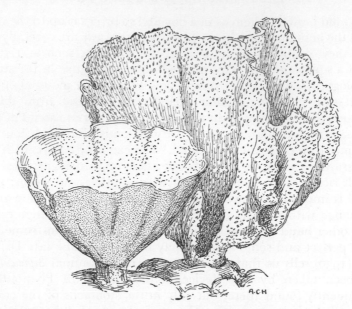

FIG. 41. Two sponges of the genus *Axinella* from a trawl haul northeast of Shetland: *A. infundibuliformis* partly in front of *A. calyciformis* ($\times \frac{1}{2}$).

(3) *carnivores* which prey upon these others.[1]  We can only mention some of the more prominent members of each group, those of the first two categories are the vitally important converters of the microscopic food into the more solid flesh which will feed the fish and other carnivores.  We shall devote the rest of this chapter to the natural history of these suspension and deposit feeders; and then in the next we will deal with the invertebrate carnivores—which are often competitors with the fish—and discuss the relations of the whole benthic community to the fisheries.

Most animals on rock or stones will be suspension-feeders, or carnivores, because little detritus can remain there for the same reason that the bottom is free of sand.  The sponges which encrust the rocks are essentially suspension-feeders.  Water is drawn in through thousands of tiny pores on their surfaces and passed through intricate branching

[1]Blegvad (1914), who worked with Petersen in the Baltic, made a pioneer study of the food and feeding of benthic animals, and classified them into three rather different categories: herbivores, detritus-eaters, and carnivores. He, however, was dealing with a shallow-water area in which the larger plants, seaweeds and particularly the sea-grass (*Zostera*) played an important part both as growing food and in supplying a rich detritus of small fragments. In the more typical deeper areas such a classification does not apply; it is the food from the plankton, either still suspended or fallen as detritus, that is all important.

canals to cavities which lead on to the larger exit openings; the water is pumped through by ciliated cells[1] in little chambers in the canal systems, and these cells also ingest the particles of food in the water, much as some protozoa do, and pass on the nourishment to the rest of the body. The sponges, which lack a special nervous system, are the simplest of the many-celled animals; examples are shown in Fig. 41 and Plate 15 (p. 210). Most hydroids, which feed on small members of the plankton, are on the borderline between suspension feeders and carnivores.

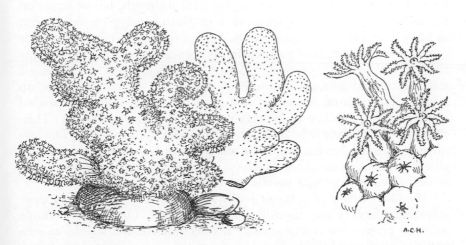

FIG. 42. The soft coral *Alcyonium digitatum* (× ½) drawn in an aquarium with the polyps expanded, and part of a colony behind showing them contracted as when brought up in a trawl; to the right is an enlarged view of some of the polyps both expanded and contracted.

While most sea-anemones capture larger prey with thick mobile tentacles heavily charged with their paralysing nematocysts, there are a few, such as the beautiful *Metridium* with its crown of feathery plumes Plate 6, (p. 83), which are adapted to gather fine plankton and suspended particles. Stephenson (1935) refers to the observations of Richard Elmhirst that ciliary currents run outwards to the lip ridges, presumably collecting food, and then inwards towards the mouth in the deep grooves between them. They live well in marine aquaria which are supplied with circulating seawater rich in fine plankton pumped straight from the sea, and may often be seen reproducing in a very remarkable manner which is called either laceration or frag-

[1]Actually each cell bears only one motile process which is technically called a flagellum; such cells are therefore strictly speaking 'flagellated' cells.

mentation; tiny pieces, as shown in Plate 6, separate off from the edge of the base, move away[1] and become new individuals with their own little mouths. They also have sexual reproduction.

The gorgonians, such as *Eunicella*, Plate 7, (p. 89) and the anti-patharians, spread out their thousands of small flower-like heads—like so many umbrellas—to catch the rain of food. Related to the gorgonians are the pale fleshy masses of *Alcyonium* whose branches quite often produce an effect not unlike swollen human hands, so that fishermen give them the vividly descriptive name of "dead men's fingers"; out of water, they are pocked with little pits, but at home on the bottom each little pit becomes a projecting polyp stretching out its hungry tentacles in all directions, Fig. 42 (p. 107). The pennatulids or sea-pens (Plate 7, p. 98) are curiously composite colonies of the same class which do not, however, grow on rock, but stand erect upon a stalk embedded in sand or mud[2]. A trawl may sometimes come up from such a ground festooned with these crimson plumes entangled in its netting: "Prince of Wales's feathers" say the fishermen. Then there are the various tube-building worms which spread out a wonder-ful fan of tentacles for the same purpose, but gather their food by ciliary currents as do the polyzoa (p. 99); so also feeds *Phoronis* whose remarkable development we discussed in Part I, p. 189.

We have seen that it is not really surprising that so many of these suspension feeders are plant-like in appearance. One more example must be given—the red or orange feather-star *Antedon* which, as seen in Plate 11 (p. 140), looks like an animated fern in autumn dress; it is an echinoderm, related to the starfish, but belonging to the very ancient group of Crinoids. This class of animals, in their more typical and ancestral form, stand on tall jointed stems and spread out a crown of branching arms like fern fronds which, by ciliary currents, pass the food they capture down channels to a central mouth. They were once a flourishing group in the palaeozoic seas of some two hundred million years ago, but today these old kinds only linger on in smaller numbers in the ocean depths. Newer forms, however, like *Antedon*, have evolved little legs—modified spines—in place of the old stalk, so now they can move about from place to place and compete more successfully in the struggle for existence. They can swim—or perhaps 'dance through the water' is a better phrase—by a graceful undulation of their ten feathery arms used like wings. I once saw more than a dozen in the Naples Aquarium take 'flight' together and dance like

[1] All sea-anemones can move slowly from place to place by wave-like muscular contractions of the base, somewhat like the movement of a snail, only much slower.
[2] *P. phosphorea* (in the Plate) is luminous, perhaps acting like a warning colour (p. 97).

a cloud of butterflies; they ranged in colour through all shades of orange, scarlet and crimson and danced as in a ballet for what seemed like several minutes, but may have been less—an unforgettable sight. Singly they can often be induced to swim in a bowl. We are now learning from the independent observations of Dr. H. G. Vevers (1955) and Mr. Arthur Fontaine that some of the brittle-stars such as the beautifully variegated *Ophiothrix fragilis* and the jet-black *Ophiocomina*

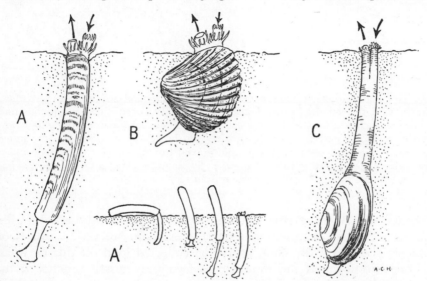

FIG. 43. Burrowing bivalves: A, the razor-shell *Ensis* and A' showing how it pulls itself below the surface with its extensible foot; B, the cockle *Cardium* and C, the clam *Mya*. The inhalent and exhalent siphons are marked by the arrows showing the currents of water going in and out. Drawn from life (A and B $\times \frac{1}{2}$; C $\times \frac{1}{3}$).

*nigra*[1] (both also shown on Plate 11), may feed almost as extensively upon suspended organic particles which they capture with strands of sticky mucus produced by numerous glands on their long curling arms. Dr. Vevers with his remarkable underwater photography (p. 139) has revealed dense populations of *O. fragilis* (as seen in Plate IX, p. 114), which, as he says, are "probably feeding almost entirely on suspended matter".

The most elaborately developed suspension-feeders are the bivalve (lamellibranch) molluscs. They are filter-feeders. Their gills have been enormously enlarged, not for respiration, but as sieving devices to collect the fine particles of food from the water which is propelled through them by cilia; a stream of water enters the mantle cavity

[1]*Ophioccomina* is also at times a carnivore (see p. 133).

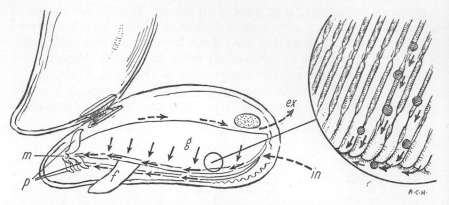

FIG. 44. The feeding mechanism of a typical bivalve mollusc, the mussel *Mytilus*, drawn with the left shell opened and the mantle removed. The continuous line arrows show how the particles of food, strained from the water by the gills *g*, are carried by ciliary currents to the mouth *m*. The broken line arrows show the water currents entering at the inhalant siphon, *in*, and leaving at *ex*. *f* is the foot and *p* the palps at the mouth. Inset: part of a gill, showing cilia, currents and moving food particles, highly magnified. Drawn from life.

through one opening (the inhalant siphon), passes through the gills and out through another opening (the exhalant siphon). Strands of mucus, also driven by cilia, carry the collected food off this network of the gills towards the mouth. So feed the mussels, anchored by 'byssus' threads (secreted fibres) to rocks, and the oysters and scallops lying on gravelly and sandy bottoms. In the same manner feed many bivalves which burrow down into the sand or mud, but have their siphons projecting above the surface. Examples are shown in Fig. 43, (p. 109), where we see the razor-shell (*Solen* or *Ensis*) which has short siphons but a long contractile foot to draw the animal down out of harm's way; or the clam (*Mya*) which has a short foot but a long contractile double siphon, or again the cockle (*Cardium*) which is similar in arrangement to the smaller *Spisula subtruncata* which is so important as the food of plaice and other fish on the Dogger Bank.

Just as the heart of a dead and decapitated animal may go on rhythmically beating for a time, so may the ciliary feeding mechanism of a bivalve mollusc, such as a mussel, be studied in action if it is opened under water. A small part of the gill should be cut away and examined in sea-water on a slide under a microscope. What a marvellous device it is! It is a trelliswork of ciliated filaments; and the cilia are arranged in different bands so that some propel the water through between the filaments and others drive little threads of mucus (at right angles to the water) along the filaments to their ends. See how small particles in the water passing through are caught up on the mucus strands—like flies on a flypaper—and hurried down the filaments to a collecting groove running to the mouth. It certainly gives the impression of a mechanism; it is almost like some throbbing loom seen in a factory. Over vast stretches of the sea-bed there may be hundreds of these little living 'machines' to the square yard; they are all converting the fine scattered rain of food from above into the solid flesh which will nourish so many of our bottom-living fish—and thus they form a main support for our great trawling industry. A drawing of the gills of the mussel (*Mytilus*) and its ciliary mechanism is shown in Fig. 44 opposite.

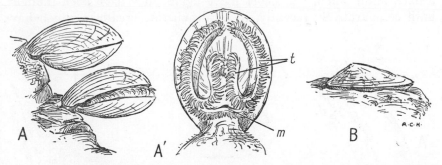

FIG. 45. Lamp-shells (Brachiopoda) from the west of Scotland. A, *Terebratula* and A′ with the shell opened to show the mouth (*m*) and coiled crown of tentacles (*t*). B. *Crania*. Drawn at the Millport Marine Station (A and B × 1½).

While I call these little animals machines, and indeed know that their working can be expressed, as can a man-made machine, in terms of physical and chemical energy exchanges, I must make it clear that I do not believe that that abstraction is the whole explanation of their life. At the end of the chapter I will cite an example of a much simpler animal which, to my mind, challenges the view that physics and chemistry, at any rate as we now know them, can account for the true nature of living things.

Feeding also on suspended particles, but by a mechanism more like that used by the polyzoa, are those other bivalve marine animals which look at first sight like molluscs but are really so very different: the Brachiopoda or lamp-shells (Fig. 45 above). Some may be attached to rock as is *Crania;* others, such as the tropical *Lingula,* live in the sand or mud like a clam and can draw themselves down out of danger by the contraction of a muscular stalk very similar in action to the foot of a razor-shell. *Lingula,* by the way, is that famous animal which appears to be unchanged and left behind by evolution; it remains today exactly as it was in the early palaeozoic age, when it left its imprints in the rock some five hundred million years ago. Surely, as Sir Julian Huxley has said, it is the senior genus of the world!

*Lingula's* scorn of change and progress, however, is an exception; the bottom of the sea is a goldmine of interest for the evolutionist. Among other animals feeding on suspended particles by filter methods are the remarkable sea-squirts or ascidians which look like humble sponges but are really distant relatives of our own vertebrate stock; they have those little tadpole-like larvae with the unmistakable chordate characters which we discussed in Chapter 2 (p. 19). Because they make this surprising metamorphosis from an active youngster to a fixed adult which will never move again, they have been thought, until comparatively recently, to be degenerate creatures which have

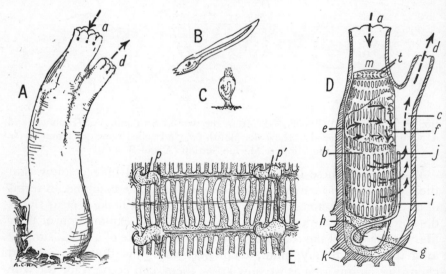

FIG. 46. A sea-squirt or ascidian *Ciona intestinalis*. A, a living animal cemented to rock by projections from the outer test (×1). B, small tadpole-like larva (×20). C, the larva just settled down to grow into adult. D, diagram of adult with half of test cut away; the water currents (driven by cilia) enter at *a*, pass through the slits in the pharynx *b* to the atrial chamber *c* and out at *d*. Part of the pharynx has been removed to show how small particles of food in the water are caught in streams of mucus passing from the endostyle *e* round each side as shown by continuous line arrows and then towards the gullet by the ciliated lobes *f* and so into the stomach *g*. *h* is the heart; *i* and *j* intestine and anus; *k*, anchoring projections. The mouth *m* is guarded by tentacles *t*. E represents a part of the pharynx wall seen under the microscope; *p*, *p'* are ciliated papillae which pass on the food-collecting mucus.

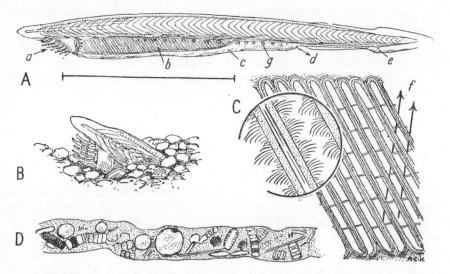

FIG. 47. Amphioxus (*Branchiostoma lanceolatus*). A, the whole animal seen from the left side (drawn from a living specimen): *a*, mouth; *b*, pharynx with gill-slits; *c*, atrial cavity and *d* its opening; *e*, anus; *g*, gonads. B, the front of the animal projecting from the gravel bottom in which it lives. C, an enlarged view of some of the gill-slits: the arrows at *f* show how particles of food are carried upwards by streams of mucus; a small part is still more highly magnified to show the beating cilia along the gill bars (*from a slide by Mr. Q. Bone*). D, a portion of the gut (× 125) showing its food, many kinds of diatoms, drawn from the photograph published by O. D. Hunt (1925).

lost their more typical chordate form. To most zoologists of the past this strange development seemed to signify a recapitulation of their ancestry from once free-swimming adults. The late Professor Walter Garstang, however, as we saw in Part I (p. 195) turned this theory inside out; he showed that the lowly fixed type is almost certainly ancestral, and that the whole of the higher chordate stock, leading upwards through the fish, has been derived (by neoteny) from an actively swimming larva of some ancient stock of similarly sedentary animals with the final suppression of the original adult form. By ciliary action the present-day ascidians (relics of the ancient race) pass water through an elaborate basket-like system of gill-slits in the walls of a large sack-like mouth cavity and so back into the sea again via an outer chamber or jacket (the atrium); as the water goes through the fine gill-slits the small food particles are sieved out and, as in the bivalve molluscs, are carried in streams of mucus driven by cilia towards the gullet. An example of a simple ascidian is shown in Fig. 46

(p. 112); some of them, however, bud off new individuals to form complex spreading colonies.

I will mention just one more example of a similar filter-feeding mechanism: that of the lancelet or amphioxus (*Branchiostoma*) which is another important animal in relation to our ancestry, being an exceedingly primitive little fish-like pre-vertebrate. It is about 2 inches long and only swims by night, spending the day buried in the sand at the bottom of the sea with just its mouth and the front tip of the body projecting from the surface (Fig. 47, p. 113). Its sieving apparatus, as in the ascidians, is again formed by a remarkable multiplication and elaboration of the typical chordate gill-slits; but I mention it, in addition, for a particular reason. In our first volume, I described a machine called the continuous plankton recorder which automatically samples the plankton as it is towed through the water. The water enters at the front and passes along a widening tunnel where it meets a gridwork of vertical bars and fine horizontal rollers, and so on into another chamber and out by an exit on the underside; up in front of the gridwork just mentioned, there winds, from a roller below, a long continuous banding of fine silk gauze which sieves out the plankton from the water and carries it through an upper slit into a storage chamber for later examination. I was rather proud of this invention when I had first made it. It was only sometime afterwards that I had the humbling experience of realising that there was nothing new in it at all; the amphioxus had done it all before—perfecting it millions of years ago!

Just as my recorder's gauze banding winds across its supporting grid-work, so in the amphioxus a net of mucus strands is drawn up from a glandular groove (the endostyle) below and passed over a remarkably similar grid-work of vertical and horizontal bars. The water passes through to an outer chamber and out by an exit (the atriopore) on the underside—again as in my machine; the continuous network of mucus strands catches the fine food particles, just as my gauze banding does, and carries them upwards. The amphioxus has such a

---

*Plate IX.* Surveying the sea-bed by photography. (*above*) *a* and *b*. Dr. H. G. Vevers's camera, mounted within and slightly above a crescent of floodlights, being lowered into the sea. (*below*) *c, d, e* and *f*. Four views of the sea-bed taken during the course of the survey. *c*, shows the track of some animal over the surface and what appear to be the heads of several burrowing worms. *d*, a sea-urchin (*Echinus esculentus*) on the edge of a pit surrounded by vast numbers of brittle stars (*Ophiothrix fragilis*). *e*, another tangled mass of brittle-stars (*O. fragilis*) with some (*Ophiocomina nigra*). *f*. A typical bit of a gravel bottom, with most of the animals out of sight below. All these photographs are reproduced by the kind permission of the Council of the Marine Biological Association of the United Kingdom.

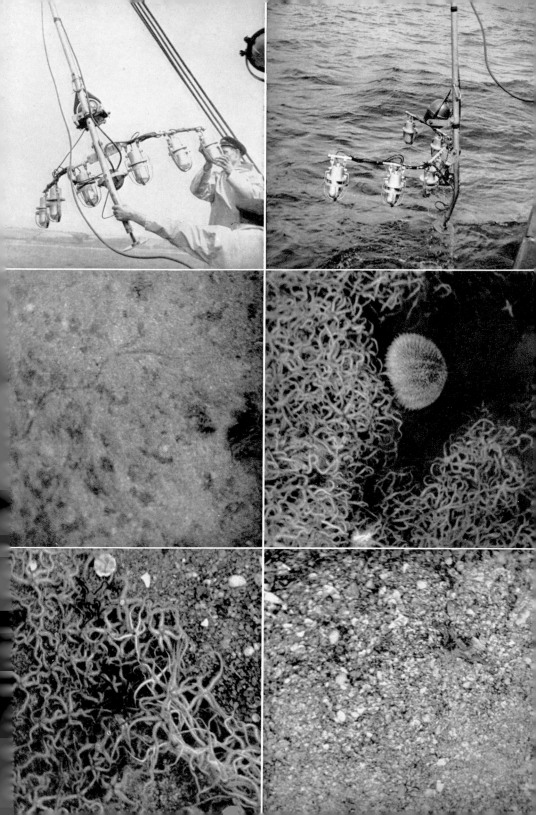

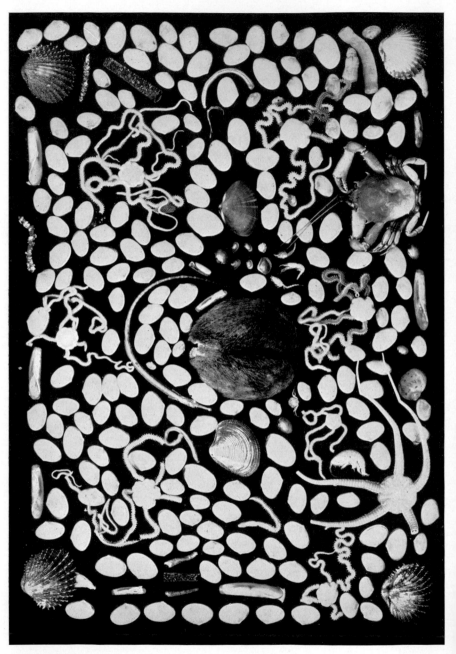

Plate X

grid-work on either side of the mouth cavity, whereas in my machine there is only one such grid-work at the back—only a trivial difference. The mucus streams coming up on either side join at the top and form one long conveyor belt, like my moving band, carrying the plankton to the gullet[1]. In Fig. 47, I show a sketch made from a photograph of this food in the gut of the amphioxus taken through a microscope by Mr. Hunt (1925). The similarity between the two systems is amazing; yet I did not consciously copy it. We see how 'inventive' natural selection can be if it is given sufficient variation on which to work; and the small changes in the gene complex seem almost infinite in variety. (Yet I do not believe that this is the whole of the evolution story, but that is another matter). Recently a new fact has been discovered about this animal. If the gill-slits get clogged with foreign matter, the muscles of the wall of the outer chamber contract violently so that the water current is suddenly reversed to cough the foreign matter out through the mouth. My machine cannot do that (but in fairness to it I must add that the continually moving gauze prevents such clogging from occurring).

Amphioxus are well-known to be common in the clean shell gravel in the region of the Eddystone near Plymouth where as many as four per square foot may be taken in a grab, as seen in Plate XI (p. 130). It is surprising to many people, however, to be told that it must also be very common in some parts of the North Sea; I have seen as many amphioxus as almost to fill a one pound honey-jar taken from the stomach of a large cod caught on the Dogger Bank.

One rather different type of suspension-feeding should be men-

[1] Amphioxus, when in the sand, sometimes lies on its back so that all I have described is actually upside down.

---

*Plate X.* All the animals shown in the photograph were picked up in a grab from just one square foot of the sea-bed in an area of fine silty sand off Bigbury Bay South Devon. This and the next photograph (*Plate XI*) were taken by Mr. E. Ford of the Plymouth Laboratory in his survey of the bottom fauna of the Channel in the Plymouth region (Ford, 1923).

The animals include a heart-urchin (*Echinocardium cordatum*) centre, a young pipe-fish (*Syngnathus* sp.) left centre, 8 brittle-stars (7 *Amphiura filiformis* spread around and 1 *Ophiura texturata* at lower right edge), 2 crabs (1 *Corystes cassivelaunus* at upper right edge and 1 small young *Portunus* sp. 'southeast' of central heart-urchin), 4 other crustaceans (an amphipod, near the *Ophiura* and a mysid, cumacean and small prawn, 'northeast' of central heart-urchin), 213 bivalve molluscs (including 188 *Abra alba* scattered over most of picture; 8 razor shells *Phaxas pellucidus*, three of which are at left edge; 4 cockles *Cardium echinatum*, at corners; 4 *Nucula nitida* and 4 *Montacuta bidentata* scattered), the gastropod *Natica alderi* at middle of right edge and 11 worms (various) scattered (but note the sandy tubes of 3 *Pectinaria*).

tioned; the combing of the water by the finely fringed limbs of small crustacea. The barnacles are, of course, familiar examples; lying on their backs, within their armour of calcareous plates, they make wide and rhythmic movements with their plumose appendages—modified limbs—and so draw in the scattered food to their mouths as if by a casting net. Several species of amphipods of the genera *Ampelisca* and *Haploops* are filter-feeders and make little purse-shaped burrows in sand or gravelly bottoms, with a little tube (of sand grains cemented together by mucus) slightly raised above the surface. They too lie on their backs, and, making a strong current with their abdominal appendages, drive water out of the burrow; as this is replaced by a fresh supply which comes in by the head, they filter off the food it carries by their fine comb-like mouth-parts. And little porcelain-crabs (*Porcellana*) sweep the water with rakelike food-collecting limbs.

News of the finding in British seas of those newly discovered animals, the Pogonophora, which are most extraordinary suspension feeders, is given in an Addendum Note on p. 314.

Now let us turn to the deposit feeders. These specialise either in collecting the already settled material from the rich detritus layer on the surface of the bottom, or in burrowing through the sand or mud near the surface and extracting the organic matter from it by passing it through their alimentary tracts just as an earthworm does the soil. Among these burrowers are many bristle-worms (polychaetes) and other worm-like creatures, such as *Phascolion* and *Phascolosoma*[1], which belong to quite a different phylum (Sipunculoidea); then there are some of those curious echinoderms of the class Holothuroidea—the sea-cucumbers as they are popularly called—which also look very worm-like, such as *Synapta*. The most primitive of all chordate animals, the acorn-worm *Balanoglossus* and its relatives, also pass the sand and mud through their bodies, but they construct definite U-shaped burrows supported by mucus not unlike those made by the common lug-worm *Arenicola* of our shores. Fig. 48, opposite, shows a selection of some of these burrowing creatures and includes yet another, *Priapulus caudatus*, which belongs to a very isolated group in the animal kingdom. This also makes a U-shaped burrow, but in a more muddy bottom;[2] by a series of swellings, which repeatedly pass down its body and fit the tube like a piston, it pumps water past itself and so brings food (from the detritus layer) down to its mouth and dissolved oxygen to its

[1]*Phascolosoma* has also been found to be at times a parasite (see p. 127).

[2]*Priapulus* occurs on some very muddy shores between tide marks as well as far out to sea. It is a cold loving polar animal and Britain is at its southern limit in the northern hemisphere (perhaps left here by the last Ice Age); a similar form occurs in the south polar seas—a remarkable distribution.

plume-like respiratory tail which greatly expands as each fresh surge of water passes it. Also it is carnivorous, having powerful horny teeth in its pharynx.

More enterprising are those which reach up to collect the rich detritus from the surface of the sea-floor above whilst they themselves remain out of harm's way down below. Many worms do this, exploring with long tentacles which spread out over the surface and pick up and convey the food to their mouths below by means of ciliated grooves; typical forms are *Amphitrite* (of the family Terebellidae) and *Trophonia*

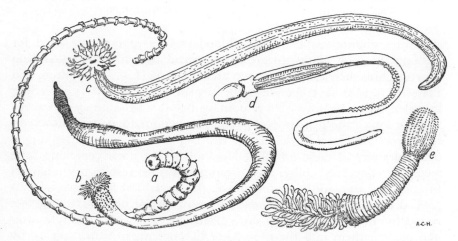

FIG. 48. Burrowing worm-like animals from widely different groups. *a. Notomastus latericeus*, a true worm (Polychaeta); *b. Phascolion strombi*, a sipuncoloid; *c. Synapta* (*Labidoplax*) *digitata*, a holothurian echinoderm; *d, Balanoglossus*, a primitive chordate; and *e. Priapulus caudatus*. (All × ½).

(of the Scoleciformidae) as shown in Fig. 49 overleaf. Some of the commonest bivalve molluscs, such as *Tellina* and *Macoma*, also feed in this way as shown in Fig. 50; with their body out of sight they extend very long hose-like inhalent siphons which move over the surface and draw in the food by ciliary action just like the long nozzle of a vacuum cleaner sucking up dust. Some of the more primitive (protobranch) bivalves such as *Yoldia* and *Nucula* are only half buried, and explore the surface and collect their food, not by their siphons, but by long extensions of their lips (labial palps).

The brittle-stars such as *Amphiura filiformis* usually lie with their bodies sunk below the silt, and search the surface with their long flexible arms. These arms have a groove on their under-surface lined by the so-called tube-feet which are little tentacle-like hydraulic

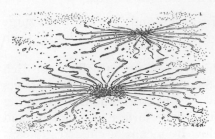

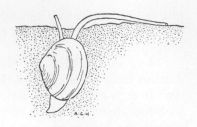

FIG. 49. Two specimens of the worm *Amphitrite* collecting food with their tentacles.

FIG. 50. The bivalve *Tellina* sucking up food with its long inhalent siphon

structures characteristic of all echinoderms; here they are used for pushing the food along towards the central mouth. The burrowing heart-urchins such as *Echinocardium* and *Spatangus* (Fig. 51, opposite, and Plate 13, p. 194) have been described by some earlier writers as feeding in much the same way—by remaining below and sending up exceptionally long tube feet to explore the surface for food; this, however, is not so. Dr. David Nichols, of my Department, who is making a detailed study of these animals, has shown that these very long tube feet are concerned only with maintaining a respiratory channel through the sand to the water above. He finds that feeding is accomplished by two distinct methods: either by special brush-like tube feet round the mouth picking up sand grains covered with organic matter and passing them into the mouth, or by currents of water (set up by the action of cilia) converging on the mouth and carrying small suspended particles of food from all over its surface. The shape of the heart urchin is modified from that of the typical symmetrical sea-urchin; it has become egg-shaped so that it can push more efficiently through the sand in one direction with its mouth facing forwards; its mouth is further provided with a shovel-like lower 'lip' to assist the pushing in of the sand grains. These urchins lever themselves through the sand by a series of paddle-like spines on their under surfaces.

Other deposit-feeders are certain gastropod molluscs, such as *Aporrhais* the "pelican's foot" Fig. 52, (p. 120), which work their way just a little below the surface of the sand or mud and then, with their proboscis, make two tubes lined by mucus to the water above; these channels serve to draw water in and out for respiration, and to allow the proboscis to be stretched out to search for food in the surrounding

[1]The tall slender *Turritella*, or tower-shell, is another common gastropod burrowing just below the surface; this, however, is mainly a ciliary feeder, making shafts, to the water above it, down which it draws the small suspended particles in the water rather than the actual detritus on the surface. It is also shown in Fig.52.

detritus layer[1]. Professor C. M. Yonge (1937), who has made a delightful study of these animals shows how different species of *Aporrhais* are
adapted to different kinds of substratum; the edge of the shell is drawn
out into wide flanges which prevent the animals from sinking in the
mud and these are much larger, with greater surface area, in a species
inhabiting soft mud than in one found in stiff gravelly mud. Another
interesting and characteristic mollusc of the sand-inhabiting benthos
is *Dentalium*, the tusk shell (also in Fig. 52) which is a member of that
small and well defined class: the Scaphopoda. Its long slender tubular
shell tapers from a wider opening at the head end of the animal to a
narrower one behind, and is slightly curved like a miniature elephant's
tusk. The wide end is buried and from it, together with the head,
projects the shovel-like foot used for digging (hence the name of the

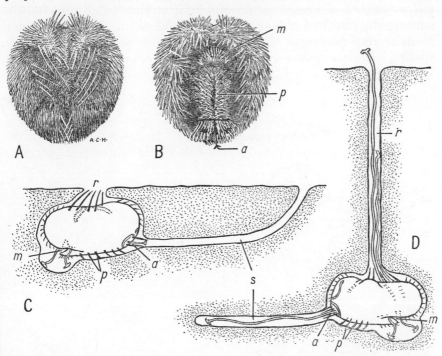

FIG. 51. Burrowing heart-urchins. A and B show the upper and lower surfaces of
*Spatangus purpureus*, ($\times \frac{1}{2}$) and C the same in side view, in its position below the
surface of the sea-bed. D, a side view of *Echinocardium cordatum* which burrows more
deeply. *a*, anus; *m*, mouth; *p*, paddle-like spines which lever the animal forward
through the sand; *r*, respiratory shaft to water above; *s*, sanitary tunnel (double in
*Spatangus* and single in *Echinocardium*) in which excrement is left behind as the urchin
moves on. C and D, which are facing in opposite directions, are re-drawn
from the figures of Dr. David Nichols not yet published (see text).

class, from *skaphis* a shovel); the narrow end sticks out through the surface of the sand and provides a 'ventilating shaft' for respiratory currents. The head of this unique animal is provided with a group of long extensible filaments with suckers at their ends, which are partly sensory and exploratory and partly for seizing and carrying to the mouth any food particles found.

We have already briefly referred to the protozoa within the rich detritus layer itself, where there are flagellates and ciliates in quantity. While we cannot, unfortunately, in this book, explore this microscopic world, I must mention just one group—indeed one of the most characteristic groups of animals from the bottom of the sea: the Foraminifera. In our earlier volume, when discussing the planktonic forms such as *Globigerina*, we saw how members of this order spread out a network of branching protoplasmic strands in all directions to capture the still smaller living things around them. The more typical kinds secrete calcareous shells of many chambers which, in different species, take on almost every imaginable design and arrangement.

FIG. 52. Burrowing benthic 'snails': *a*, the towershell *Turritella* crawling on a sand surface; *b*, the pelican's foot shell *Aporrhais*, on the surface and *b'* when buried (the arrows indicating water currents); *c*, the elephant's tusk shell *Dentalium* in position below the sand surface and *c'.c''* showing how it pulls itself down with its extensible foot. All drawn from living specimens (× 1½) except *b'* which is diagrammatic and redrawn from Yonge (1937).

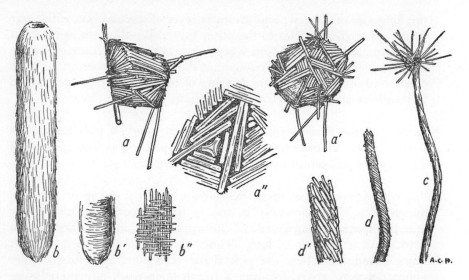

FIG. 53. 'Houses' of microscopic size built of sponge spicules picked up by arenaceous foraminifera (Protozoa (×35)). *a, a'*, examples made by *Psammosphaera rustica*, with *a″* giving the detail of a small part to show the fitting into place of spicules of different size. *b*, external and *b'* internal view of the house of *Technitella legumen* with a small part highly magnified to show spicule arrangement. *c, Marsipella cylindrica* and *d*, the test of *M.spiralis* with a portion *d'* further enlarged. All except *a″* drawn from specimens collected by the late Mr. E. Heron-Allen and now in the British Museum (Natural History); *a″* is redrawn from Heron-Allen and Earland (1912).

Others, however, instead of having a shell, build around themselves grains of sand or other particles, to form a shelter like those constructed by the aquatic larvae of caddis-flies. Many make just a rough covering of sand, but some—and to these I particularly want to call attention—build houses which are little short of marvels of engineering and constructional skill. I use the word 'skill' advisedly. With the late Dr. E. Heron-Allen who made a special study of these forms, I share the view that the building of these devices cannot be simply a matter of physico-chemical mechanism alone.

Let us briefly consider the 'houses' built by just one or two different species of these remarkable microscopic animals. *Technitella legumen* constructs a long cylindrical case entirely of sponge-spicules it has picked up from the sea-bed (Fig. 53*b*, above); Heron-Allen and Earland (1912) described it as follows:

"The shell wall consists of two distinct layers of spicules: an outer layer, in which the spicules are all laid with their long axes parallel to the long axis of the test; and an inner layer of spicules laid with their long axes at right angles to the outer layer. We thus get as close an approximation to "woof and warp" as is possible with a rigid, non-flexile material, and it is obvious that the strength of the test must be enormously increased by the crossing of the two layers, as resistance to tensile strain is given in two directions instead of one."

Next let us take *Psammosphaera rustica* which builds a polyhedral but almost spherical chamber, again of sponge spicules, as also illustrated in Fig. 53*a*. I will again quote the same authors:

"Hardly any two specimens exhibit an identical shape or external appearance. This diversity is due to the methods of construction and the material employed. The apparent mode of construction is to select a number of long slender spicules often 2 or 3 mm. or more in length. These are placed like tent poles at various angles about 0.5 mm. apart, forming a rough open-work figure enclosing a central space between the points of intersection of the poles. The open spaces in the wall are then filled in with shorter fragments of spicules carefully selected for length, so as just to fill the required space. The animal thus secures the nearest possible approach to a spherical chamber obtainable with the material employed, the salient angles being the points where two or more of the "tentpoles" join. The long spicules employed as "tent-poles" project irregularly all over the surface of the test in perfect specimens, and probably serve a secondary purpose as catamaran spars in supporting the animal in the surface layer of ooze. They are, however, very fragile, and are frequently more or less damaged, if not destroyed, in the process of cleaning the dredged material."

*Marsipella spiralis* makes a long cylindrical case, but here the sponge-spicules, in a single layer, are always built into the wall in a spiral, giving added strength to the structure. To my mind these various Astrorhizid foraminifera present one of the greatest challenges to the exponents of a purely mechanistic view of life. Here are minute animals, apparently as simple in nature as *Amoeba*, without definite sense-organs such as eyes, and appearing as mere flowing masses of protoplasm, yet endowed with extraordinary powers; not only do they *select* and pick up one type of object from all the jumble of fragments of other sorts on the bottom, but they build them into a design involving a comparison of size. They build as if to a plan. Here indeed is a mystery worth looking into.

# CHAPTER 6

# MORE ABOUT THE BENTHOS AND
# ITS RELATION TO THE FISHERIES

I N OUR review of the principal members of the benthos which convert the fine scattered food into more solid fare for the fish, we have so far said little about their varying abundance and distribution; these matters and their causes are naturally of much consequence in relation to the fisheries. Here we must return to Petersen and his grab to which we briefly referred in the last chapter (p. 104).

For the first time Petersen showed us just how many animals of different kinds there may be per square foot of the sea-bed in different parts of the sea. We have seen that his grab was designed to take out of the bottom a bite of a definite area, usually 1/10th of a square metre, which is just about a square foot: a bite of the bottom soil with all its contained animals. (Sometimes he used a grab of twice that size). He grabbed all over the western end of the Baltic, the Kattegat and the Skagerak and found that he could recognise eight different 'animal communities', to which he gave names derived from the generic or specific names of the dominant animals concerned: for example, his 'Macoma' community contained various bivalve molluscs and polychaete worms but was dominated by the bivalve *Macoma baltica*—or his 'Echinocardium-filiformis' community contained various bivalves, gastropods and worms, but was dominated by the burrowing sea-urchin *Echinocardium cordatum* and the brittle-star *Amphiura filiformis*[1]. Within certain areas he consistently got the same groups of animals associated together and he thought that they must be ecologically related to one another in much the same sort of way as are the different species in the various plant associations recognised by botanists. Similar communities, but with different species, have now been found from the same kinds of sea-bed in all latitudes from the polar seas to the tropics. Petersen's methods certainly revolutionized the study of

[1]Petersen's name for this community, combining the generic name of one species with the specific name of another, was not unnaturally looked upon with disfavour by systematic zoologists; it is now called the "Echinocardium-Amphiura" community.

the benthic faunas and gave us quite new quantitative standards for comparing the relative wealth of life in different areas; it is, perhaps, doubtful, however, whether the members of his communities really have the association relationship one with another that he supposed. It appears more likely, from the work of those who have followed Petersen in other areas, that they are groups of animals brought together by their liking for particular types of bottom and by the availability of food.

Mr. E. Ford (1923), using Petersen's grab in the Plymouth area, found that there are many minor associations, some similar to and others different from those defined by Petersen, depending on variations in locality, depth, type of substratum, season of the year, etc. But overriding these he found he could classify the various minor groupings into two main and distinct series of species, according to the kind of bottom-deposits they come from. In one series are the animals found in Grades VI, VII and VIII of Allen's scale (p. 103), i.e. in the finer grades, from medium sand to silt; those in the other are found in the coarser gravelly deposits of grades II, III and IV. These seem to be the really valid communities, based upon the nature of the substratum. Their significance may be judged by the way so many genera, particularly of bivalve molluscs, have different representative species in the two series; while there are also a number of other genera which are limited to one or other series. Ford illustrates this most clearly in tables of the species in the two series shown side by side and quotes the following statement made by Petersen in 1915:

". . . closely related species, especially those of the same genus, are scarcely ever found living in one and the same area of a given water; they may meet and fight out their war on a frontier line, but are never found to cover the same area of distribution altogether. Each has its own region, its own community. The competition must be greatest between those species which are most closely related."

The force of this has been increasingly realized by students of ecology and evolution in recent years. "This", writes Ford, "appears to me to provide the key to the proper relationship existing between the two series. They are independent associations largely built up of their own characteristic species belonging to genera which are common to both." Plates X and XI are photographs which Mr. Ford has kindly allowed me to reproduce from his paper, each showing all the animals collected in *one haul* with a grab which sampled 1/10th of a square metre, but taken from different localities; the first is of a

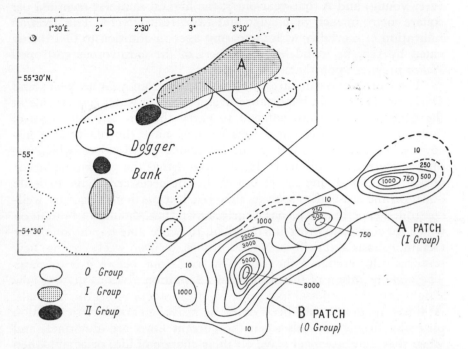

FIG. 54. *Upper left:* a chart of dense patches of the bivalve mollusc *Spisula subtruncata* of different ages on the Dogger Bank in the autumn of 1922, as surveyed by F. M. Davis (1923). The O, I and II groups represent animals aged less than one, one, and two years respectively. The scale is given by the degrees of latitude at the side: one degree, of course, is 60 miles. *Lower right:* more detailed chart of two of the same patches, A and B, showing contours of quantities expressed in numbers per square metre (also from Davis, 1923).

community from a bottom of silty sand and the second is one of the other series from 'clean shell gravel'. They give a clear idea as to the quantity of food available for bottom-living fish on different grounds.

The late Mr. F. M. Davis (1923, 1925) of the Lowestoft Laboratory made extensive surveys of the fish-food on the Dogger Bank, also using the Petersen grab. He found the species not evenly spread over all the bank, but in great patches suggesting the areas in which the larvae had settled most successfully. Fig. 54, above, is taken from his charts showing the distribution of the patches of the bivalve *Spisula subtruncata*, so important as food for plaice; at top-left the outlined, but unshaded areas represent patches of very young specimens less than a year old, the shaded areas are one-year-olds and those shown black are two year olds. It also shows the population densities in two patches, B (very young) and A (one-year-olds); the highest numbers recorded per square metre in each were 8,250 and 1,007 respectively. This gives an indication of mortality with increasing age; in addition to their being eaten by fish, he found large numbers of the carnivorous gastropod *Natica* preying upon them (see p. 128).

The current-systems are known to vary from year to year; and Davis emphasises the importance of appropriate water movements at the time the larvae are hatched to carry them to suitable types of bottom. As a supplement to this we now have the remarkable discoveries of Dr. D. P. Wilson, of Plymouth (1948-54) to which we briefly referred in Volume I. He has found that the planktonic larvae of many bottom-living invertebrates do not necessarily have to settle down on the sea-bed as soon as they reach a particular age; by well-controlled experiments he has clearly shown that, should the bottom on which they descend prove uncongenial, they are able to postpone their metamorphosis and drift on again for days, or even weeks, trying 'new pastures' till perchance they meet the right one before it is too late. The demonstration of this wonderful adaptation gives us quite a new insight into the dispersal and survival of the stocks of benthic animals. At times, no doubt, vast fleets of larvae must be carried to destruction on unfavourable grounds when the current flows are abnormal, and when they can no longer stave off their change of life; or again, when they are carried right over and off the edge of the continental shelf.

Apart from vagaries of current flow causing variations in the number of young which may survive, it has been shown, by Dr. Gunnar Thorson (1946, 1950) for Danish waters, and by the late Dr. Colin Rees (1951, 1952) for the North Sea, what marked fluctuations there may be in the number of these larvae in different years. As part of the plankton, I devoted a chapter in the first volume to the adaptive significance of these pelagic stages in the development of so many benthic animals; we saw how in different ways their larval life has been evolved as a compromise between two rival selective advantages: on the one hand to reach reproductive maturity as soon as possible to propagate the race, and on the other to remain floating as long as possible to spread the species over the greatest area. For a detailed and beautifully illustrated account of these various larval forms, and for a consideration of their ecology in relation to their later benthic life, the student should consult the magnificent monograph by Dr. Thorson (1946) to which I have just briefly referred.

So far we have been considering mainly the suspension and deposit feeders which provide the greater part of the food for the bottom-living fish; we must now pass to those members of the benthos in the

third category: the carnivorous animals. We shall presently see that
Dr. Thorson has recently estimated that these predators are much more
serious competitors with the fish for the limited supply of food than has
been generally recognised in the past; before, however, we come to this
we must say a little more about their general natural history and what
animals the more important kinds prey upon.

Among the coelenterates it is the more typical sea-anemones which
take the larger prey—animals swimming unwarily near their tentacles,
particularly shrimps and other crustacea, and also fish if not too big.
Many bristle-worms (polychaetes) are voracious carnivores such as

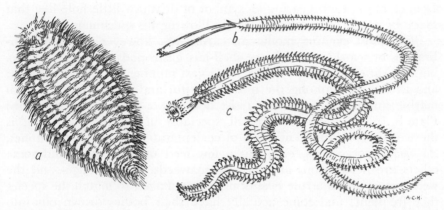

FIG. 55. Burrowing carnivorous bristle-worms (Polychaeta) *a, Aphrodite* showing
underside (for upper side see Plate 15, p. 210); *b, Glycera* and *c, Nephthys,* the last two
with mouths everted to show 'teeth' (Drawn from living specimens ($\times \frac{2}{3}$) at
Plymouth.

*Aphrodite, Nephthys* and *Glycera* shown above; they shoot out their
capacious mouths (inside out), grip their victims with powerful horny
'teeth', and roll them in again. *Aphrodite,* popularly known as the sea-
mouse, is worthy of special mention; it is of unusually stout proportions
for a worm, and its segmented-worm nature is only visible on the lower
surface, for its back is covered with a curious matted feltwork of fine
fibres. Down its sides are tufts of brilliant iridescent bristles which,
shining with rainbow hues, as shown in Plate ˙ 5 (p. 000), make it a
very conspicuous animal when it is washed uˑ dead or dying on the
shore after a storm. In life it burrows out ot sight in the substratum,
and would be better called the 'sea-mole' than 'sea-mouse'; travelling
through the 'soil', it hunts out and devours the more ordinary bristle-
worms, just as a mole burrows after earthworms. Dr. Thorson tells

me that the sipunculid 'worm' *Phascolosoma porcerum* in turn attacks *Aphrodite,* piercing it with its proboscis and feeding as a parasite.

Among the molluscs, some of the gastropods are the great predators —particularly forms like the whelk, *Buccinum undatum,* and its allies (Fig. 56, opposite). The smaller *Natica* causes great destruction on the beds of bivalve molluscs such as *Spisula* and *Mactra,* which, as we have seen, are so important as the food of plaice and other flat-fish. It seizes and holds its prey with special divisions of its foot, as shown in the same figure, and, pressing its proboscis against the victim's shell, drills a neat round feeding hole by means of its radula[1]. Vast quantities of empty shells of bivalves may be dredged up from the Dogger Bank, each bearing its symbol of death: a little hole like that made by a collector of birds' eggs in blowing his specimens.

The most exciting molluscan carnivores, however, are the nudibranchs or sea-slugs, which are shell-less gastropods, as land-slugs are, but of a different group. There are a vast number of different species; and as they are among the most beautiful and gaily coloured of all marine animals, I could not resist devoting a whole plate to them: Plate 8, (p. 99). They nearly all specialise in feeding—'browsing' is the word—upon different kinds of coelenterates: hydroids, anemones, *Alcyonium,* gorgonians, etc.; but a few feed upon sponges and some others are herbivorous and feed on seaweeds. The sponge- and the weed-eaters are as a rule beautifully camouflaged to match the species they frequent; and some actually have their bodies drawn out into seaweed-like fronds as in the elaborate deception presented by *Dendronotus* (Fig. 2 in Plate 8). Now before discussing the carnivorous forms I shall, for reasons we will see, digress for a moment to say a word or two more about the plant-eaters. In the same plate (Fig. 9) I have included a young specimen of such a species which is not in the same group as the true sea-slugs (Nudibranchia); it is *Aplysia punctata,* the so-called sea-hare, which belongs to a different branch (Tectibranchia) of the same order and, having reduced its shell to a mere vestige, has become slug-like in form by an independent evolutionary line. It is a coastal species, as, of course, all the weed-eaters must be, but its planktonic larvae settle down in the shallow water well out below low-tide level; here the young sea-hares browse on a purple-red seaweed and at this stage are coloured exactly like their background as shown in the Plate. Now as they grow older they migrate landwards

[1]A radula is a remarkable structure found in the mouths of all typical gastropods; it is a long ribbon, bearing a vast number of transverse rows of sharp horny teeth which can be drawn backwards and forwards as a rasping organ—indeed as a flexible file.

and, when mature, lay their eggs among the dark olive-green sea-weeds of the shore; and they have by then become a similar colour themselves. Thus the plant eaters are perfectly camouflaged; such an adaptation must be brought about largely by the selective action of fish which we know (p. 22) must have a well-developed colour vision[1]. This being so, what about the striking appearance of the others: the carnivorous sea-slugs?

The coelenterates, upon which the sea-slugs feed, are armed with those extraordinary nematocysts, which normally shoot out their stinging threads at any attacking enemies (see p. 95); the slugs,

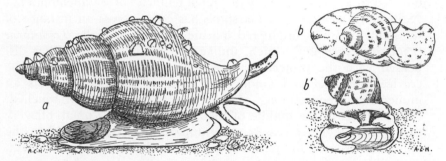

FIG. 56. Carnivorous snails of the sea-bed. *a*, the whelk, *Buccinum undatum* ($\times \frac{1}{2}$); *b*, *Natica*, walking on a vertical surface, ($\times$ 1) and *b'* holding a bivalve mollusc, and drilling into its shell. Drawn from life (note barnacles on whelk).

however, have not only evolved a technique for preventing the discharge of these 'firearms' as they take their living meal, but they can actually store the 'loaded' nematocysts in their own tissues and use them for their own protection against other predators! It is in the gaudy coloured papillae on their backs that they keep these stolen weapons. It seems reasonable to suppose, as did both Professor Garstang and Sir William Herdman, that the vivid hues associated with them serve as a warning coloration such as we find in so many terrestrial animals with stings, poisonous bites, noxious tastes etc. (p. 97). They each (as quoted by Poulton, 1890) particularly likened the coloured papillae of the Eolid sea-slugs to the conspicuous tussocks of poisonous and irritating hairs on the backs of the caterpillars of the tussock-moths (*Orgyia*) which can be pulled out, without fatal results to their owner, but with unpleasant consequences to the pecking bird.

[1]The actual change in colour of *Aplysia* may well be due to the storage of the same pigments as are in the plants it eats; but its whole form, especially when young, is just like the seaweed on which it lives.

This interesting comparison is illustrated in Fig. 57 (p. 131). Sir Edward Poulton after discussing this similarity writes:

"Mr. Garstang has now tested this suggestion by experiment, and he finds that fish will not attack the Eolids under normal conditions. He therefore threw one of them (the orange variety of *Cavolina farrani*) into the tank containing young pollack (*Gadus pollachius*), which generally swallow any object while it is descending to the bottom. The Eolid was swallowed and rejected after a second or two by two fish, which then shook their heads as if experiencing discomfort. Similar movements were made when the fish were induced to seize the specially defended tentacles of sea-anemones . . . "Still more recently Mr. Garstang has come across an instance of the same kind in a bright red marine worm, one of the *Terebellidae* (*Polycirrus aurantiacus*) which, unlike the rest of its family, has dispensed with the protection of a tube, and creeps about in the crevices of stones and among the roots of *Laminaria*. It has an immense number of long, slender tentacles, and when touched, coils itself up in the middle of them. The tentacles break off very easily, and evidently possess some unpleasant attribute. When the animal is irritated the tentacles become brilliantly phosphorescent, so that they are conspicuous by night as well as day. Mr. Garstang obtained experimental evidence of the validity of this interpretation. He placed a specimen in one of the fish-tanks in the Plymouth Laboratory: only one pollack ventured to seize the worm, but ejected it immediately, and would not touch it again. Another fish made three vigorous attempts to swallow it, but finally left it. Another, a very voracious rock-fish, actually swallowed it, but immediately afterwards began to work its jaws about as if experiencing discomfort. Mr. Garstang then cut the head and

---

*Plate XI.* All the animals in this photograph were taken like those in the previous one (*Plate X*) from one square foot of the sea-bed, but this time from shell-gravel half a mile off the Eddystone Rock. Another of Mr. Ford's photographs (Ford, 1923).

The animals include 4 amphioxus (*Branchiostoma lanceolatus*) at upper and lower edges, 1 young heart-urchin (*Echinocardium* sp.) below central shell, 2 small sea-urchins (*Echinocyamus pusillus*) above central shell, 2 crabs (*Portunus pusillus* and *Ebalia tuberosa* to 'northeast' and 'southeast' of central shell), 2 amphipods (*Maera* sp. and *Ampelisca typica* to 'northwest' and 'southwest' of central shell) 24 various bivalve molluscs (including 1 large *Arcopagia crassa* in the centre, 5 *Venus fasciata* which are largish shells near the top and near the bottom corners, and 5 *Glycymeris glycymeris* of which the largest is in the middle near the bottom), and 5 various worms scattered over plate (including a polynoid worm 'NNE' of central shell and 2 *Glycera* sp.).

Plate XI

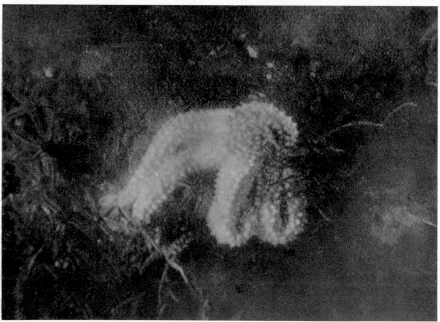

*Plate XII*

tentacles away from the body and threw both pieces into the pollack tank: the tentacles were untouched, but a fight took place over the body, which was torn into several pieces and swallowed with great relish."

The whole field of adaptive coloration in the sea, both possible camouflage and warning colours, is one which would well repay a more thorough investigation by modern experimental behaviour-study methods. These may give us a solution to the problem of the extraordinary variability in the colours of the sea-anemones already

FIG. 57. A comparison in adaptation between an eolid sea-slug (*right*) and a caterpillar of the tussock-moth (*left*); for explanation see text (p. 129).

mentioned (p. 98); then there are the starfish of which many are as brilliantly coloured as the anemones, and the multi-coloured brittle-stars such as *Ophiothrix fragilis* which show quite as big a range of colour variation, as seen in Plates 11 and 15 (pp. 140 and 210). A point which must be borne in mind is the fact that the colour red appears as a dull neutral colour in all but very shallow regions, because the red rays of light are absorbed by the water so much more quickly than are those nearer to the blue end of the spectrum. How very quickly this occurs was recently brought home to me by the splendid series of colour photographs of scarlet gorgonians (soft corals) taken at various depths by my former pupil, Mr. Derek Bromhall, diving with aqualung equipment around Hong Kong.

Among the invertebrates perhaps the starfish of different kinds are the most voracious carnivores. The common *Asterias rubens* (Plate 11) and *Marthasterias glacialis* (Plate 16) feed largely on bivalve molluscs. They pull open the shells with the sucking tube-feet on their powerful muscular arms, after the bivalve's weaker muscles, which hold the

---

*Plate XII.* Photographs of the viewing screen of Dr. H. Barnes's apparatus as seen on the research vessel when the television camera is lowered on a cable to scan the sea-bed many fathoms below the surface. (*above*) *a:* An anemone, *Bolocera*, and a small squat-lobster, *Munida*. (*below*) *b:* the starfish, *Marthasterias*, and to the left, several brittle-stars, *Ophiothrix fragilis*.                    (*H. Barnes*)

shell closed, have given way through fatigue; once the victim is exposed, *Asterias* everts its capacious stomach inside-out, smothers the animal and begins to digest it on the doorstep, as it were.   They also eat gastropods, polychaete worms, small crabs and other crustacea, and at times (perhaps when other food is scarce) younger members of their own kind.   The many-armed sunstar *Solaster papposus* (Plate 11) and the large long-armed starfish *Luidia ciliaris* (Plate 15) frequently prey upon *Asterias; Luidia* has also been found to contain the remains of brittle-stars, the holothurian *Cucumaria,* and small specimens of sea-urchins, both *Echinus* and the heart-urchins *Spatangus* and *Echinocardium.* That beautiful scarlet or crimson *Palmipes* ( =*Anseropoda*) *placenta,* (Plate 11) so flat and thin that it looks almost like the fallen leaf of a maple tree, presents us with a puzzle.   Among its prey are, quite often, swift-moving crustacea, which are swallowed whole.   How can it capture these?   In Fig. 58, below, is a sketch of a specimen which has half-swallowed a prawn (*Processa canaliculata*), drawn from a photograph taken by Mr. Hunt (1925), who records finding in their stomachs remains of amphipods, mysids, cumaceans, small swimming-crabs (*Portunus*) and hermit-crabs.   He writes that "as many as ten crustaceans have been found in a single stomach, all in comparatively fresh condition."   There can be no doubt that starfish are most serious competitors with commercial fish for the available supplies of food on the sea-bed, and none more so than *Astropecten* (Plate 11) which is characterised by the little lines of spines along the margins of its arms. Mr. Hunt, who examined 125 specimens, writes: "Of these 76

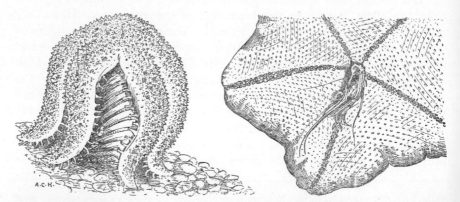

FIG. 58.  Starfish in the act of feeding.  *Left,* the common starfish *Asterias rubens* opening a scallop; *right, Palmipes* (=*Anseropoda*) *placenta* with a partially swallowed prawn (*Processa*).  The former drawn from life and the latter from a photograph published by Mr. O. D. Hunt (1925); both are $\times \frac{3}{4}$.

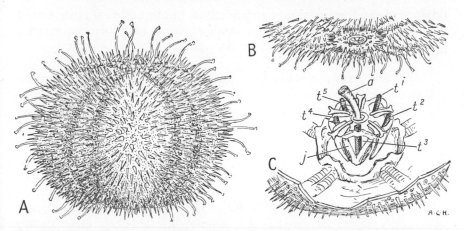

FIG. 59. The sea-urchin *Echinus esculentus*. A, seen from one side with its tube feet extended. ($\times \frac{1}{2}$) B, looking at the mouth on the underside. C, a dissection to show the 5 teeth $t^1$–$t^5$ (shaded) each sliding up and down in V-shaped jaw frames, *j*, and worked by complex muscles which have been omitted for clarity; *a*, is the cut alimentary canal. The anus is at the upper pole. A and B from living specimens.

contained molluscan remains, 35 echinoderm remains, 19 crustacean remains and 3 remains of polychaetes. The list of molluscs . . . shows a close correspondence with the molluscan diet of plaice." Then, after working out the frequency of meals and the average weight of food taken per individual, he goes on:

"The average number of *Astropecten* on the grounds throughout the year, derived from the catches of *Astropecten* made by the S.S. *Salpa* during 1923, is estimated as at least 1 specimen per 100 sq. metres, or 10,000 per sq. kilometre. From the foregoing an approximation may be made as to the amount of food consumed by this species in a given area in a given time. This works out at 730 kilograms per square kilometre per annum, or enough to support 73 kilograms of plaice, a value equal to the average catch of plaice per square kilometre per annum on the North Sea grounds as deduced from figures given by Howell."

Turning to the brittle-stars, we find that they are not entirely deposit- or suspension-feeders; some, like *Ophiura* and *Ophiocomina* (both in Plate 11), are carnivorous as well, feeding particularly on polychaete worms and small crustacea. The typical large sea-urchin *Echinus esculentus* (Plate 14, p. 195, and Fig. 59, above) is also both a deposit feeder and a carnivore. Its alimentary canal is nearly always full of a mixture of sand, small stones and detritus, but in addition Hunt found many fragments of sedentary animals such as tube-forming worms, polyzoa, hydroids and barnacles. He writes:

"Its strong teeth are evidently used for the detachment and mastication of such organisms, which form their chief food, though it undoubtedly takes much of the bottom material into its stomach, and must derive some nourishment from this source alone."

The remarkable arrangement of the powerful teeth of *Echinus,* making up the so-called 'Aristotle's lantern', is also shown in the sketch in Fig. 59 overleaf.

Passing to the crustacea, we need do little more than note that many of the decapods are predators. Among the shrimps and prawns *Processa, Crangon* (common shrimp) and *Pandalus* eat smaller crustacea, polychaete worms and very young bivalves, while the prawn *Palaemon* has been known to catch and eat small fish (*Gobius*) and large and active shrimps; among the crawling forms (reptantia) which are carnivorous *Galathea* and *Munida, Eupagurus* (hermit-crabs) and the burrowing crab *Corystes* may be mentioned particularly. The last-named, which lives buried under the sand and feeds largely on small bivalves and polychaetes, is of special interest and is shown on Plate 10 (p. 137). Its second antennae are enormously lengthened and provided with fringes of hairs, so that they interlock to form a breathing tube up to the water above; the water is now drawn *down* the tube into the gill-chamber, i.e. from in front, whereas usually crabs drive the water forward from behind.

The hermit-crabs (*Eupagurus*) deserve some attention. As everyone will know, they have become specially modified to live inside empty gastropod shells and are often associated with sea-anemones or hydroids which become attached to their borrowed shell. Our largest and commonest, *E. bernhardus* (Fig. 60, opposite) starts life by inhabiting the small dog whelk shells of the shores, but then as it grows bigger it migrates seawards to occupy successively larger shells of true whelks. It may now come to have on its back either a colony of one of the creeping moss-like hydroids *Hydractinia* or *Podocoryne* or the large anemone *Calliactis parasitica*. This association appears to benefit both; the crab is protected (from being attacked by fish) by the stinging cells of the coelenterates, and these, no doubt, in return receive fragments of food which fly up as the hermit tears apart its prey. The smaller hermit-crab *E. prideauxi* starts in a small shell, like its cousin, but very soon is covered by another kind of anemone, the very beautiful cloak

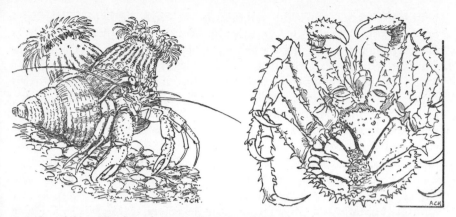

FIG. 60 *(left)*. The hermit crab *Eupagurus bernhardus* in a whelk shell with two anemones *Calliactis parasitica* on its back ($\times \frac{1}{2}$); this should be compared with *E. prideauxi* with a different anemone seen in Plate 10 (p. 137).

FIG. 61 *(right)*. The stone crab *Lithodes* seen from underneath to show the remarkable asymmetry of the abdomen ($\times \frac{1}{2}$); its upper surface is shown in *Plate 10* (p.137).

or strawberry anemone *Adamsia palliata* dappled with crimson spots; this not only covers the shell, but expands out to cover part of the crab as well. The two now grow at about the same pace, so that the crab has no need to find a new home, for its covering, its living cloak, grows with it; and as it walks, its cloak trails its fringe of tentacles along the ground to pick up morsels of food, as shown in Fig. 2 of Plate 10 (p. 137). Surprising though it may seem, the big spiny stone-crab *Lithodes,* shown in Fig. 3 of the same plate is closely related to the hermit crabs; if you turn it over you will see that its abdomen is quite asymmetrical, as shown in Fig. 61 above, telling us that its ancestors (probably smaller) were in fact once hermits living in shells[1]. These large stone-crabs are very common in the northern North Sea, and one, covered with barnacles, is seen in the trawl haul of Plate 13 (p. 194); they do not occur in the southern North Sea or English Channel where their place seems to be taken by the true spiny spider crabs (*Maia squinado*) which we see in Plate 16 (p. 211).

When I had first sketched out this chapter I had gone on at this point to say that of all the bottom-living carnivores the most important (i.e. in considering the community as a whole) were the fish themselves. Since writing that, however, I had last year (1956) the good fortune to

[1]The large tropical and land-living coconut crabs (*Birgus*) are also hermit crabs, but they have not only abandoned their shells, they have left the sea to climb coconut palms.

be invited to take part in a symposium on *Perspectives in Marine Biology* organised by the Scripps Institution of Oceanography at La Jolla, California; there I heard a most exciting paper given by Dr. Gunnar Thorson which certainly calls for a revision of this view. As I now write, his paper is not yet published, but it will be (Thorson, 1958) before my book appears and he has kindly allowed me to see a copy of it so that I can refer to it more exactly. I cannot, of course, deal with all the different aspects of these bottom communities which he discussed; I must confine myself to a very brief account of what he had to say about the balance between the predators and food animals.

In discussing the prey-predator relationships in the benthos Thorson remarks upon the little that is known about how much the animals actually eat. Regarding fish he refers to the work of Dawes (1930, 1931) and Bückmann (1952) who show that the plaice takes from 3 to 5 per cent. of its own weight of food a day during the warmer half of the year and only about 1/10th of this in the colder half. He also quotes Blegvad (1916) who examined hundreds of stomachs of many kinds of bottom-living fish and found their contents to make 2·2 to 4·0 per cent. of their total body weight; and the same author further had shown that such fish took on an average 6 hours to empty their stomachs and 4 to 5 hours to fill them again. Thorson thinks it reasonable to assume that most fish do not take more than an average of 5–6 per cent. of their own weight of food a day; in striking contrast to this he points to the high weight of food taken by most invertebrates at a single meal.

I have not the space to do justice to the many instances of recorded invertebrate feeding rates which he quotes; I can merely give one or two examples. Alpers at Naples found that the gastropod *Conus mediterraneus,* feeding on the worm *Nereis cultrifera* took 25 to 50 per cent. of its own volume in a single meal; Martin Johnson found in turn that *Nereis vexillosa* fed on other worms half as long as itself; and Mead showed that young and newly-settled starfish (*Asterias forbesi*) ate up to 3 times their own volume of clams (*Mya arenaria*) in 6 days. So the list goes on to include many different kinds of animal. In summarising, Thorson shows how very voracious the young invertebrate predators are, taking on an average some 25 per cent. of their own weight in food a day; active adults, without a definite growth stop, take 15 per cent a

---

*Plate 9.* CRAWFISH AND LOBSTERS
1. Crawfish, *Palinurus vulgaris* ($\times \frac{1}{3}$). 2. Lobster, *Homarus vulgaris* ($\times \frac{1}{2}$). 3. Norway lobster or Dublin Bay prawn, *Nephrops norvegicus* ($\times \frac{1}{2}$). All drawn from living specimens at the Scottish Marine (Fisheries) Laboratory, Aberdeen.

A.C.H.

*Plate 9*

A.C.H.

*Plate 10*

day, but some of the more sluggish adults which have stopped growing may take relatively little.  In short it seems that the growing invertebrate predators consume on an average at least four times as much food a day as do the bottom-living fish.  This, says Thorson, seems reasonable when we realise that the life span of the invertebrates is so much shorter than that of most fish.

Next Thorson recalls a calculation made by Petersen (1915) of the standing crop of fish food on the bottom of the Kattegat when he found that a 1,000,000 tons of food (lamellibranchs, gastropods, polychaetes and crustacea) had to be shared by 5,000 tons of flatfish and 75,000 tons of invertebrate predators.  Petersen, assuming that the rate of consumption per weight of body was the same for both, concluded that only 6 to 7 per cent of the so-called 'fish food' was eaten by the fish.  But, says Thorson, since we have seen that the invertebrates eat about 4 times as much food as the fish," we must recognize the amazing fact that only 1 to 2 per cent of the 'fish food' is actually eaten by fish; the rest is taken by the invertebrates." He goes on to point out that if for some reason the standing crop of 'fish food' is increased, the invertebrate predators with their shorter life cycles and quicker growth would be able to take advantage of it long before the fish could.

This certainly gives us food for thought.  We see what unwelcome pests most of the invertebrate predators are.  Will future farmers of the sea be able to eradicate some of them and so step up the quantity of fish carried on a given area?  I shall return to this later (p. 303). Not all the predators, however, represent material going entirely to waste; while the gastropod *Natica*, for example, is so destructive of the bivalves which form the food of the plaice, it is itself a favourite prey of the common dab.

I would like to refer to much more in Dr. Thorson's stimulating discussion, but space will only permit me to make one further point: his solution of a mystery which has puzzled us for so long.  Since most of the predators have a much longer life span than their prey they are likely to be on the bottom in large numbers when a new generation of prey settles down.  The problem has been to know how the newly-

---

*Plate 10.*  A FEW CRABS
1. Swimming crab, *Portunus holsatus* ($\times \frac{1}{2}$).  2. Hermit crab, *Eupagurus prideauxi* carrying the cloak anemone, *Adamsia palliata*, ($\times \frac{1}{2}$).  3. Spiny stone-crab, *Lithodes maia* ($\times \frac{1}{2}$).  4. Edible crab, *Cancer pagurus* ($\times \frac{1}{2}$).  5. Burrowing crab, *Corystes cassivelaunus* ($\times \frac{1}{2}$).  All drawn from living specimens at the Scottish Marine (Fisheries) Laboratory, Aberdeen.

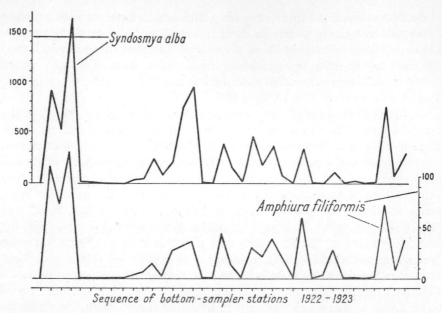

FIG. 62. Two graphs showing the striking similarity in the distribution of the bivalve mollusc *Syndosmya* (=*Abra*) *alba* and that of the brittle-star *Amphiura filiformis* as found by Mr. E. Ford at a sequence of positions on the sea-bed off South Devon (Ford, 1923).

settled young, for example, of small bivalves, can survive for the first month or two of their lives when every square inch of the bottom is being searched for prey every day by a network of brittle-star arms. Just how big a puzzle it has been was well-emphasised many years ago by Ford in his paper of 1923. In Fig. 62 I reproduce a remarkable graph of his showing the relative numbers of the small bivalve *Syndosmya* (=*Abra*) *alba* and the brittle-star *Amphiura filiformis* at 37 different positions sampled by his grab in Bigbury Bay near Plymouth. The positive correlation between the two sets of figures is fantastically good. "What does this mean?" says Ford, and he goes on to write as follows:

"According to Blegvad both species are essentially detritus feeders so that their frequency in and restriction to a soil at Bigbury in which the finest deposits are well represented, would not be inconsistent with this mode of feeding. On the other hand, Petersen says 'At places where the Amphiurae live in such quantities that they form a dense net over the sea-bottom . . . but little of the tiny (bivalve) fry will be able to develop . . .'

Later on in the same publication he (Petersen) continues: 'I conclude that the Mactra fry and other small organisms sink to the bottom in great quantities over the whole of the Kattegat; on the too soft bottom they probably die; but the network of Amphiurae as well as other animals at many places will certainly cause their disappearance in the course of a few hours'."

At last, after more than 30 years, Thorson has solved this puzzle. He has shown that just when the larvae of the bivalves settle down the Amphiuran brittle-stars enter a 'passive period' for about two months. During the first month the distended reproductive organs, ovary or testis, fill the body and the stomach is pushed to one side and even degenerates; then during the second month, after spawning, the gut is gradually reformed. During these two months most of the young bivalves which settled at the beginning of the period will have grown to such a size that they are too big to be eaten by the brittle-stars. The bivalves and brittle-stars can now devolop side by side both succeeding or failing together according to the same supply of food: hence the remarkable correlations found by Ford. "The significance of these 'passive periods'," Thorson writes, "for the species composition of an *Amphiura* community can hardly be over estimated." He goes on to show that such passive periods among predators during the maximum season of upgrowth of their prey seems to be a common and perhaps a normal feature on the sea-bottom. He gives examples among the predatory gastropods and points to many crustacea which do not feed during the breeding season. Finally, he shows that these passive periods are still more advantagous than appears at first sight. They usually begin a month before spawning so that the voracious predator young will not begin to settle for perhaps another three weeks, i.e. seven weeks from the beginning of the period; this time lag allows the young of a prey species which have settled early in the period to have reached a size too big to be attacked by very young predators. "So", writes Thorson, "a good stock survives the onslaught of the young predator hordes." This, of course, shows the nice balance brought about by natural selection.

We must now leave the grab and dredge, and turn to some new methods of examining the sea-floor which are being developed. Dr. H. G. Vevers (1951, 1952) late of the Plymouth Laboratory, pioneered with a specially designed underwater camera which, lowered on a cable with an accompanying battery of lights, he made to hop over the sea-bed and take a picture at every stride; he made lines of photographic observation over many different types of ground in this area. The camera can be set to take pictures of 1 square metre of the bottom or less; in the surveys so far published, he took areas a quarter of this size; i.e. squares with a side of just over 19½ inches. One of his most striking discoveries by this method was that of the astonishing swarms of brittle-stars in confined areas, their arms all overlapping, as seen in Plate IX, p. 114; this plate shows four photographs of the bottom taken with his camera. It is surprising that these animals can find sufficient food when in these great concentrations; as already remarked (p. 109), he thinks it likely that they are feeding entirely on suspended matter. Underwater cameras are now being used from a number of marine laboratories for surveying the sea-bed.

Fast upon the invention of his apparatus has come underwater television. Dr. Barnes of the Millport Marine Station was the first to suggest the importance of using television for oceanographic research, and began his experiments in 1950; in the following year came the tragic loss of the submarine *Affray* and the Admiralty made rapid progress in developing their own equipment, which was successfully used to finally identify the wreck in deep water. By August of the next year their television camera had advanced so well that it was used for the first time on an expedition by the R.R.S. *Discovery*, to look at the sea-floor down to depths of 300 metres—along the continental shelf from the Channel to the coast of Portugal, and then out to the banks round the Azores. I had the privilege of being invited to join the expedition; it was a remarkable experience to sit in a cabin on deck looking into the viewing screen and have the sensation that one's chair was swinging close over the ocean floor some 1,000 feet below the ship. Starfish, shells, worm-castings and sometimes fish could be clearly seen; but most surprising were the striking ripple-marks in the sand on bottoms as deep as 150 metres suggesting much stronger currents at those depths than usually expected. In the meantime Dr. Barnes, working with a different objective in view, had produced an apparatus which enables us to study the life on the bottom in much greater detail; looking into his viewing screen it is possible to see, almost natural size, the movements of the tube-feet of a sea-urchin

---

*Plate 11.* BRITTLE-STARS, STARFISH AND A FEATHER-STAR
1. Common brittle-stars, *Ophiothrix fragilis* (×1) showing three colour varieties.
2. Black brittle-star, *Ophiocomina nigra* (×1). 3. Sand brittle-star, *Ophiura texturata* (×1). 4. *Astropecten irregularis,* a starfish common on sandy sea-bed (×½). 5. Common starfish, *Asterias rubens* (×½). 6. Sun-star, *Solaster papposus* (×½). 7. Leaf-star, *Palmipes* (=*Anseropoda*) *placenta* (×½). 8. Cushion-star, *Hippasteria phrygiana* (×½). 9. Feather-star, *Antedon bifida* (×1). All drawn from living specimens: Nos. 1, 2, 3, 7 and 9 drawn in the Plymouth Laboratory, Nos. 4, 5, 6 and 8 on board the Scottish Fishery Research Ship "Explorer" in the northern North Sea.

A.C.H.

*Plate 11*

Plate 12

going about its private business, quite unsuspecting the prying eyes within a ship in another world far above it. I have already referred (p. 9) to the astonishing views he has given us of the density of animal plankton in parts of the Clyde sea area. In Plate XII (p. 131) I reproduce two photographs taken of his viewing screen when the camera was being used for examining the sea-bed.

A study of the ocean floor at the great depths far out beyond the continental shelf lies outside the scope of our book which is concerned essentially with the seas immediately around the British Isles. However, as we are discussing new methods, let us note and acclaim the achievements of two great expeditions which in recent years have added much to our knowledge of the deep-sea deposits and of the benthic life at depths of several miles down.

The first is the Swedish *Albatross* Expedition of 1947 led by Professor Hans Pettersson which was specially concerned with driving long steel tubes into the ooze of the ocean bed and obtaining core samples up to nearly 70 feet in length. The device used was the ingenious piston core-sampler invented by Dr. B. Kullenberg. Each long steel tube, of only 2 inches diameter, is loaded with a detachable weight so that it is lowered on a cable to the bottom and then dropped end on into the ooze like a huge hollow needle pricking its surface. Now, a

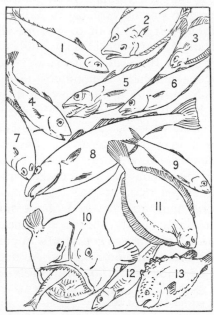

*Plate 12.* PART OF A NORTH SEA TRAWL CATCH ON THE DECK (*90 miles N.E. of Aberdeen*)
Painted as soon as the catch had been released from the 'cod-end'. A key to the different species is given below. The whole plate $\times \frac{1}{4}$ (diam.).

1. Mackerel, *Scomber scombrus* (probably caught on the way up).
2. Megrim, *Lepidorhombus whiff-iagonis*
3. Dab, *Limanda limanda*.
4. Haddock, *Gadus aeglefinus*.
5. Hake, *Merluccius merluccius*.
6. Whiting, *Gadus merlangus*.
7. Long rough dab, *Hippoglossoides platessoides*.
8. Cod, *Gadus callarias*.
9. Herring, *Clupea harengus* (probably caught on the way up).
10. Angler, *Lophius piscatorius*.
11. Witch, *Glyptocephalus cynoglossus*.
12. Argentine, *Argentina sphyraena*.
13. Lump-sucker, *Cyclopterus lumpus*.

piston, closely fitting its inside and situated at its lower end, is pulled
up the tube by an internal cable on which the whole is suspended; and a
remarkable thing happens. A vacuum at such a depth and pressure is,
of course, impossible, so that the ooze is forced into the tube; instead,
however, of it rising up the tube as does ink in a fountain-pen
filler, the long tube itself is drawn down, because the force required
to drive in its thin steel walls is less than that required to lift the column
of ooze. When the piston reaches the closed top of the tube through
which the cable passes, it can go no further without taking the tube
with it, and that is just what it does; it pulls out the tube and brings
it to the surface carrying the precious core within it. Long samples of
ooze which have been settling for perhaps up to ten million years are
brought up in an undisturbed state; from the different kinds of shells
of tiny animals like *Globigerina*, which once lived at the surface, experts
can read the history of the sea tracing past glacial and inter-glacial
periods by the cooler and warmer water species found.

The second recent deep-sea expedition is that of the Danish ship
*Galathea* led by Dr. Anton Brunn which had for its main objective
the dredging for animal life in the greatest known depths of the ocean.
They succeeded in putting down their dredge into that long narrow
trench nearly nine miles deep off the Philippine Islands; from this and
many other deeps they drew up living animals including delicate
sea-anemones. In the introduction to our first volume (p. 8) we saw
that living in water under great pressure was no obstacle to animals
provided they had no spaces or bubbles filled with air or gas, for all
liquids are only very slightly compressible; the internal body fluids of
the animal will be at the same pressure as the water outside and the
two pressures will exactly balance one another. Among the many
species new to science which they obtained, quite the most exciting
was a mollusc of a kind thought to have become extinct in the early
palaeozoic times of some four hundred million years ago; it is another
living fossil, one which may well cause us to revise our ideas of molluscan
evolution for it appears to be segmented like a worm. It has been
named *Neopilina galatheae* and should be as famous as the coelacanth.
We must return, however, to our shallower seas.

To close this chapter a few words must now be said about our
fisheries for shell-fish: i.e. certain molluscs and the larger crustacea.
Actually most of these are strictly coastal and do not concern us in our
study of the open sea, but there are some we should refer to. Among
the bivalve molluscs, the oyster[1], mussel and cockle are truly inshore

[1]Oysters do occur in small numbers in deeper water and were dredged for off
the Dutch coast by Brightlingsea boats at the end of last century.

forms, but the large scallops (*Pecten maximus*) are fished up from banks which may lie some way from the coast; they are caught in dredges of 4 to 6 foot span which are towed several at a time by a single boat. There are rich beds in the English Channel off Beachy Head, the Normandy coast, and off Brixham, off Southern Ireland and the Isle of Man, and in the Clyde Sea area. The smaller and delicious "queens" (*Chlamys opercularis*) may occasionally be brought in by trawlers from various grounds in sufficient quantities to be marketed; but they are

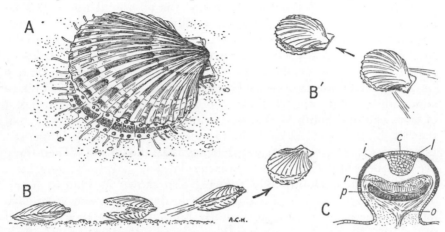

FIG. 63. The queen scallop, *Chlamys opercularis*. A, at rest on the sea-bed; note the tentacles and eyes along the two mantle edges. B, showing the swimming action when escaping from a starfish: jets of water are shot out by a rapid closing of the valves; they may also, as in B', swim forwards by squirting out jets at each side of the hinge. C, a section of an eye as seen through a microscope, *c*, the transparent cornea; *i*, the pigmented iris; *l*, the crystalline lens; *o*, optic nerve; *p*, pigment behind the retina *r*.

never the object of a special fishery. The remarkable powers of these animals in "flying" through the water when approached by their star-fish enemies are shown in Fig. 63 above. Among the gastropods, the periwinkles are, of course, entirely littoral, but the whelks (*Buccinum undatum*) may be taken at considerable depths and are dredged for like scallops or caught in baited pots on a number of grounds, particu-larly off the east coast, or occasionally they may be landed by the smaller trawlers.

Turning to the crustaceans, the common shrimp (*Crangon vulgaris*) and several prawns, *Palaemon* (=*Leander*) *serratus*, *P. elegans*, *Pandalus montagui* and *Processa canaliculata*, are all caught in shallow water in bays and estuaries around our coasts. The largest prawns, however, on our markets, *Pandalus borealis,* are caught off Norway in quite deep water: from 30 to 60 fathoms. This was a fishery developed after their discovery in large quantities by the naturalists of the Norwegian fishery department. Professor Hjort, who was largely responsible for the development of this fishery, always believed that there might be a similar stock of prawns to the west of Scotland; and recently an allied species *P. bonnieri* has been found in fair quantities in the Clyde area by the naturalists at Millport.

Lobsters (*Homarus vulgaris*) are fished for all round our coasts by baited creels or pots, and are occasionally caught in trawls on stony grounds some twenty miles from land; they are, however, essentially dwellers on the rocky bottoms near the coast. Crawfish (*Palinurus vulgaris*) of which one is shown for comparison with a lobster on Plate 9 (p. 136) are also lovers of rocky bottoms, but do not, as a rule, come so close inshore. They are fished for by pots and trammel nets off the coast of Cornwall and South Wales, but strange to say there is only a small market for them in England; in France, of course, as the langouste, this species is esteemed a greater delicacy than the lobster. Then there are the beautiful orange-red Norway lobsters (*Nephrops norvegicus*), sometimes called Dublin Bay prawns, also shown in Plate 9 (one). They are often abundant far out to sea in depths between 20 and 50 fathoms where they like a soft muddy bottom. While they occur all round the British Isles on suitable grounds, they are particularly numerous off our north-east coast and North Shields has always been a prominent centre for them (Storrow, 1912, 1913); they are not fished for by special methods, but are caught by the smaller North Sea trawlers. It is again surprising that, like the crawfish, they are not eaten more in England; the species has a remarkable range of distribution and occurs in the Adriatic to provide the Italians with their "Scampi", a dish that we, as tourists, always find so delicious.

The edible crab, *Cancer pagurus,* (Plate 10, p. 137) is the only crab for which there is a fishery in Great Britain; it is fished at many points but notably along the east coast and in the south west. The swimming crabs (*Portunus* spp.), however, also in Plate 10, are said to be eaten in the Channel Islands (Cole, in Graham 1956). Our crab fishery, like that for the lobster, is a coastal one and does not really concern us here; it is largely carried out by similar methods, i.e. with creels and pots, but sometimes in Cornwall trammel nets may also be used. The crabs are actually more inshore animals in summer than in winter. In the autumn they migrate off-shore into deeper water where the females extrude their eggs and attach them to their small abdominal appendages; in the spring they return to shallow water carrying their eggs which hatch in June and July into the little zoea larvae (described in Part 1, p. 176).  In addition to their to-and-fro migrations, some have been shown, by tagging experiments, to migrate considerable distances along the coast; journeys of 90 miles have been recorded.

CHAPTER 7

# THE TRAWL, LINE AND
# SEINE-NET FISHERIES

So much of our knowledge of the distribution and relative abundance of the bottom-living fish comes from the landings of trawlers at our fish-markets, that it will be well to give a brief sketch of the development of trawling and other methods of demersal fishing before proceeding to the natural history of the fish themselves.

While trawling seems to have begun at the beginning of the seventeenth century or even earlier, it has only grown into a great industry during the last hundred years.  Opinions differ, but many believe the first trawl to have been evolved from the simple type of seine net still used by long-shore fishermen to surround their fish and drag them ashore.  Made in the form of a large bag, it was pulled over the sea-bed towards the shore by two boats, which, being one on either side, kept its mouth wide open; its catch, like that of the seine, was emptied out on the beach.  Next came the idea of using a very long wooden beam to hold the mouth open, so that it could be managed by a single boat and be hauled up at sea without coming in to land. This is the beam-trawl (Fig. 64); while it has now been superseded on all the steam trawlers of to-day by the larger and much more efficient otter trawl, it is still used on a few small sailing smacks, and is invaluable for the amateur who may want to trawl from a yacht, or motor-boat[1].  At each end of the beam are iron supports and runners which allow the trawl to be pulled smoothly along. The head-rope, or the upper lip of the net is lashed to the beam, and the foot-rope, which forms its lower lip, drags along the bottom; the latter, being much the longer, sweeps backwards in a curve and so, as explained for the otter-

[1]Small otter-trawls may also be used from such craft but they require a lot of practice to use successfully.

trawl (p. 1), does not disturb the unsuspecting fish till they are covered by the net and almost already in the bag.

The trawl may well have been developed from the seine net as just suggested, but some believe it had quite a different origin, thinking it was evolved from a large form of oyster dredge; to support their claim there is the remarkable fourteenth century account of an invention called the "wondyrchoun". G. L. Alward in his *The Fisheries of Great Britain and Ireland* (1932) gives a translation of a petition in the Parliament of 1377, the last Parliament of Edward III[1]. Mr. P. T. V. M. Chaplais, Reader in Diplomatic at Oxford, has

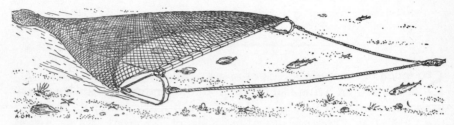

FIG. 64. The old-fashioned beam-trawl.

kindly made a more exact translation for me from the mediaeval French as follows:

"Also your said commons beg to inform you that, as in several parts of your said kingdom, in creeks and havens of the sea where there used to be good and plentiful fishing to the great profit of the Realm, which (fishing) is being rapidly ruined for a long time to come by some fishermen who seven years ago secretly contrived a new type of instrument which, among themselves, they call wondyrchoun, made like an oyster drag of outsize dimensions, to which instrument is attached a net so closely meshed that no kind of fish, however small, that enters therein can escape, but must stay and be taken . . . with which instruments called wondyrchouns in the said several parts the aforesaid fishermen take such quantity of the said small fish that, not knowing what to do with them, they feed and fatten their pigs on them all the year round to the great damage of all the commons of the Realm and to the destruction of the fisheries in such places; and they ask for redress thereof."

Alward goes on to say that a commission was appointed to enquire into

[1]*Rotuli Parliamentorum* (Record Commission) Vol. II, p. 369.

the matter and that its members met at Colchester; and he further gives the following particulars from their report:

> "The 'wondyrchoun' was three fathoms long and ten of men's feet wide and the net had a beam ten feet long, at the end of which were two frames formed like a colerake; that a leaded rope weighted with many great stones was fixed on the lower part of the net between the two frames, and that another rope was fixed with nails on the upper part of the beam, so that the fish entering the space between the beam and the lower net were caught. The net had meshes (maskes) of the length and breadth of two thumbs. They said the net ought to be used in the deep water, and not in the waters of colne and pont or in any other like places."

He then says that no action appears to have been taken in consequence of this report, "but that later on trawling, which no doubt is the mode of fishing described, was prohibited in many private waters." He regards the petition and the report of the Commission as of great importance, "for here", he says, "we have the first reliable trace of the trawl."

Dr. C. L. Cutting, who in his *Fish Saving* (1955) has given us such a splendid history of fish processing from the earliest times and also included much on the history of actual fishing, writes as follows:

> "In the seventeenth century trawling, probably introduced from the Zuider Zee, was quite common in bays and inlets on the south-east coast, the fish being transported to London by road. In March 1617, Mr. William Angell, the 'King's Fishmonger', issued a certificate to John Farsby, of Barking, 'to tralle for place and souls in such places as he can best find fish to be in and is usually fished bye any Cost men of Kent or elsewhere', and to bring 'weekly his fish to London yf wind and wether doe serve'."

Mr. Michael Graham, in his delightful book, *The Fish Gate* (1943), reproduces a rough sketch of an unmistakable beam-trawl found scribbled on the back of State papers from the reign of Charles I; in these papers, dated 1635, he says "The King's Most Excellent Majesty took into consideration the great destruction made of fish by a net or engine now called the trawle."

Whether trawling began at the mouth of the Thames or, as many still believe, in the west-country, it is certain that the Devon men

FIG. 65. Old sailing smacks: a nineteenth century sketch of the return of a North Sea fishing fleet by the late Mr. Ernest Dade from *Sail and Oar* (1933). Below this sketch he writes "The old smacks brought a very powerful odour with them when they returned after six or eight weeks at sea. They could be smelt some miles away."

played a great part in the development of British trawling[1]. The Brixham trawling-fleet of red-sailed smacks expanded so much that it became difficult to dispose of the catch in the towns and villages of Cornwall and Devon; in the latter half of the eighteenth century many of these west country fishermen moved up to Rye and Dover to supply the London market. In the early part of the nineteenth century they moved round to join the Thames men in the harbours of Ramsgate, Barking and Harwich to work the grounds of the southern North Sea. A little later Yarmouth became the great trawling centre with a fleet of some seven hundred smacks; soon, there started what was called the 'fleeter' system, in which a large number of boats remained out on the fishing grounds for weeks at a time while their catch was collected every few days by fast cutters to be carried direct to Billingsgate. Typical smacks are seen in another of Ernest Dade's charming sketches

[1]Some believe that the Devon trawlermen played a part in the defeat of the Spanish Armada; the Devon fishermen almost certainly did, but we do not know if at that time they were using the trawl or fishing by line. Others think that knowledge of the trawl first came to Brixham from Holland when William of Orange landed in 1688, but again I do not know of any evidence to support the idea.

shown in Fig. 65 opposite. By the eighteen-forties many boats were
pushing north to fish off the Yorkshire coast and land their catches at
Scarborough to supply the summer visitors. At first they returned to
the southern ports during the winter; in one year, however,—so the
story goes—encouraged by the good price obtained for their fish, a
number of boats stayed north longer than usual and were caught in a
great gale. One of the smacks, which was separated from the rest,
was driven hard by the wind before the crew could haul their trawl,
and over unknown grounds; when at length they managed to get
their net in-board, although badly damaged, it was found to be full of
the finest soles. After the gale the smack went back to hunt for this
rich ground and so discovered what came to be known as the Silver
Pit: the richest ground for soles in the North Sea; it lies at the extreme
south-west end of the Dogger Bank[1]. News of the great find quickly
spread and soon so many boats had come north that Scarborough was
neither able to take all their catch nor give them the facilities they
needed for stores and repair. They began to use Hull as a port, and
in the eighteen-fifties many Brixham families settled there to establish
the first Humber trawling centre. Grimsby, being nearer to the sea,
was now rapidly developed as a special home for the fishing industry,
by the enterprise of the Manchester, Sheffield and Lincolnshire
Railway (which later became the Great Central). Hull and Grimsby
have ever since been friendly but keen rivals and have side by side
grown into the great deep-water fishing ports they are to-day.

Steam tugs used to tow the smacks out of harbour when there was
no wind, as we see in another of Dade's drawings in Fig. 66 overleaf.
One day, when there was still no wind outside, one enterprising smacks-
man, from Sunderland I believe, employed a tug to continue towing his
vessel while he put his trawl down; thus he made a good catch of fish
whilst all the rest of the fleet was idle. The news again travelled
quickly and very soon steam tugs were chartered at several centres to
be used as trawlers. In 1881 the first specially built steam trawler,
*The Zodiac*, was launched at Hull, for the Grimsby and North Sea
Steam Trawling Co. The great change over to steam now began in
earnest. In 1886 Grimsby had 820 sailing smacks; but in 1902 there
were only 29 left, and the number of steam-trawlers had risen to close
on 500. It was the same at Hull, which, like Yarmouth, had developed
the fleeter system extensively.

The smack fishermen, who worked the coastal grounds and came

[1]It is now called the Outer Silver Pit in contrast to the Little Silver Pit off the
Lincolnshire coast. In the story of its discovery I follow the account given by F. G.
Aflalo (1904); there are several variations of it given by different authors.

frequently into port, had a reasonable if hard life, but the fleeter system was different. It was a practice which kept the men for six or eight weeks on the Dogger Bank under frightful conditions; and there was much danger and loss of life in transferring the catch day after day, often in appalling seas, from the smacks to the carrier in small rowing boats. What had been a magnificent calling, and still was in the coastal

FIG. 66. A smack being towed out to sea, another sketch by the late Mr. Ernest Dade. This was how steam trawling began: the employment of a tug when there was no wind.

smacks, became on the Dogger an almost intolerable hell of industrialism. The good and the bad of the old days have been splendidly told by Walter Wood in his *North Sea Fishers and Fighters* (1911); like Ernest Dade's North Sea sketch book of last century, published long afterwards as *Sail and Oar* (1933), it is indispensable for an understanding of the past. I quote from Walter Wood as follows:

"There were no sanitary arrangements whatever in the sailing smacks, whose domestic economy was throughout of the most primitive description. They were as different from the splendid latest types of steam-trawlers as was the old emigrant ship from the *Olympic* . . . The marvel is that in past days men and boys could be found to undertake the work, and probably the smacks could never have been provided with crews if it had not been for Boards of Guardians and reformatories. Legions of miserable children have

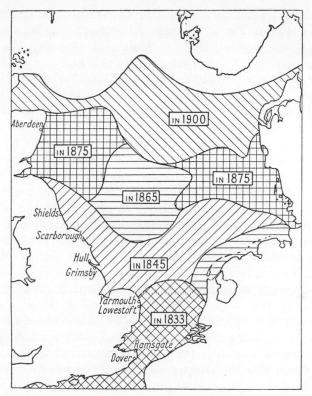

FIG. 67. A map to show the spread of trawling in the North Sea during the nineteenth century; redrawn from Alward (1911).

been sentenced to the Dogger, to perish there, or become men and heroes. Those who survived and remained did at least get inured to sufferings and hardships, and provided the finest race of seafarers in the world—and that they remain to this day[1]."

[1]Our book is of natural, not social, history, and I must not take up more space in the main text with such digressions; nevertheless, I cannot resist adding the following further quotation from the same book, as a footnote to our nineteenth century civilization:

"One of the worst features of the old sailing days was the apprenticeship system, which had many elements of inhumanity and barbarism in it. Grimsby became notorious for the number of unhappy little fellows who were sent to prison rather than return to a life of slavery and degradation on the Dogger. ... They were at the beck and call of any man, brute or otherwise, and so hard and incessant was the labour, so dull and uninviting was the life in many cases, that a single trip to the Dogger was enough for even a young and robust lifetime. Once ashore, nothing would induce many of the apprentices to go back to sea. There was no alternative; they were taken before the magistrates, and sent to gaol. Time

*Continued overleaf*

The rapid spread of trawling in the North Sea during the last century is shown in Fig. 67 overleaf. Aberdeen began trawling in 1882. Milford Haven began much as Hull and Grimsby did: Brixham fishermen, pushing up the west coast to fish and land their catch at Tenby for the summer visitors, soon found that their activities outgrew this market; the Great Western Railway then built the docks which made Milford Haven into an important fishing port in the 'nineties. Similarly, further north, came the rise of Fleetwood. One may wonder perhaps why it was that trawling only developed so rapidly after the middle of the century, for the great expansion was taking place before the coming of the steam trawler. Why could it not have come, say, a hundred years earlier? The answer is, of course, in steam after all. The expansion could only take place when the railways had provided the means of carrying the landed fish quickly and cheaply to London and other big centres of the population. Railway transport and dock building has played a great part in the development of British fisheries. The Great Eastern Railway developed Lowestoft as a fishery harbour so successfully that the smack fleet of Yarmouth transferred to this adjacent port. By fishing local waters these picturesque sailing smacks of Lowestoft, as at Ramsgate and Brixham, continued, until comparatively recently, to make a good and healthy living in competition with the steam-trawlers going to more distant grounds. Now, alas, they have gone and one regrets their loss from the sea as much as one does that of the windmills from the landscape.

Before the coming of the trawlers, bottom-living fish were landed by hook and line by a large number of small sailing boats, like the sturdy cobles of Yorkshire and Northumberland, from many small fishing towns and villages as well as the larger centres such as Scarborough. These characteristic craft are well shown in two more of Dade's lively sketches, in Figs. 68 and 69; they had flat bottoms towards the stern to allow them to be pulled up a sloping beach, often on wheels by horses, as shown in the second picture. It is interesting to look back and see what the line fishermen were catching some three hundred years ago. Our great naturalist John Ray records in the *Itinerary* of his journey north with Philip Skippon in 1661 a number of fish seen at Scarborough:

after time the boys declared in the police courts that they would rather go to hard labour than back to sea—and to prison they were committed. It was publicly and frequently declared that under the old sailing and apprenticeship system boys spent more time in gaol than on board their masters' smacks. Yet there were considerable possibilities of success, as many prosperous men to-day have proved."

FIG. 68. Yorkshire cobles tacking in to land. Another sketch by the late Mr. Ernest Dade.

"We saw ling, cod fish, skate, thornback, turbot, whiting, and herring. They take also conger, bret, haddock, and mackrell. They have an artificial harbour or pier, made of vast stones, piled one upon another without cement, for security of their vessels of trade. The like, though not so large, is at Lyme, in Dorsetshire, called the cob. We observed in ling the *intestina caeca*, which they call kelk, to be larger and fewer in number than in the cod-fish. The turbot hath three large *intestina caeca* a little below the stomach, which is also very large. We saw there among others, a long, large, cartilaginous fish, which they call a hay, (or hoe, a northern name for the picked dog-fish[1]) not much unlike (they say) to a dog-fish."

[1]Spur dog-fish (*Squalus acanthias*).

FIG. 69. At Filey (Yorkshire) the cobles were pulled up on wheels by horses. A sketch, like the last, from Ernest Dade's *Sail and Oar* (1933).

In the following year he visited Tenby and writes:

"Great variety of fish taken near this town, viz., cod, ling, mackrel, thornback, soles, plaice, turbot, scarbut, holybut, conger, hake, dog or hound-fish, horn-fish or sea-needles,[1] haddocks, gurnards red and white, herrings, sprats, mullet, and basse, suins[2], sharks, dunhounds, bream, flukes grey and white, cowes, bleaks or pollacks, ballon[3], smelts, lobsters, crabs, porpess, grampus, siels, hews, bullheads, butter-fish, dots, bret or brit (brill), bowmen, oysters, shrimps, limpings (limpets?), smooth and rough cockles, flemings, white and black hay-fish, cuttle-fish."

These quotations are taken from the *Memorials of John Ray* published by the Ray Society in 1846;[4] my attention was drawn to them by seeing them quoted in Dr. Raven's magnificent biography *John Ray, Naturalist,* (1942) in which will be found collected so many other interesting observations made by Ray in preparation for his *History of Fishes.*

The smaller inshore boats, now fitted with engines, still fish with hook, line and lobster-pot along the coast, as at Flamborough and

[1]Garfish (*Belone belone*).
[2]Sea trout (*Salmo trutta*).
[3]Ballan wrasse (*Labrus bergylta*).
[4]The editor of the *Memorials* had added in parenthesis, after most of the English names, the scientific names of 1846; these I have omitted as many of them have been changed and the modern ones will be found elsewhere in the text. I do not know what kind of fish Ray meant by scarbut, cowes, hews, or dots; there were no latin names following those in the 1846 *Memorials*. Dr. Tucker suggests that flemings were clams (*Mya arenaria*) and tells me that in those days 'bret' was the name for turbot and that their 'turbot' was our halibut.

Robin Hood's Bay; but, sad to relate, they and their adventurous crews have diminished much in number under the competition with the trawlers from the major ports. Their way of life and methods of fishing have been brilliantly portrayed in the novels of Leo Walmsley, particularly in his *Three Fevers* (1932).

Line fishing, before the days of trawling, was by no means confined to the small boats along the coast. Early in the fifteenth century decked vessels from Bristol, Lynn, Scarborough, Boston and Cromer—and even Walberswick in Suffolk—were going to Iceland to fish (Cutting 1955); and then in the sixteenth century, after the discovery of Newfoundland by Cabot in 1497, British craft joined those of other nations exploiting the Grand Banks: in 1528 for instance, 149 ships from our east coast ports are recorded as taking part. The fish they caught were, of course, brought back in salt. In the eighteenth century, however, came a great development in the landing of fresh fish by what were called 'well' smacks which had a large compartment amidships separated by water-tight bulkheads from the rest of the ship forward of it and aft of it. This compartment or well served as a huge aquarium, or aquatic store, in which the fish were kept alive as they were caught; the top was decked in, except for a hatchway, to hold the water in as the vessel rolled or heeled over under sail, and numerous holes bored in the sides allowed a free exchange of water with the sea outside so as to keep it in good condition. Fig. 70 below,

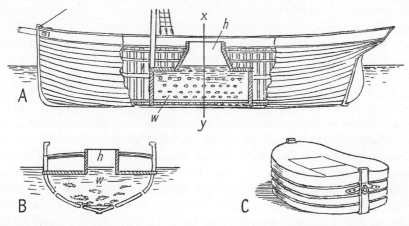

FIG. 70. A. A 'well' smack of the eighteenth century for bringing back fish alive: *h*, the hatch at deck level; *w*, the well communicating through holes to the sea outside. B, a section through the line XY in A. C, one of the floating chests used at Harwich in the same period for keeping fish alive till sold. A and B are redrawn from Alward (1932) and C from Holdsworth (1884).

shows a sketch of such a vessel. Harwich became an important centre
for these 'well' smacks in the eighteenth century, fishing by line
mainly for cod on the Dogger Bank; Cutting (1955) records that in
1774 forty out of sixty-two such vessels were fishing there. Greenwich,
Gravesend and Barking were also important centres and many of the
well smacks transferred their fish at Gravesend into smaller boats
which were then rowed to Billingsgate Market. Floating chests were
used at many ports for keeping fish alive till sold. The well smacks
unfortunately went out as trawling came in. The trawlers caught more

FIG. 71. A deep-sea long-liner hauling in a line as she steams towards the dhan-
buoy anchored at the far end.

than did the line fishers in the same time; their fish, however, were
nearly all so suffocated in the trawl by their gills being closed by the
pressure of other fish in the cod-end, that too few were in good enough
condition to be kept alive.

To-day, in addition to the steam-trawlers, there are a number of
steam-vessels of similar design which fish by line, particularly for the
larger cod and halibut, on grounds—as some to the west of Scotland—
which are so rough that they would tear a trawl to pieces. They are
known as long-liners, for they lay long lines with baited hooks along
the bottom. Each line, anchored and marked with a dhan buoy at the
ends, is a little over half a mile long and usually carries about 120
large hooks on snoods (small lines each 1½ fathoms) attached to the
main line at about 3½ fathom intervals. Fig. 71 above, shows a
sketch of the arrangement. Some 20 to 30 lines will be set by one
vessel at a time, i.e. some 10 to 15 miles of line and some 2,500 to
3,800 hooks fishing at once, according to whether fishing in deeper or

shallower water. Hauling is done by a special steam-driven winding device.

After this digression on fishing by line let us return to modern trawling. Together with the change-over to steam came the replacement of the beam by the otter-trawl (Fig. 1, p. 2). Instead of the mouth being held open by a rigid bar, the same result is produced by the action of two wooden otter-boards, which, as we saw in the introduction (p. 1) act as kites and pull outwards on either side and so keep

FIG. 72. A modern steam-trawler (drawn from a photograph) and the wide sweep of her trawl.

the headrope tightly stretched to the full width of the trawl. Fore and aft on each side of a trawler are the two large inverted U-shaped structures of steel stepped on the deck and projecting slightly over the sides; these are the gallows, and from them hang the otter-boards before the trawl is launched. The trawler carries two trawls, one on each side, and they are usually used alternately; some skippers, however, have a preference for port or starboard side and tend to use that side continuously. Fig. 72, above, shows a sketch of a modern trawler.

When ready for launching—'shooting' is the correct fishing term— the trawl to be used, which has been lying along the deck between the

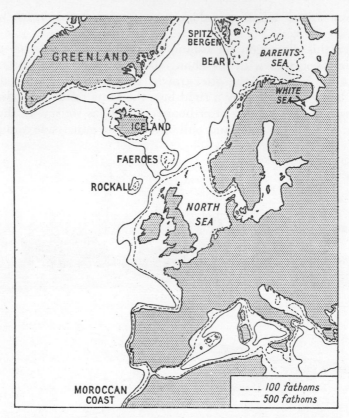

FIG. 73. The main areas fished by British trawlers of to-day.

gallows, is linked to the otter-boards, unrolled and put into the water. It will be pulled by two steel warps, each coming off a separate drum on the huge steam winch; after passing round a series of bollards, one warp goes to the otter-board at the forward gallows and the other to that at the after gallows on the same side, so that when they are veered away the trawl will be lowered into the water. As the trawl with its heavy boards sinks, the ship steams slowly forwards in a gradual curve to expand it and bring it astern; the two warps, now coming aft from the pulleys on the gallows, are brought together to pass over the same towing block—on the port or starboard quarter as the case may be—and let out together till the trawl is on the bottom. After it has been towed along the sea-bed for perhaps three or four hours, depending on the nature of the bottom and the size of catch expected, it is hauled up by reversing the whole process; and this is what I have already described in the opening paragraphs of our introduction. The photographs in Plate XIII (p. 162) show the cod-end full of fish and the catch on the deck.

Instead of a span of a little over 30 feet, as had the old beam-trawl, the new otter-trawl measures 80 and its catching power has increased enormously. It has been still further increased in recent years by connecting the otter-boards to the trawl by long cables so that they are now far out to the sides; this has the effect of frightening and driving the fish in towards the trawl in the middle, as the cables sweep over the bottom in a wide arc on either side, as shown in Fig. 72 (p. 157). By the nineties the whole of the North Sea was being fished south of a line from the north of Scotland to the north of Denmark; so intense did it become that, early in this century, large areas were on an average being scraped over two or three times a year. It was no wonder that signs of overfishing began to show; to this we will return in a later chapter. In the meantime larger trawlers were being built to go to more distant grounds. Grimsby sent the first steam trawler to Iceland in 1891 and Hull soon followed; in 1905 Hull pioneered the fishing in

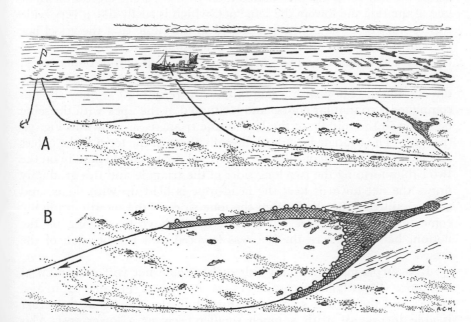

FIG. 74. At work with a Danish seine. A, laying the net: the vessel seen returning to the buoy after following a triangular course and so laying down the ropes and net on the sea bed as shown. B, after picking up the buoy the net is towed forward like a trawl till it is closed by the ropes coming together when it is hauled up.

the Barents Sea and the western ports began to send trawlers far down the coast of Morocco after hake.[1] To-day the huge deep-water trawlers push far to the north, to Bear Island, Spitsbergen and Greenland, fishing not only in summer but through the darkness of the arctic winter. Britain's trawling grounds of to-day are shown in Fig. 73 (p. 158).

While the deep-water trawlers have been getting larger, more powerful and more efficiently equipped with echo-sounding and position-finding apparatus, with radar and other modern inventions to fit them for going further and further into the difficult waters of the Arctic, the scene in the North Sea has also been changing somewhat. Led by the Danes and the Dutch there has been an enormous development of fishing by seine net out in the middle of the North Sea; this net can be used from quite a small vessel, sometimes smaller than a herring-drifter. The seiner puts out a buoy with a flag on it and then "steams" (actually they are nearly all motor-craft) for a distance of about 100 yards, making a bearing about 30 degrees from the line which marks the flow of the tide, and meanwhile letting out a cable. She now turns a sharp angle to the right, travelling at right angles across the tide for a distance of about 60 yards. As she crosses the mid-line of the tide she lowers the seine net, which is really like a very wide trawl; one side of its mouth is fastened to the cable that the vessel has been dropping, and the other side to a similar cable that the vessel continues to drop as she proceeds towards the next corner of her track. Here she now turns again at a sharp angle to the right, heading back directly for the buoy with a flag on it. On reaching the buoy she has completed a triangular course and is situated at the apex with the seine net lying in the middle of the base of the triangle, as shown in Fig. 74 (p. 159). The triangle is, indeed, literally there in the form of the cables and net at the bottom of the sea. The vessel now starts to haul in on the two cables forming the two long sides of the triangle and this gradually draws the net towards her; the head-rope is held up with floats, and as it is pulled along the bottom the long sides of the mouth gradually come together to enclose all the fish which have been lying on the bottom between where the net was lowered and the position of the vessel.

It is surprising how many fish such a seine net will gather up at one time. The whole process is very speedy, and is repeated again and again; and the gear is so much lighter than the trawl that the seiner is able to operate with a much smaller crew at a lower cost. This

[1] A note should just be made of the pareja method of trawling used by the Spanish and adopted by some of our companies fishing for hake; in this, two vessels take part and tow a wide fast trawl between them. Paired trawling has also been introduced for catching herring.

method, however, is only suitable for comparatively shallow water, and the seine boats have not the capacity to go far afield. Nevertheless, over wide regions of the southern North Sea the Danish seine has proved a most efficient instrument; and now a very large fleet of Danish and Dutch seiners are working where once the smaller trawlers fished from Grimsby, Lowestoft and other North Sea ports. In recent years we have followed suit to some extent. There are a number of seining vessels now working from Grimsby and Lowestoft; some of the herring drifters, too, are converted to use the seine net during the spring, when there is little herring-fishing, and they change back to drifting for the summer and autumn. In Scotland there has been a big development of the Danish seining method in the Moray Firth. Plate XIV (p. 163) shows three photographs from a remarkable film made by the Scottish Home Department of one of these seine-nets actually fishing on the sea-bed, taken by a frogman swimming with a watertight cine-camera. Two show the plaice in large numbers being chevied along by the footrope and passing into the bag of the net; the other shows the cod-end with some young fish actually escaping through the meshes: a picture which will be referred to again when we discuss the overfishing problem and its remedies.

CHAPTER 8

# THE STORY OF THE PLAICE

WE come now to the sea-floor fish themselves. I will introduce them by selecting one kind for special treatment, as I did with the herring among the pelagic species, but here to illustrate the life and habits of a characteristic demersal fish. I choose the plaice, *Pleuronectes platessa,* for this short study, for three reasons: it is one of the more important food-fish of the North Sea; a great deal of research has been done on it by our English naturalists of the Fisheries Laboratory at Lowestoft; and, thirdly, it is a good representative of the flat-fish family (Pleuronectidae) which is one of the most successful and beautifully adapted of all the groups of bottom-living bony fish.

We all know a plaice as well as we know the herring. It is, indeed, 'as flat as a pancake': flattened about what, in a more typical fish, would be its vertical and longitudinal plane—i.e. flattened as if it had been passed on its side through a mangle. It is so modified that it lies on the bottom on its left side with its right side uppermost. Its head is remarkably twisted, so as to bring both its eyes on to the upper or right-hand side, and the margins of the body are provided with continuous fins. The original right side of the body—the 'upper side'—is dark and dappled with red spots; the left or 'under side' lacks pigment and is white. The plaice swims by undulating its flat body in a series of waves passing from head to tail, and so skims horizontally forward like a billowing magic carpet. After swimming for a short distance a little above the bottom, it glides down to come to rest again; as it settles, it wiggles its marginal fins, so that they throw up a shower of sand or fine gravel to fall upon its edges and thus obliterate its outline. This may be well seen at almost any marine aquarium. At rest the plaice is beautifully camouflaged, as all flatfish are. It is shown on a gravel bottom in Wilson's photograph on Plate XIX (p. 222) and in colour in Plate 15 (p. 210); one is also included, in a characteristic attitude, in the foreground of the picture of the cod on Plate XXIV (p. 243).

Like nearly every other bony fish of commercial importance—the herring being the outstanding exception—plaice lay floating eggs: little spheres of glass-like transparency which drift in the currents of the sea as part of the plankton. A large female plaice lays up to half a million eggs at one spawning; as the eggs are extruded they are fertilized in the water by the milt discharged from attendant males. Recently Mr. G. R. Forster (1953) has published a most interesting account of this as seen in the Plymouth aquarium; I quote as follows:

"The two plaice were swimming in mid-water about 2 ft. 6 in. from the bottom, the female lying slightly diagonally across the back of the male their vents being close together. The female, considerably larger than the male, was quivering violently and emitting a rapid stream of eggs. Mr. F. J. Warren, who was also watching the tank, saw a stream of milt coming from the male. After about 20 sec. the fish separated and settled on the bottom. The eggs were being eaten very rapidly by a shoal of sea-bream (*Pagellus centrodontus* de la Roche). The beginning of the spawning was not seen but the whole act did not take much longer than three-quarters of a minute as the tank had been under observation about half-a-minute earlier. When captured afterwards the female was found to be almost completely spent, but may have spawned previously."

Plate XIII. (above) a. The cod-end of a trawl about to be untied. (below) b. The catch on deck: a view from for'ard looking aft towards the trawl winch and wheel house; note the gallows aft. (The dark patch on the water is the shadow of the trawlers' smoke above it)  (J. H. Fraser)

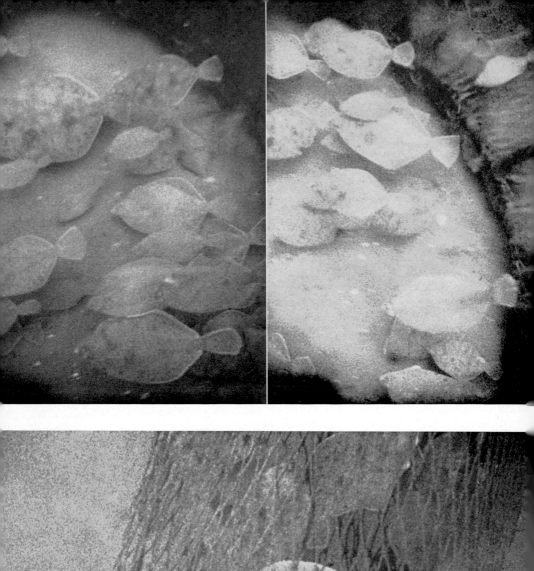

The discovery that most sea-fish lay such eggs was one of the first economic contributions of marine research. Towards the end of last century, when the trawl was increasing in size, there was an outcry by certain sections of the industry, demanding a limit to the size of the trawl which they thought must be destroying the spawn on the sea-bed. There was a Royal Commission to investigate the matter; but in the meantime the tow-net had given the answer. G. O. Sars, the great Norwegian naturalist, first showed that the eggs of the cod float in the plankton, and Professor McIntosh of St. Andrew's University soon followed by demonstrating the same for many other species; they proved that the fears of the industry, like the eggs, were groundless. Research ships, by travelling backwards and forwards in lines across the North Sea and stopping at intervals to take vertical hauls with a standard type of plankton-net,—usually the Hensen net[1]—can chart the relative quantities of different kinds of fish-eggs in various parts of the sea at different seasons.

The greatest concentration of plaice eggs is shown to be in the Flemish Bight in mid-winter, over the deeper water at the northern entrance to the English Channel—i.e. half-way between the Thames estuary and the coast of Holland, where there is a tongue of rather more saline water coming into the North Sea from the south. Here, it has been estimated, some sixty million plaice assemble every year for spawning. There are lesser concentrations off the Yorkshire coast (to the east of Flamborough Head), off the north-east coast of Scotland, in the Irish Sea, and north-west of Heligoland. The instinct to migrate to these regions to spawn has no doubt been evolved by the better survival of the young from eggs so placed. Experiments have been made by liberating drift-bottles[2] at some of these points; those dropped into the sea at the position of the main Flemish Bight spawning ground

[1] A photograph of this net is shown in Plate XXIV of the first volume (p. 289).

[2] These, as described in Part I (p. 15), are sealed bottles made so that they just float. Each displays through its glass sides a notice in several languages asking the finder to break the bottle and to send off an enclosed postcard giving the date and place of its recovery; so the main currents of the North Sea have been worked out.

---

*Plate XIV.* Remarkable photographs taken by that daring pioneer frogman, the late Commander Hodges, R.N., showing a seine net in action at the bottom of the sea. These are shots taken from a film specially made for the Scottish Home Office, Fisheries Division, and reproduced by their kind permission. (*above*) *a* and *b:* Plaice, large and small, being chevied along the bottom by the approaching net seen coming into view at the top right-hand corner. (*below*) *c:* The cod-end filled with plaice as it is pulled along the bottom; note a young plaice escaping through the meshes in the right of the picture: important proof that a wide mesh saves the lives of many undersized fish, allowing them to grow to marketable size.

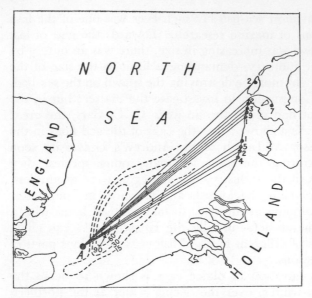

FIG. 75. The main spawning ground of the plaice in the southern North Sea shown by the broken lines which contour the number of eggs found (per cubic metre of sea) by Wollaston (1923). Superimposed upon the map is the course taken by drift bottles, which were liberated at A and later picked up on the Dutch coast, thus demonstrating the current carrying the floating eggs and young fish towards the nursery grounds against that coast.

have all been recovered from points along the coast of Holland, as seen in Fig. 75 here.[1] The plaice, unconsciously, is performing just such

[1]In the first volume I reproduced in Fig. 5 (p. 18) a chart showing the results of drift-bottle experiments made by the late Mr. J. O. Borley when investigating the likely path taken by plaice eggs and larvae. In addition to the main drift from the southern spawning ground towards the Dutch coast, it also showed that bottles liberated on the spawning ground off Flamborough were all picked up on the shores of the Wash, indicating a drift of larvae to these nursery grounds. The existence of this chart, which I had taken from one which used to be in the museum of the Fisheries Laboratory at Lowestoft when I was on the staff there in the early 1920's, came as rather a surprise to the present-day workers there. Mr. Michael Graham in a recent (unpublished) Progress Report on the work of the Lowestoft Laboratory has included some comments on this which Mr. A. J. Lee, who worked up the data, has kindly allowed me to quote:

"*The Borley/Bidder drift-bottle experiments.* Just before the first World War the late J. O. Borley organised extensive liberations of surface and bottom drift-bottles on a plan approved by the late G. P. Bidder. Presumably owing to the war, the cards were never reported on until attention was called to them by the inclusion of a chart, based on a few returns, in the material Professor A. C. Hardy was collecting for his book *The Open Sea*. On examination, the cards were found to show that the chart in question came from returns during a period of north-easterly winds, not typical south-westerly winds, which means that the conception of plaice larvae usually drifting from the Flamborough Off grounds to the Wash needs some modification. Repetition in the current year has shown that plastic envelopes from the same position strand at widely scattered points on the coasts between the Tyne and Norfolk, depending on the wind, but that bottles with one metre drogues mostly travel across the North Sea and are returned from Scandinavia. The bottom bottles from the Borley/Bidder experiments did, however, show a cyclonic eddy in the deeper water, which would doubtless carry plaice larvae with it in the usual disturbed conditions of the area and season, thus perhaps accounting for the Wash as a nursery . . ."

an experiment—its eggs are little drift-bottles, carrying its babies to the most suitable nursery-grounds, where they may settle down to begin their life in the shallow coastal waters.

Apart from the findings of the drift-bottle experiments, we can follow the drift of the eggs and fry, from week to week, by making repeated tow-net surveys from a research ship. The little larval fish develops within its sphere, curled round its supply of yolk—just as we see the baby pilchard in Plate VIII (p. 79) before hatching from its egg. H. J. Buchanan-Wollaston, who made the pioneer surveys of plaice-egg drift before and just after the first World War, showed (1915, 1923) that the usual drift was in a north-easterly direction at a speed of $1\frac{1}{2}$ miles to 3 miles a day. In about fifteen days—taking longer or less if the sea is colder or warmer than usual—the little fish hatches out and wriggles free: a tiny creature, just a quarter of an inch in length. Like all young larval fish it comes into the world carrying a good food-reserve in its still quite large spherical yolk-sac; in eight or nine days the sac and its contents are almost completely absorbed, and the young plaice—still a member of the pelagic community—starts to feed upon the small plants of the plankton as it drifts—taking only the smallest of the diatoms at first. As it grows it begins to take animal food, and the small planktonic tunicate *Oikopleura*, described in Part I (p. 153), has recently been shown (J. E. Shelbourne, 1953) to be particularly important; it also eats the young stages of copepods and mollusc larvae but it still likes its vegetables and takes a few of the larger diatoms as well. It is at first a perfectly normal-looking symmetrical young fish; when, however, it is a month old that strange metamorphosis begins which in another $2\frac{1}{2}$ weeks, converts it into a 'flatfish'. The shape of its body changes to the adult form; by a difference in the growth rates on the two sides, the whole skull becomes twisted in an extraordinary deformation to bring the left eye over on to the right side. In the meantime it is coming down from the plankton and taking up its life on the bottom. This metamorphosis, which is shown in Fig. 76 overleaf, occurs normally just as the young fish has been carried over the coastal 'nursery' grounds, and when it is still barely threequarters of an inch long.

Here come in some of the factors which may make for good or poor brood-years. If, during the time of the larval drift, there should be an abnormally long period of northerly and north-easterly winds, then the flow of water up through the Channel into the North Sea will be much reduced (or at times almost reversed), so that many larvae will not be carried as far as they would normally be. Or if there should be a stretch of south-westerly winds, the flow will be greatly accelerated

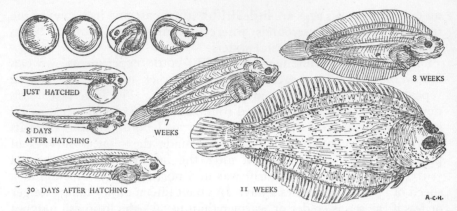

JUST HATCHED

8 DAYS
AFTER HATCHING

7
WEEKS

30 DAYS AFTER HATCHING

11 WEEKS

8 WEEKS

A·C·H.

FIG. 76. Successive stages in the development of the Plaice from the curled up embryo in the egg to a young fish specially adapted to living on the sea-bed; note the large yolk-sac of the newly hatched young and the later remarkable twisting of the skull which brings the two eyes on to the right and future upper side. (All ×5).

and the larvae carried much further. It is such changes in weather-conditions, as well as differences in the amounts of planktonic food available or in the abundance of predators, which give rise to the fluctuations in the strength of the different year-classes of plaice. We saw (p. 59) similar fluctuations in the herring stocks.

Hjort was, I believe, as explained in our earlier volume, the first to suggest that these fluctuations in year classes might be due to food being in shorter supply during early development in some years than in others, and there I showed how the findings of some of the Danish fishery naturalists were supporting his views; now, since Part I was published, has come some striking new evidence. Mr. J. E. Shelbourne of the Ministry of Fisheries Laboratory at Lowestoft, to whom I have just referred, has recently followed patches of plaice larvae drifting in the sea; he kept over them in the ship and saw just how they farde with the different quantities of planktonic food which happened to eb available at the time. He has kindly allowed me to quote the following extract from his unpublished Progress Report for 1956:

"Two patches of plaice larvae were followed, each as it happens for a period of twelve days: the first in January and the second in March. The plankton accompanying the first patch was much lcss than that accompanying the second patch, in respect especially of copepod nauplii, *Oikopleura* and *Fritillaria*,[2] all of which are good

[1]Such effects of wind are further discussed on p. 227.
[2]An animal similar to *Oikopleura* (see Part I, p. 155).

food for larvae. In bad food conditions, there was no evidence of growth and survival beyond the yolk sac larval stage, and distinct signs of increasing weakness as yolk reserves became exhausted. In good food conditions, on the other hand, it was clear that a good proportion of the larvae were advancing beyond the yolk sac stage, and that those in the transition stage of development between yolk exhaustion and reliance on external food sources, were, in the main, visibly thicker and stronger."

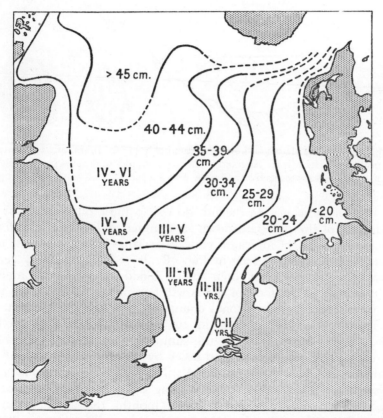

FIG. 77. A map giving the average age and size of plaice in different parts of the North Sea and showing how the fish tend to move further from the coastal nursery grounds as they get older. From Garstang (*Rapp. Cons. Explor. Mer., 11, 1909*).

Until they are two years old the young plaice remain on the coastal nursery banks; as they get older, they tend to move further and further away from the coast towards the middle of the North Sea. The chart in Fig. 77 above, shows the distribution of plaice in the North

Sea according to their age and length; the average age and length is shown for each area enclosed by the contour lines. At one year old they are about 3 inches in length, at two years about 5½ inches, and at five years nearly 14 inches. We tell the age of a plaice, not by its scales (which are very small and difficult to read) but by its otoliths or ear-stones—calcareous bodies formed in the sacculus of the membranous

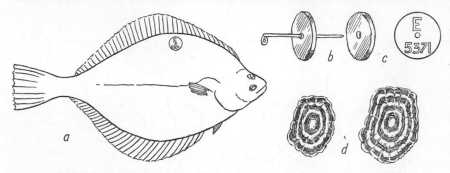

FIG. 78. *a*, a marked plaice; *b*, showing method of fixing the mark, and *c*, the number and country of origin (E for England). *d*, two examples of otoliths (×3) indicating ages of 3 and 4 years respectively (drawn with special lighting to show up rings).

labyrinth of the ears. As the fish grows, so the otolith enlarges; and the density of the part laid down in summer and winter is different, giving us a series of alternate concentric rings of opaque and more translucent material as seen in Fig. 78 above. This possibly reflects a calcium difference in their diet. Todd (1915), who made a detailed study of the food of the North Sea plaice, showed that there was, in fact, a marked seasonal change in this; the mature fish take principally polychaete worms in the winter and bivalve molluscs (*Solen, Spisula, Mactra,* etc.) in the summer. There is also a seasonal difference in the quantity of food taken by the adults. From March to October nearly every fish examined will have food in its stomach, but in November the number found feeding drops suddenly to less than 10 per cent.; during the next three months the average number feeding at any time rises slowly to 50 per cent; full feeding is observed again in March. Young plaice in their first year or two eat largely small crustacea, particularly amphipods. Some remarks on their feeding, in comparison with other flatfish, will be found on p. 203.

The onset of sexual maturity in the plaice appears to be a matter of size rather than of age, and so will vary in different parts of the North Sea according to the relative abundance of food available on the bottom. The females mostly become mature at a length of between

12 and 16 inches. This is usually achieved at ages of four to five years, but a few may reach this size at three, or even two years old; the males mature earlier, at a length of 8 to 12 inches. This was shown by the work of Wallace (1907-15). The actual growth-rates of individual fish may be studied, not under the artificial conditions of an aquarium, but in the sea itself; by tagging experiments. Many thousands of plaice (as also of other fish) have been marked with little numbered buttons

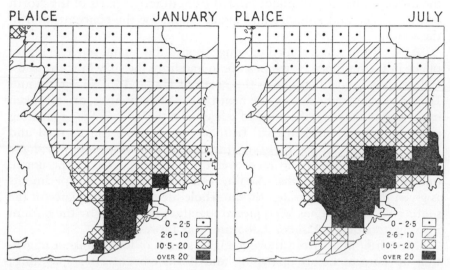

FIG. 79. Plaice distribution in the North Sea: charts showing the average quantities, in hundredweights per 100 hours fishing, caught in these standard rectangular areas during January and July (1920-1935) by steam trawlers landing fish at British ports, compiled from the statistics published by the Ministry of Agriculture and Fisheries.

and set free, and many hundreds of them have been caught again after varying intervals. Usually there are two little buttons, one on each side, held together like cuff-links by strands of silver wire passing through the muscles just below the dorsal fin (speaking morphologically) as shown in Fig. 78 opposite. Before the fish is liberated it is carefully measured. A reward is then paid to fishermen who recapture such marked fish and return them whole together with a note on where they were caught. From these experiments we have learnt a great deal. By re-measuring the fish on its return we know how much it has grown in a definite interval of time and in different parts of the sea; we know how far and in what ultimate direction it has travelled in this period;

and from the percentage of marked fish returned we may get a good indication of the rate of mortality caused by fishing. In some experiments in the southern North Sea as many as 70 per cent of marked plaice have been caught again in a single year, and the actual number must be higher than this; some marks are never noticed till the fish reach the kitchen, and some fishermen do not bother to return them, or, as in one case I know of, a fisherman may hang the mark on his watch-chain as a lucky souvenir! The charts in Fig. 79, overleaf show the average quantity of plaice landed from different parts of the North Sea in winter and summer and again emphasise the concentration in the south.

Apart from minor feeding migrations, the main movements of plaice in the southern North Sea are to and from the spawning-grounds. Fish marked and liberated to the north of Holland in November and December, if caught during the next two or three months, are all taken in the region between the point of release and the centre of the spawning ground in the Flemish Bight. In other experiments fish marked and liberated in the Flemish Bight in March, after spawning was over, have been caught at points scattered over the North Sea well to the north, during the next six months. An illustration of some actual experiments is given in Fig. 80 opposite. So the whole life-story of the plaice of the southern North Sea has been pieced together, bit by bit, by the patient investigators of the Fishery Laboratory at Lowestoft.

Most fish, apart from movements in search of food, make a migration up current before spawning and down current after spawning; these are technically known as *contranatant* and *denatant* migrations respectively. Observations on the plaice in areas other than the southern North Sea have given us some valuable additional information. Circulating round the Shetland Islands there is a clockwise current which carries round the eggs and larvae in the spawning season; before spawning the mature fish make an anticlockwise migration round the islands against the current (Bowman, 1933). On the east coast of Scotland plaice as far south as the Forth migrate north against the current to spawn in the Moray Firth. Some two thousand young of these fish were taken in tanks from St. Andrews Bay and set free at the Shetlands; it was found that when these fish became mature they did not try to return to spawn in the Moray Firth, but joined the local fish in their migration round the islands. However, marking experiments in Icelandic waters show us that plaice do not always migrate against the current before spawning (Tåning, 1934). As at the Shetlands there is a clockwise current round Iceland. The plaice spawn in the warmest water on the south-west coast, the eggs and fry are carried round the north coast to the nursery grounds on the north-east side. When these fish become mature some do indeed migrate back to the spawning ground via the northern route against the current; but the recapture of marked fish has shown quite clearly that some of the fish take the shorter and easier way—travelling *with the current* round the southern side.

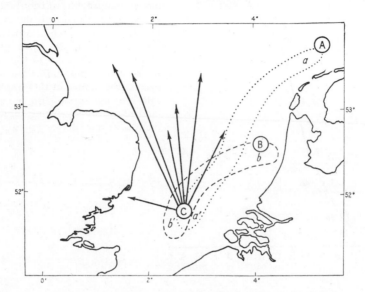

FIG. 80. A demonstration of plaice migration in the southern North Sea. Plaice marked and liberated at A in December and at B in November were recaught in the areas *aa′* and *bb′* respectively during the following January to March. Plaice caught, marked and liberated on the spawning ground at C in March were recaptured during the summer months at points indicated by the arrows. From Garstang (1905).

We cannot leave this fish without a brief mention of one of the most interesting experiments towards the future farming of the sea, that planned and carried out by Professor Walter Garstang when he was director of the Lowestoft Laboratory from 1902 to 1908; indeed all the early English work on the plaice was begun under his leadership (Garstang, 1905, 1912). Experiments on the transplantation of plaice had already been successfully made by the great Danish pioneer C. G. J. Petersen; Garstang applied the method to see if it would be possible to increase the yield of the North Sea fisheries. Tagging experiments had shown that the rate of growth in different parts of the North Sea varied according to the available food. On the coastal banks of Holland

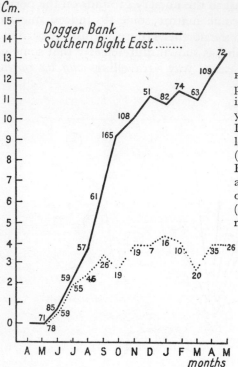

Cm.

Dogger Bank ———
Southern Bight East ........

FIG. 81. An experiment with marked plaice: graphs showing the average increase in growth (in centimetres) of young plaice caught on the crowded Dutch coastal grounds in April and released either on the same grounds (dotted line) or taken to the Dogger Bank (continuous line). The figures against the points on the graph indicate the numbers of fish recaptured (and re-measured) during subsequent months. From Borley (1912).

A M J J A S O N D J F M A M
*months*

there are immense numbers of young plaice crowded on the ground and heavily competing for the limited resources; on the Dogger Bank, in contrast, there is an exceptionally rich food supply, though it is not a nursery ground for plaice. No doubt the greater variability of currents in different years over the Dogger region, as compared with the more stable coastal streams up the Dutch coast, provide the reason for the evolution of a breeding migration which results in this overcrowding of the coastal areas, while the rich Dogger Bank is unexploited by the young. The Dogger, of course, is a great feeding ground for adult plaice which, as they grow older, push out towards it from the coasts. If the currents cannot be relied on to carry the young plaice to this El Dorado of food, man and steam together may do so. Experiments were made in the transplantation of young plaice from the coastal area to the Dogger. Large tanks, with sea-water continually pumped into them to provide a plentiful supply of well-oxygenated water, were placed on the deck of the Lowestoft research trawler as it fished off the coasts of Holland. Of the young plaice caught only those of about 8 inches in length were used for the experiment; they were measured and marked, and half of them were liberated at once at the point of capture and the other half carried in the tanks on deck to be set free on the Dogger Bank. Thousands of fish were so treated. Fig. 81, opposite, shows the results of one such experiment in graphic form: the continuous line shows the average increase in length of those fish recaptured in each of the subsequent fourteen months on the Dogger Bank, while the dotted line shows the same information from the coastal area. We see that in little over a year the Dogger Bank fish have grown nearly three times as much. The experiment has been repeated several times with the same striking results.

Here is a practical way of increasing the wealth of the sea. Garstang dealt with it when he delivered the first series of the Buckland lectures in the spring of 1930; the following is a quotation from the summary in *Nature* (Garstang, 1930)[1]:

". . . the Dogger Bank, with an area as large as Wales, lies outside the track of normal plaice migration, and yet possesses enormous reserves of the favourite food of this fish. The one unimpeachable method of raising the size of plaice in the North Sea is to utilise this great reserve for the purpose, and to transplant every year some millions of the small overcrowded and slow-growing fish from the coastal banks to this great feeding ground, on which it has been shown repeatedly that the plaice transplanted grow three, four, and even six times as rapidly as on their native shores.

Science is useless without enterprise. Great Britain looks to the traditional enterprise of the great Humber fishing ports to take up this matter as a commercial proposition. Let Grimsby and Hull take the first step towards cultivating the 'Great Fish Farm' which lies at their very door."

The International Council considered the matter and appointed a special committee, of which Professor Garstang was a member, under the Chairmanship of the late Dr. E. S. Russell; it met at Lowestoft on November 3rd of the same year and a number of distinguished figures were present including Mr. Henry Maurice, President of the Council, and Professors E. Ehrenbaum, Johan Hjort, W. Mielck, and Otto Pettersson. It published the following report[2]:

[1]The lectures were published in full in the *Fishery News* and subsequently in a booklet from this journal's office in Aberdeen: *The Buckland Lectures: First Series for 1929*, (1930).
[2]*Rapp. Cons. Explor. Mer.*, 74, 109, 1931.

"The Committee having considered the estimates contained in the appendices annexed hereto, is of opinion (A) that the probable cost of transplanting one million plaice from the Horns Reef area to the Dogger Bank would be £3,000, including the cost of control, (B) that the probable yield from these plaice in two years would be from £7,400 to £10,000, (C) that the yield from the plaice if left on the Danish grounds may be estimated at £1,000, (D) that the favourable effect on growth rate on the Danish grounds cannot be estimated.

It draws the conclusion that the probable profit of the operation would be from £3,400 to £6,000, after allowance has been made for all contingencies. It accordingly recommends that this large scale transplantation should be undertaken as soon as possible."

But nothing was done. It remains a policy for the fish-farming of the future, when there will be more international agreement and regulation of fisheries; at present no single country or association of trawler-owners will finance such an undertaking, when the boats of all other nations and associations will benefit equally from the results[1].

I must not take up more space with just one species; for a fuller account of its natural history, its fishery, and its migrations the reader should consult Mr. R. S. Wimpenny's excellent Buckland Lectures which are published as *The Plaice* (1953). We must now turn, in the next chapters, to the many other different kinds of bottom-living fish; and we must remember that our story of the Plaice is only one example of many life histories which have been worked out for other fish of commercial importance by the naturalists of our governmental and other marine laboratories, and those of other countries.

CHAPTER 9

# HAGS, HOUNDS, SHARKS AND SKATES

A THOROUGH treatment of all the different species of bottom-living fish in the seas around our islands would require a large book to itself. We must be content here with only a rapid survey, and for a more detailed and systematic account I would again refer the reader

[1] I have just learnt that the Ministry of Fisheries are now carrying out some larger scale experiments.

to the books of Francis Day (1880-84) and J. T. Jenkins (1936) mentioned on p. 68. We will begin by considering two animals which are not fish in the strict sense of the word, but cyclostomes—those primitive vertebrates which have neither paired fins nor jaws, and to which we briefly referred when describing the lampreys found attached to basking sharks (p. 93). The cyclostomes are animals of great interest to zoologists; for they show us, in many parts of their bodies, a form and functioning which, being simpler than in the fish help us to visualise some of the steps taken in the evolution of the more advanced types. They present us with a glimpse of the likely past, in showing us the probable state of ancestral soft parts which can never be preserved for us in the fossil record; they give us the clue, for example, to the origin of the thyroid and pituitary glands, the pineal eye, the pancreas, the kidneys and many other structures.

There are two main groups of cyclostomes: the lampreys (Petromyzontia) and the hagfishes (Myxinoidea); their common representatives are compared in Fig. 82 overleaf. The lampreys are long eel-like animals with the mouth opening at the very front of the body in the middle of a large circular sucker; this is provided with many horny so-called "teeth", which, however, are quite different in structure and development from the true ivory teeth of higher forms. Inside the mouth is a powerful muscular tongue, also equipped with these horny "teeth", which can be pushed through the mouth to be worked backwards and forwards as a rasp. The lamprey attaches itself with its sucker to the skin of some large fish, and then takes a meal by rasping away the flesh and conveying it backwards into the mouth by the movements of its tongue. Fish with healed scars of lamprey wounds are not infrequently found. Between meals it may often be found resting attached by its sucker to a stone. Behind the eye on each side is a row of seven small openings which lead into pouches containing the gills and opening internally into a separate branchial duct in the midline below the gullet. The lamprey does not breathe by taking in water through the mouth and passing it out through the gills, for this would be impossible when it was using its mouth either as a sucker or in feeding; by the elastic expansion and muscular contraction of the gill-pouches it continually pumps water in and out of them through their side openings.

All lampreys breed in fresh water, where they pass through an ammocoete larval stage, and some species spend much of their life there. The ammocoete is a little eel-like creature which spends most of its time buried, all but its front end, in the mud at the bottom of the river. It is not unlike the little pre-vertebrate amphioxus which lives in the

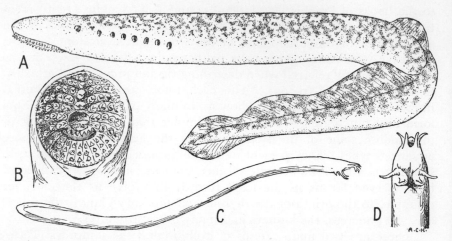

FIG. 82. A, The sea-lamprey, *Petromyzon marinus* ($\times \frac{1}{4}$) and B, an enlarged view looking into its mouth to show the horny teeth within the circular sucker-like rim. C, the hag *Myxine glutinosa* ($\times \frac{1}{3}$) and in D an enlarged view of the head seen from below showing the mouth between the ten tacles on the underside.

same way in the sea-bed (p. 114); and they both feed in a very similar fashion by filtering out small organic particles, flagellates and other tiny organisms from the stream of water taken in by the mouth and passed out through gills. Between the ammocoete and the amphioxus there are indeed a number of striking resemblances which suggest a relationship—but of what kind? Is the amphioxus really primitive, or degenerate, or again is it derived by neotony (as explained in Part 1, p. 195) from the larva of some past cyclostome? That is another story, and, as expert opinions differ, it is too long a one to embark on here. I will, however, just call attention to a very remarkable chordate animal, which has recently been discovered as a fossil in the Silurian rocks of Lanarkshire (E. I. White, 1946). Two specimens were found, 6 and 7 inches long; they show a series of muscle segments down the body which are in the primitive form of those of our amphioxus, but they have well-developed eyes which the latter entirely lacks. Dr. White, who described them, regards the animal as "in my opinion, undoubtedly the most primitive of the 'vertebrate' series of which we have knowledge"; and he called the new genus *Jamoytius* in memory of his friend, the late J. A. Moy-Thomas, a brilliant Oxford zoologist and expert on fossil fish, who was killed in a car accident while on military service in the last war.

The sea-lamprey, *Petromyzon marinus*, after spending some two or

FIG. 83. Some unusual sharks from British waters. *a*, the six-gilled or brown shark *Hexanchus griseus*. *b*, another shark with six gills, the frilled shark *Chlamydoselachus anguineus*. *c*, the spiny shark, *Echinorhinus spinosus*. *d*, the hammerhead *Sphyrna zygaena*. with a view of the underside of the head to show the widely separated nasal openings, *e*, the humantin, *Oxynotus centrina*. Drawn in the British Museum (Nat. Hist.).

three years as an ammocoete, passes to the sea after metamorphosis and only returns to fresh water to spawn; it grows to a length of about 3 feet. Lampreys are sometimes called slime-eels on account of the enormous quantities of mucus they produce from glands in the skin.

The hag or hag-fish, *Myxine glutinosa*, belonging to the other group of Cyclostomes, is entirely marine and is smaller, not exceeding two feet in length. Its mouth, instead of being in the centre of a large sucker, lies in a groove on the underside of the head with four short tentacle-like processes sticking out in front on either side; it has, however,

a rasping tongue similar to that of the lamprey. Hagfish are sometimes also called borers, because they enter the mouth, gill-cavity or
open wounds of dead and dying fish and eat their way inside, devouring
everything but skin and bone. They are a curse to line-fishermen, who
frequently find many of the fish on their hooks completely destroyed.
It is said that they are now less common in the North Sea because,
since the great extension of trawling, there is less long-lining from
small coastal boats than there used to be. At one time it was thought
that they would actually attach themselves, like lampreys, to healthy
fish and rasp their way inside, and so were often spoken of as parasites;
there is, however, no evidence for this. Indeed, recent observations
show that they feed on all manner of benthic animals, and that their
habit of eating their way into dead and dying fish is by no means their
only or even their typical mode of life—they just seize on dead fish
when the opportunity of such a good meal presents itself. Hags
appear to be rather local in distribution and are found more on our
east coast than to the south or west; they are said to be particularly
common in the Moray Firth, off St. Abbs Head, off the mouth of the
Tyne, and between Redcar and Flamborough on the Yorkshire coast.

   We begin our account of the true fish with the cartilaginous
elasmobranchs, whose general characters we have already discussed
(pp. 29-34). Several of the larger sharks we have dealt with among
the pelagic fish, but the tope, toper or whitehound *Eugaleus galeus*[1]
lives mainly on the bottom; although occasionally entangled in drift-
nets, it is more frequently found taking bait. Day describes it as a
'fierce and ravenous fish' and while quoting a record of one 7 feet long
caught in Dublin Bay says 'it is not rare up to 6 feet in length'. It
appears to feed entirely on fish and to be commoner on the south and
east coasts than on the west. Another still larger bottom-living shark
should just be mentioned, although it is a great rarity in our waters:
the hammer-head, *Sphyrna zygaena* (Fig. 83, overleaf). It is at once
recognised by its remarkable hammer-shaped head carrying the eyes
far out to the sides. These extensions also carry the nostrils with them
and so allow the animal to smell out its food over a wider area; this is
probably the most important feature of the adaptation. It reaches a
large size; a specimen 13 feet 7 inches long was taken at Ilfracombe in
1865. *Mustelus mustelus*—the smooth hound, sometimes ironically
called Sweet William on account of its unpleasant odour—is not unlike
the tope in general form, but is smaller; it feeds largely on crustacea.
It is not uncommon on our south-western coasts and is frequently taken
by trawlers working from Plymouth.

   [1] =*Galeus vulgaris*, Day.

*Plate XV.* (*above*) *a.* The common dog-fish (*Scyliorhinus canicula*) swimming. (*below*) *b.* The male of the same species curled round the female in copulation.
(*Douglas Wilson*)

Plate XVI. (*above*) *a*. The angel shark (*Squatina*) (*below*) *b*. The spotted ray (*Raia montagui*)                     (*Douglas Wilson*)

*Hexanchus griseus,*[1] the six-gilled or brown shark, is usually a very rare visitor here, though a common Mediterranean species; it and the next species are distinguished from all our others by having six gill-slits on each side instead of the normal five. While this shark has in the past been extremely rare in the Scottish lists, two remarkable records have been made recently (Rae and Wilson, 1953, 1955): in July 1952 a line fishing vessel caught a number 60 miles northeast of Sule Skerry (Orkney Is.) and brought thirteen of them into Aberdeen; six more were caught in Scottish waters in 1954. It is clearly a bottom-living shark, for the records of its stomach contents include fish like haddock, dabs, plaice, and angler fish. A drawing is included in Fig. 83. It may reach a very large size; Day records one measuring 26 feet 5 inches captured at Polperro in Cornwall. The frilled shark, *Chlamydoselachus anguineus,* is a much rarer species and I believe was not included in the British list until two specimens were taken by trawlers fishing deep off the west of Ireland in 1935 and 1936. It is one of the most remarkable of living sharks for, apart from its six-gill slits and the frilly margins to their covering flaps, it has its mouth almost at the very front and its nostrils up on the side of the head instead of under the snout; it is also shown in Fig. 83.

There are three species of shark commonly known as dogfish: *Scyliorhinus* (formerly *Scyllium*) *caniculus* (Plates XV and 14, p. 195) the rough hound or lesser spotted dogfish; *S. stellaris,* the nursehound or greater spotted dogfish (Plate 16, p. 211) and *Squalus acanthias*[2] the spur-dog, or piked dogfish (Plate 13, p. 194) which belongs to a different family from the other two. The spur-dog can easily be distinguished by the prominent spine immediately in front of each of its dorsal fins, its much more pointed snout, its prominent functional spiracle[3] and its uniform dark grey colour. A living specimen should be handled with care, because, associated with the dorsal spines are poison glands which can cause a quite unpleasant sting. The rough hound and the nurse hound are both spotted with dark spots—like a cheetah—upon a lighter ground; yellowish-grey on the former and reddish-grey on the latter; they may, however, be more easily distinguished by noting that the rough hound has the pelvic fins wide

---

[1] = *Notidanus griseus,* Day.

[2] = *Acanthias vulgaris,* Day.

[3] The spiracle is a small opening leading from the back of the mouth cavity to the outside and is to be seen close behind the eye. It is, in fact, a much modified gill-slit; but instead of letting water pass out, it allows it to enter and so provides a respiratory current when the mouth opening is blocked with food. If you watch a spur dog in an aquarium you will see the spiracle rhythmically opening and closing; in the rough dog it is vestigial and very small.

F&F—N

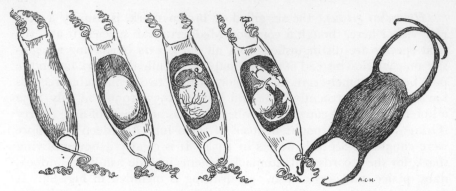

FIG. 84. Egg cases of the dogfish, *Scyliorhinus caniculus,* (*left*) with three opened to show the large egg and developing embryos with yolk sac, and one of the skate *Raia batis* (right). Drawn at the Plymouth Laboratory.

apart and the first dorsal fin just half-way down its back, whereas the other species has its pelvic fins close together and the first dorsal fin nearer to the tail. The rough hound is smaller and does not exceed $3\frac{1}{2}$ feet in length whereas the nurse hound reaches 5 feet; the spur-dog is intermediate in size between the two. The rough hound and spur-dog are very abundant round all our coasts but the nurse hound, frequenting deeper water, is not so commonly taken, and does not extend so far north as the other two; it also likes a more rocky bottom. The spur-dog feeds almost entirely upon other fish, whereas the rough and nurse hounds are more general feeders, taking quantities of crustaceans and molluscs as well as fish.

The two hounds produce large horny egg-cases, the 'mermaid's purses', characteristic of so many elasmobranches (Fig. 84, above); the spur dog, however, is viviparous, carrying its young in the uterus—usually three or four but sometimes as many as eleven—until they are nine or ten inches in length or occasionally even over a foot. Actually the spur-dog does produce a thin horny envelope enclosing all the embryos in each uterus during early development, but this ruptures when they are about $2\frac{1}{2}$ inches long. These facts are taken from the work of E. Ford (1921) who has made a very good comparative study of the life-histories of these three species which should be referred to by those wanting more information. As noted in Chapter 2 (p. 34) fertilization is internal in the elasmobranch fish and the so-called claspers of the male are organs for directing the sperm into the female and not for holding her as was originally thought; pairing has only rarely been seen, but Dr. Wilson was lucky enough to secure the excellent photograph on Plate XV (p. 178) showing the male coiled completely round the female. The smaller and rarer black-mouthed dogfish, *Pristiurus melastomus*, (Fig. 85) is occasionally taken on the west of Scotland, as was the one shown here, but is really a more southern species, being common in the Mediterranean; it is beautifully marked with a bold marbled pattern.

Like the spur-dog most other selachians bring forth their young alive; the tope (*Eugaleus*), which we have already referred to on p. 178, may carry as many as thirty-two young at a time. In nearly all of them some connection is established with the mother to assist the young in nourishment and respiration. In some, as in the smooth hound *Mustelus mustelus*, there is indeed an arrangement which reminds us of the complicated mammalian placenta; numerous maternal processes from the walls of the oviduct fit closely into pits in the highly vascular yolk sacs of the young. While the typical rays and skates, about to be described, lay eggs in large horny cases like those of the dogfish, *Torpedo*, the electric ray, is viviparous; its embryos have their gill-plates drawn out into long threads which appear to serve as organs of absorption.

FIG. 85.  The black-mouthed dogfish, *Pristiurus melastomus*.

Two other sharks will just be mentioned and included in Fig. 83 (p. 177). One, the spiny shark, *Echinorhinus spinosus*, while only an occasional visitor, is a large and striking fish; it reaches a length of up to nine feet, and may be recognised by the very large spiny denticles which stud its surface and the posterior position of its two dorsal fins. The other, the humantin, *Oxynotus centrina*, an even rarer straggler to our waters from the coasts of Portugal, is noteworthy for its peculiar spines situated within its large dorsal fins. Tucker (1949) gives interesting British records of the related *O. paradoxus*.

The skates and rays are shark-like elasmobranch fish which have become remarkably flattened for life on the sea-bed with an enormous enlargement of their pectoral fins. We saw in Chapter 2 (p. 30) how the typical elasmobranchs, lacking the hydrostatic swim-bladder, were dependent upon their paired fins to act as elevating planes for raising and lowering their bodies. The skates and rays have developed these fins as great wing-like expansions and actually swim by making wave-like undulations pass backwards down the margins instead of using their tails as propellers.[1] They look more as if they were flying than swimming as they glide gracefully through the water; I have tried to show this in my sketches in Fig. 86 below. They are as beautifully adapted for benthic life as are the bony flatfish like the plaice, sole and turbot, being just as flat, but in the opposite plane; they are also as beautifully camouflaged on their upper surfaces (see Plate XVI, p. 179). When we see a ray at rest on the bottom of an aquarium we at once notice the large spiracle, behind the eye, opening and closing in regular breathing movements; with the mouth buried in the sand, the respiratory current is taken in entirely through this

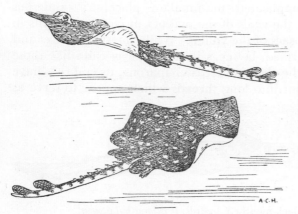

FIG. 86. Thornback rays, *Raia clavata*, sketched swimming in the aquarium of the Millport Marine Station.

opening, although it is forced out through the gill-slits, which, like the mouth, are on the underside. We can see very well how these fish have been evolved because we are fortunate in having in our seas one representative of the family Rhinidae, the angel-fish (sometimes called the monk-fish) *Squatina squatina*,[2] which is intermediate in form between the sharks and the rays, as seen in the same Plate. This fish, also known as the fiddle-fish on account of its shape, occurs all round our islands, inhabiting deeper water in winter but coming nearer the coast in spring; Day describes it as a voracious ground-feeder and 'especially partial to flatfishes'.

Before coming to the true rays we should mention the famous cramp-fish, or electric ray, *Torpedo nobiliana*, which is capable of giving the unwary handler quite a considerable electric shock. It is not uncommon in the English Channel and is occasionally taken in

[1] *Torpedo*, the electric ray, is an exception; it has a prominent tail fin and uses this for propulsion and not its 'wings'.
[2] = *Rhina squatina*, Day.

Scottish waters.[1] It is recognised by having a much more rounded (in fact almost disc-like) body as compared with other rays (Fig. 87, overleaf); and its upper surface normally bears prominent round spots, but there is much variation and they may be absent. The electric organs are broad crescentic areas lying on either side of the body just inside the greatly expanded pectoral fins; they are made up of a vast number of vertical hexagonal columns which are subdivided into smaller compartments each containing an electric plate supplied with nerve-endings. In development these electric plates are shown to be derived from transformed muscle-fibres and have been evolved as powerful organs of offence and defence. "There can be little doubt" writes Norman (1931), "that the Torpedo makes use of the organs to kill or benumb its prey, and of two specimens of the common Torpedo, taken in the estuary of the Tees, one had an eel weighing two pounds and a flounder of one pound in its stomach, and the other a salmon weighing nearly five pounds, none of the victims showing any marks or blemishes on their bodies." He goes on to say that the power of the shock "is usually of sufficient strength to knock down a fully grown man if he accidentally steps on one of these fish lying buried in the sand in the shallow water."

Dr. Douglas Wilson (1953) has made some very interesting observations on the feeding of *Torpedo nobiliana* in the Plymouth aquarium. He has kindly allowed me to quote the following passages:

"In the 1930's some time was spent observing *Torpedo* in the hope of discovering the manner in which the prey is captured. The rays observed never attempted to secure squid or dead fish thrown into the tank; but round fishes, such as cod (*Gadus morrhua* L.) and pollack (*G. pollachius* L.), if kept in the same tank, gradually disappeared one by one. In March 1935 a *Torpedo nobiliana*, 2½ to 3 ft. long, was seen with the tail of a cod, about 20 in. long, sticking out of its mouth. The cod was really too big for the ray and took over an hour to disappear. For several days afterwards the ray had a bloated appearance. Later in the same year I arrived at the tank in time to see a pollack disappearing into the mouth of the same or a similar ray . . . When the aquarium was reopened after the war further specimens of *Torpedo* were obtained, but in general they were unwelcome owing to the apparent impossibility of feeding them except with living fish. The same difficulty had occurred with *Rhina*[2] *squatina*, but had been overcome by drawing dead fish through the

[1] The rarer species *T. torpedo* is also occasionally taken at Plymouth and has been kept in the Aquarium there (Wilson, 1953).    [2] =*Squatina*

FIG. 87. *a*, the sting ray, *Trygon pastinaca*, with enlarged view of poison spine (*a'*) and *b*, the electric ray *Torpedo nobiliana* drawn at the British Museum (N.H.).

water on the end of a wire. When the fish arrived near its mouth, the *Rhina* gave a very quick upward thrust of the head and rose from the ground to seize it. In *Rhina* the large mouth is at the extreme anterior end and is well suited to this habit. It was thought that *Torpedo* might similarly react to a dead fish drawn smartly through the water to within striking distance, though how it would attack it was a matter for speculation. The mouth of *Torpedo* is relatively much smaller than that of *Rhina* and is situated underneath the head well behind the anterior end, a poor position, apparently, for seizing actively swimming prey.

In the autumn of 1952, when two medium-sized *Torpedo nobiliana* (each about 2 ft. long, one a male, the other a female) had settled down in the largest tank, the feeding technique used for *Rhina* was tried and at once proved successful. A dead pout, *Gadus luscus* L., on the end of a wire fixed to a bamboo pole, was pounced upon by the male ray as soon as it was drawn to a position a few inches above the bottom in front of the ray. With a very quick movement the ray sprang forwards and upwards and made to envelop the fish, its wings (pectoral fins) and snout (the straight anterior border of the head) being curled around ventrally. The stiff wire prevented the completion of the manoeuvre, and as the pout was pulled away and upwards the ray adopted first a vertical position, with the wings surrounding the prey, and finally turned over upside-down in mid-water. It could then be seen that the pout was between the jaws of the ray, whose wings, snout, pelvics and tail were all bent or bunched upwards (that is ventrally) as if to surround it. The pout was unhooked from the wire, and the ray righted itself and flattened itself out on the bottom, by which time the meal had been swallowed. Much the same performance was repeated with another pout, after which the ray lost interest and on that day gave no further display."

After making several further observations on feeding, he goes on:

"*Torpedo* catches relatively large active fishes, and it seems a reasonable conclusion that it is able to do so because it can numb and quieten them with its electric organs. But before this conclusion can be accepted the giving of the shock during capture needs to be demonstrated.

A dead horse mackerel, *Caranx trachurus* (L.)[1], about 9 in. long, was fixed to the end of a waterproof electric flex. Each wire of the double flex was soldered to an electrode and the electrodes were inserted into the muscular tissues of the fish, one at each end. The flex was connected to a Pye Scalamp Galvanometer. The fish was now trailed in the usual way. Several times the fish touched the back of the ray but no deflection of the galvanometer occurred. Eventually the ray (the female) pounced, and at that instant when it folded its wings and head on to the prey a strong shock was registered. The ray failed to secure the fish. After several more attempts without any response the female was abandoned and the male was tried. As soon as the bait arrived in the proper position the ray pounced and again a strong shock was registered."

He then records a number of instances when its electrical powers were seen to be used in a defensive manner; dogfish, nurse-hounds, conger eels and angel-fish were all seen to give a sudden start and then rapidly retreat on making contact. Perhaps the prominent "bulls-eye" markings, which usually adorn the upper surface, may serve as a warning device to would-be predators.

It is amusing to recall that *Torpedo* was the instrument of the first electrotherapy; W. Radcliffe in his entertaining and learned *Fishing from the Earliest Times* (1921) relates that "according to Galen and

[1]Now called *Trachurus trachurus* (L).

Dioscorides the shock, whence or however obtained, relieved chronic headache, while a contemporary of the latter recommends a person suffering from gout in the feet to stand "bare-legged on the shore and apply the Torpedo." There is a story, I believe, recording that this arose because the Emperor Tiberius trod on one while bathing at Capri and found that the resulting shock greatly benefited his gout.

Passing now to the typical skates and rays belonging to the genus *Raia*, we find that there are no fewer than eleven distinct species taken in our waters; these are becoming increasingly important as commercial fish—and with anchovy sauce how good they can be! The late Dr. G. A. Steven, who has made interesting studies of the natural history of the different species and their relative importance in the south-western fisheries (1932, 1933, 1936), devised a simple system for their rapid identification (1931); unfortunately lack of space forbids giving its full detail. First the skates: the common skate *Raia batis* (Plate 14, p. 195) and the long-nosed *R. oxyrhynchus*, can be distinguished by their darkly pigmented and black-spotted undersides from all the rays which are white bellied species; *R. batis* has a much shorter and less pointed snout than *R. oxyrhynchus*. Then the rays (i.e. white-bellied species) may be separated into three groups—the long-nosed, the circular and the short-nosed rays. The long-nosed are *R. fullonica*, the shagreen ray; and *R. marginata*, the bordered ray (also called the white-bellied skate). The circular rays, having the tips of their wings decidedly rounded, are *R. undulata*, the marbled ray; *R. naevus* the cuckoo ray; and *R. circularis* the sandy ray. The short-nosed species have their bodies of a typical diamond shape, due to the pointed wing-tips and short but well-defined snout; they are *R. clavata* the thornback ray (Plate 16, p. 211); *R. brachyura* the blonde ray; *R. montagui*,[1] the spotted ray (Plate XVI, p. 179); and lastly *R. microcellata*, the painted ray.

Steven showed how these various species make up very different proportions of the catches of different classes of fishing-vessel: liners, steam-trawlers or sailing beam-trawlers in the Plymouth area. The composition of the total landings of all classes of vessel for the major ports of Cornwall and Devon he gives as follows: *clavata* 37 per cent, *naevus* 19 per cent, *fullonica* 16 per cent, *montagui* 15 per cent, *batis* 7 per cent, *brachyura* 4 per cent—the remaining five species together making up the odd 2 per cent. They feed largely on fish and crustacea. Three species at least, *clavata*, *brachyura* and *fullonica*, tend to occur in shoals, sometimes all of one sex. The thornback, *R. clavata*, is the most widely distributed species in the Channel area, at all depths and on all kinds of bottom. Absent from the Channel is *R. radiata*, the starry ray which

[1] = *R. maculata*, Day.

is an arctic species, but not uncommonly taken off the northern Scottish coasts; I figure it in Plate 13 (p. 194).

The rays and skates produce horny egg-cases not unlike those of the common dogfish, as seen in Fig. 84. The late Dr. R. S. Clark published a fine series of photographs of all the young rays and skates (1922) and of the adults in his revision of the genus *Raia* (1926). Young rays feed almost entirely upon small crustacea such as amphipods and shrimps and as they get older turn to crabs and also fish. The adult thornback, says Steven (1932) "sometimes feed entirely on fish . . . Of several hundreds of stomachs examined, not one was found to contain anything but fish, mainly herring (sometimes as many as six in one stomach) and not more than half a dozen empty stomachs were encountered." He then makes an interesting observation on their feeding: "Of the foraging habits of the Raiidae little is known. It is nevertheless certain that they depend upon 'scent'—or at any rate on some sense other than sight—for the finding and recognition of their food or prey. For in long-line fishing, where the catch depends upon the fish finding and taking the bait, there is no difference at all in the magnitude of day and night hauls . . . They differ markedly from Turbot which, being sight feeders, are seldom caught in any number on the lines during the night, but are readily taken by day." Sir Julian Huxley has told me how in Australia he has seen giant rays detecting their prey by touch and then shifting their mouth over it; with the eyes on top they cannot, of course, see underneath.

Of quite a different family is the sting-ray, *Trygon pastinaca* (Fig. 87, p. 184), which, although not common, may be taken all round our coasts. It may be distinguished from the true rays by lacking a caudal fin, so that it has a long whip-like tail; it also lacks dorsal fins, but in their place on the back of the tail is the huge serrated poison-spine— said in very large specimens to reach a length of 15 inches. It whips its lash-like tail round its prey and drives home the stinging spine. The spine is said to be formed by the enlargement and fusion of denticles in the tail region; although I believe this point has not yet been satisfactorily demonstrated. Norman (1947) says that these stinging spines are shed from time to time and replaced by new ones growing from underneath; and sometimes two or three may be found in a single specimen.

To end our brief review of the rays, two exciting species will just be mentioned: the eagle ray, *Myliobatis aquila,* and the horned ray or devil-fish, *Mobula giorna;* they are compared in Fig. 88 overleaf). The horned ray is a Mediterranean species but just comes into the British list; Day records that there is a specimen of 45 inches span in the

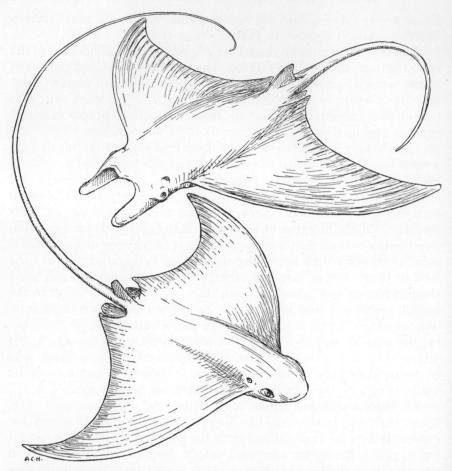

FIG. 88. *Above,* the devil-fish or horned ray, *Mobula giorna,* and *below,* the eagle ray, *Myliobatis aquila.* Drawn in the British Museum (Nat. Hist.) ×¼.

Royal Dublin Society's Museum which was caught off the south of Ireland in 1830. The eagle-ray has been recorded from all round the British Isles on a number of occasions, including many times from the North Sea. Recent records are two caught in trawlers working off Aberdeen in November 1952 and two more (off Cape Wrath and West Orkney) in November 1953 (Rae and Wilson, 1953, 1954).

As an appendix to the elasmobranchs we must just make a brief reference to a member of quite a different order from the sharks and rays—*Chimaera monstrosa,* the rabbit-fish, of the order Holocephali, which is shown in Plate 2 (p. 19); sometimes it has been called the

King of the Herrings, but I have never discovered why. It is one of the very few members left living to-day from a group of fish (the bradyodonts) which were once very important in palaeozoic times; it occurs in the deep water down the edge of the continental slope, and is only rarely caught—chiefly by trawlers when fishing for hake on the edge of the shelf[1]. As its name implies, it is a monstrous-looking fish, at any rate in shape. The male has an extraordinary toothed organ on the top of its head, thought to be used as a 'grappling-iron' in pairing with the female; Norman (1931) says that marks and scratches observed on females at the base of their dorsal fins are believed to have been made by it. The male is also provided with the typical elasmobranch 'claspers' which are modified parts of the pelvic fins and serve, as we have seen in the dogfish, a different function from that of actually clasping. It has a pointed snout and a body which is stout in front and tapers away to a long thin whip-like tail. The pectoral fins are large, wing-like, and pointed; and it has a strong spine in front of the first dorsal fin. The gill clefts are covered by an opercular fold so that there appears to be only one opening. Its teeth are fused together to form large grinding plates in the upper and lower jaws. The remains of fish, crustacea, brittle-stars and polychaete worms have been found in its gut, all ground into very small pieces; so it certainly feeds on the sea bed. *Chimaera* is, as we have said, one of the cartilaginous fish, yet in its vertebral column we see a remarkable development of a calcified bone-like substance—not true bone but something very like it.

When I recently accompanied the Scottish Fisheries Research Ship "Explorer" on a trawling cruise in the northern North Sea we were lucky enough to bring up no less than twenty specimens of *Chimaera* in a single haul of only half-an-hour's duration in the deep water down the edge of the slope leading to the Norwegian Deeps.[2] Only two of these were males, and one of them, that in Plate 2, I painted as soon as it came up; whilst its shape is grotesque, there is a certain beauty in its colour. Over the lighter parts of the body there is a delicate pearly iridescence of which one has no idea from just seeing preserved specimens; and its vivid green eye was like a jewel which almost appeared to have a glow of emerald fire in it. The long rat-like tail was quite fleshy and robust in the fresh specimen, but within a hour of death it had withered into a thin and almost string-like ending. Using Aberdeen fishing records the late Sir D'Arcy Thompson (1917) deduced a migration of *Chimaera* between spending summer in the Atlantic depths and winter in the northern North Sea.

[1] A still deeper *C. mirabilis* is occasionally caught.
[2] 61° 01′ N; 03° 00′ E (3 Aug. 1956).

# CHAPTER 10

# BOTTOM-LIVING BONY FISH

BEFORE coming to the typical bony fish we must mention one species that should be set apart from all the rest: the fish that belongs to the Sovereign—the sturgeon, *Acipenser sturio*. By an un-repealed Act from the reign of Edward II it is decreed that "the King shall have the wreck of the sea throughout the realm, whales and great sturgeons" either taken from the sea or elsewhere. It is said that it is very good to eat, having an excellent firm flesh. It is not, however, just because it is a "royal" fish that we must treat it first; zoologically it belongs to a different order from all the rest: the Chondrostei (Gk. *chondros*, gristle, *osteon*, bone). Without doubt it is the most primitive of all our (British) bony fish.

The sturgeon, shown in Plate XVII, p. 214, is in fact another 'living fossil' from the past: one of the few remaining members of an order which diverged in the Jurassic era from a much earlier and larger group of fish[1], one which flourished from the mid-Devonian to the Cretaceous. We have just seen at the end of the last chapter a carti-laginous fish, *Chimaera*, on the way to becoming something like a bony fish; the sturgeons, as the name of their order implies, are bony fish which are doing the reverse by losing most of their bone and becoming largely cartilaginous. It is not their cartilage, however, which makes them primitive; they are in fact descended from ancestors strong in bone and, while their main skeleton has lost so much of it, they are characterised by prominent rows of large diamond-shaped bony plates down their backs and sides.

As is well known, the sturgeon ascends large rivers to breed, particularly those of Russia, where its spawn provides us with the delicious caviar. It must, however, spend some considerable time in the open sea and so should certainly be included here; yet we know next to nothing about its sea-life: less indeed than that of the salmon. From the few records quoted by Day it appears to feed on bottom-living invertebrates; small crustacea, bivalve molluscs, and the so-called

---

[1]These are the palaeoniscoid fish of which there are still two genera living to-day in the rivers of Africa: *Polypterus* and *Calamoichthys*.

sea-mouse *Aphrodite* (p. 127) have been found in its stomach together with sand which also completely filled the intestine. Specimens 7 or 8 feet in length are not uncommon and Day refers to the case of one 11¼ feet long in the British Museum which was caught in the North Sea off Heligoland. A few are regularly reported entering the Severn and Trent, sometimes ascending as far as Shrewsbury and Nottingham respectively; but they do not spawn in our rivers. From time to time odd specimens are caught by trawlers in both the North and Irish Seas. Jenkins writes:

> "It is certainly remarkable how nearly every year one or more examples of the sturgeon are taken in the same place on the west coast; this has come under the author's personal observation repeatedly in the fishery boats and draw-nets (seines) off Pwllheli, on the south coast of Caernarvonshire."

Records from waters round Scotland, given by Rae and Wilson (1952–1956), show an increase recently; 10, 13 and 11 being taken respectively in the years 1953, 1954 and 1955; one died in an excess of misplaced homage, and was covered with distinction, by burying itself in the condenser pipe of one of Her Majesty's aircraft carriers: H.M.S. *Glory*!

We now come to the typical bony fish which constitute the order Teleostei (Gk. *telos, teleos*, completion; *osteon*, bone); their usual character has already been discussed when dealing with fish in general (Chap. 2). We are, of course, in this book concerned with the *open* sea and so we shall not include a number of purely coastal fish, some of which are specially adapted for life between the tide-marks ; these interesting species have been discussed by Professor Yonge in his beautiful volume *The Sea Shore* in this series.[1] The most successful groups of demersal teleosts on the continental shelf are the cod-like fish (Gadidae), the flat-fish (Pleuronectidae) and the gurnards (Triglidae); the first two families, not including the great rarities, have in our waters fifteen and eighteen species respectively. Apart from these large groups there are many other kinds to be included. Unless otherwise stated the information regarding the feeding of these fish is taken from the extensive researches of R. A. Todd (1905, 1907).

How are we to deal with all these different fish? Should we take

---

[1]These shore fish include the members of the genus *Cottus*, the gobies (*Gobius* spp.) the sea-snails (*Liparis* spp.), the suckers (*Lepadogaster* spp.), the blennies (*Blennius* spp.), the gunnel (*Pholis gunnellus*), the viviparous blenny (*Zoarces viviparus*), and the sand-smelt (*Atherina presbyter*).

them group by group in zoological order? I think not; that is done in the works of reference. Our book is essentially a natural history of the sea; we want to get some idea of the various kinds which may be found living together in different parts of it. And besides, few zoologists agree upon the exact order in which these should be placed. Let me take you out on a trawler which is going to fish on a wide variety of grounds in the northern North Sea and we shall see just what is caught as we go along. As explained in the introduction, I was fortunate last summer (1956) in being invited to accompany the new Scottish fishery research trawler *Explorer* on a special survey of the stocks of fish in the region between the north of Scotland and Norway. Instead of taking long hauls of 3 or 4 hours duration on only a few grounds, as would a commercial trawler, we took short hauls of half-an-hour at many different places. A complete record of all the fish caught was kept by Mr. S. D. Devlin of the Scottish Home Department Staff who most kindly gave me a copy of his log. As I have explained in my preface, I learnt much from his long experience of the fish of the North Sea. I made watercolour drawings of them as soon as they came out of the trawl and these are reproduced in Plates 12 to 15; they include most of the species met with and each plate represents the fish typical of different regions and, in some, a few invertebrate animals as well. Usually I shall comment on the different kinds just as we meet them, but I will reserve a fuller discussion of the prominent members of the cod family until the next chapter; they are treated separately—as were the herring and the plaice—on account of their special importance both in the fisheries and in the general ecology of the sea.

Plate 12 (p. 141) is a painting of one of the hauls we made at a position some 90 miles N.E. of Aberdeen from a depth of 74 fathoms. It is intended to give an idea of the general appearance of the pile of fish as soon as it has gushed from the cod-end on to the deck. It shows, of course, only part of the catch, and except for a little rearrangement to include as many different kinds as possible, the fish are just as they tumbled out of the trawl. The outlines of the fish were rapidly sketched in and then one of each species was taken and drawn more carefully, but in the same attitude; behind the selected fish is shown the general background of the commoner kinds. It was not a large haul, but we must remember that the trawl was only fishing for half-an-hour. Whiting were most numerous with 62, followed by 57 long rough dabs, 29 haddock, 7 cod, 4 witch and just ones and twos of other species; at the next haul the commoner kinds were haddock 203, whiting 142, long rough dabs 133, gurnard 14, spurdogs 8 and cod 6. We shall leave the whiting, cod, haddock and hake—the last conspicuous with its very sharp teeth—until the next chapter. The pelagic fish, the mackerel and herring, we have already dealt with; they were probably caught on the way up. In passing we may note that the herring looks very different from one caught in a drift-net, as we shall see if we compare it with that in Plate 1 (p. 18); it is much more blue because it has had nearly all its scales rubbed off—a condition typical of trawl-caught herring. Now let us turn to the others.

At the bottom of the picture, in the middle, is a beautiful little fish that I had never seen before—an argentine. There are two species in our seas: *Argentina silus* and *A. sphyraena;* they are deep-water members of the salmon family and both very much alike. The one shown in the plate is the smaller of the two, *sphyraena;* but we took some of the other species later in the cruise when further to the north and east. Both are characterised by a line of brilliant silver plates down their sides, flashing as if they were a line of mirrors, but may be distinguished by differences in the number of their fin rays.[1] In these northern waters they are commoner than was originally supposed. As explained in Chapter 1 (p. 3) we had, for purposes of research, a small-mesh net fixed to the upper surface of the trawl to catch the smaller fish escaping through its standard meshes; in this net as many as 127 argentines were taken in one haul and 73 in another, mostly *A. sphyraena,* and again further over towards Norway there were 273 of the other species (but mostly in the trawl proper). Jenkins says that Argentines are sometimes caught in considerable numbers by trawlers fishing in deep water off the west of Ireland and that he has frequently seen them for sale on hawkers' barrows in Preston.

Another surprise in this first haul was a lump-sucker *Cyclopterus lumpus* which I had previously decided to leave out of the book, thinking it to be an entirely coastal species. It certainly is more often taken close against the shore, but as we see here it may extend well over the floor of the North Sea, and to a considerable depth. Its body is covered with little protuberances giving it a somewhat toad-like appearance; but it is bright with a pink hue on its lower parts. Its pelvic fins are fused together to form a completely circular sucker on its underside and with this it anchors itself to stones; this is an adaptation found in a number of shore-living fishes enabling them to hold on against strong wave action. The lump-sucker lays a very large mass of eggs, some 100,000 together, usually in some sheltered crevice in the

[1] *A. sphyraena* has 13–14 rays in each of its pectoral fins, 11 in the pelvic and 50–53 scales along the lateral line; for *A. silus* the corresponding figures are: 17–18, 12–13, and 60–65.

rocks; the male then stands on guard for weeks on end, driving away possible predators and aerating the eggs with a fanning motion of his fins. Dr. Wilson records in his *Life of the Shore and Shallow Sea* (1935) that sometimes at low tide these devoted parents "are attacked by rooks and carrion crows which rip them open and feast on their internal organs."

Dominating the picture is the large angler fish, *Lophius piscatorius,* in the foreground; it is sometimes also called the monk or frog-fish. It must certainly be regarded as one of the most remarkable of our demersal fish; while related to the deep-water pelagic angler fish described in the first volume (p. 243), it has become adapted for life in comparatively shallow water. The mouth has an enormous gape from side to side, and like the oceanic anglers, the first fin-ray of the dorsal fin has moved forward on the head to form a fishing-rod furnished with a lure—a little flap of skin—at the end of its line. Many naturalists have questioned whether this is really used for capturing prey; from the observations of Dr. Wilson at Plymouth (1937), however, there is now no doubt about it. Let me quote from his account:

---

*Plate 13.* FISH AND INVERTEBRATES FROM ANOTHER NORTH SEA GROUND (*150 miles N.E. of Aberdeen*)

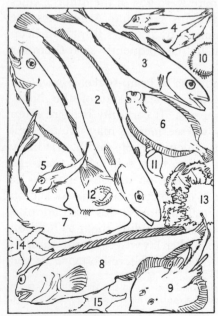

Painted, as was *Plate 12,* on the Scottish Fishery Research Ship "Explorer" from fish taken freshly from the trawl. A key to the different species is given below.

*Fish*

1. Pollack, *Gadus pollachius* ($\times \frac{1}{4}$).
2. Ling, *Molva molva* ($\times \frac{1}{8}$).
3. Coal-fish or Saithe, *Gadus virens* ($\times \frac{1}{8}$).
4. and 5. Colour varieties of the grey gurnard *Trigla gurnardus* ($\times \frac{1}{6}$).
6. Lemon dab *Microstomas kitt* ($\times \frac{1}{6}$).
7. Spur-dog or piked dogfish, *Squalus acanthias* ($\times \frac{1}{4}$).
8. Catfish, *Anarrhichas lupus* ($\times \frac{1}{6}$).
9. Starry ray, *Raia radiata* ($\times \frac{1}{6}$).

*Invertebrates* ($\times \frac{1}{4}$)

10. Heart urchin, *Spatangus purpureus.*
11. Whelk, *Buccinum undatum.*
12. Cockle, *Cardium echinatum.*
13. Stone-crab, *Lithodes maia.*
14. Common starfish, *Asterias rubens.*
15. Cushion-star, *Hippasteria phrygiana*

A.C.H.

Plate 13

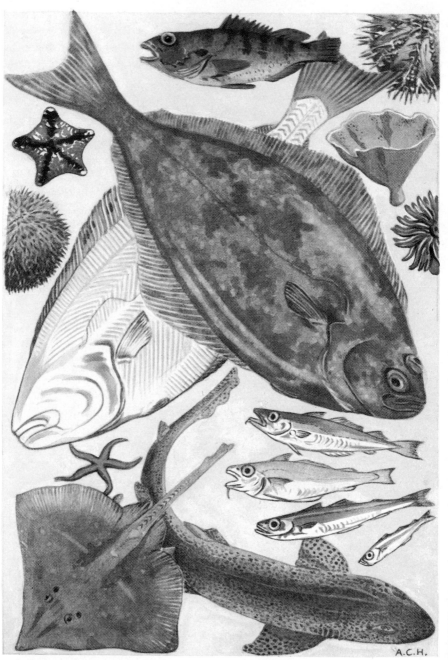

Plate 14

"An angler when hungry erects the lure immediately any suitable fishes come anywhere near and endeavours to attract one of them close enough to be caught. The lure is quickly jerked to and fro, and as the rod is almost invisible the bait (in my specimens always forked and 'fly-like', not vermiform) simulates some tiny creature darting about. An attracted fish rushes up in an endeavour to catch it; the bait is skilfully flicked out of its way just in time and, with a final cast, is dashed down in front of the mouth which may open very slightly. The intended victim, still following the bait, turns slightly head downwards; it is now more or less directly head on to the angler's mouth. The jaws snap faster than the eye can follow, and the tail of the prey is next seen disappearing from sight through the firmly closed mouth. As far as I have been able to observe the bait is not actually touched by the victim before it is caught, as has sometimes been supposed. Touching the bait with forceps does not cause a reflex snapping of the jaws.

---

*Plate 14.* FROM A TRAWL-HAUL NORTH OF SHETLAND
Fish and invertebrates painted on the Scottish Fishery Research Ship "Explorer" from specimens taken freshly from the trawl. A key to the different species is given below.

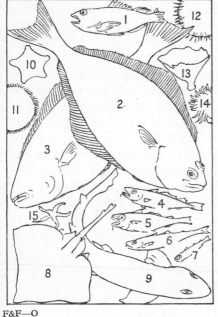

Fish

1. Red fish, *Sebastes viviparus* ($\times \frac{1}{3}$).
2. and 3. Upper and lower surfaces of the halibut, *Hippoglossus hippoglossus* ($\times \frac{1}{8}$).
4. Poor-cod, *Gadus minutus* ($\times \frac{1}{2}$).
5. Pollack-whiting or Norway pout (*G. esmarkii* ($\times \frac{1}{2}$).
6. Blue whiting, *G. poutassou* ($\times \frac{1}{2}$).
7. Silvery pout, *Gadiculus argenteus* ($\times \frac{1}{2}$).
8. Common skate, *Raia batis* ($\times \frac{1}{2}$).
9. Rough hound or lesser spotted dog-fish, *Scylliorhinus caniculus* ($\times \frac{1}{4}$).

*Invertebrates*

10. Starfish, *Porania pulvillus* ($\times \frac{1}{2}$).
11. Common sea urchin, *Echinus esculentus* ($\times \frac{1}{3}$).
12. Another urchin, *E. acutus* ($\times \frac{1}{2}$).
13. Sponge, *Axinella infundibuliformis* ($\times \frac{1}{4}$).
14. A deepwater anemone, *Bolocera tuediae* ($\times \frac{1}{2}$).
15. Orange variety of Scarlet Sea-star, *Henricia sanguinolenta* ($\times \frac{1}{3}$).

The moving lure has a strong attraction for healthy hungry fishes of several kinds. Small pollack, whiting, pout and bass were the species actually observed to be attracted to it, but probably most pelagic fish that capture moving prey by sight would at least swim up to investigate the darting object."

The inshore specimens here observed were all comparatively small ones up to 18 inches in length; further out in the deeper water they grow to over 3 feet and are landed in considerable numbers by our trawlers, giving an average annual catch of about 2,000 tons. The young angler, as shown in Dr. Wilson's splendid photograph in Plate XVIII (p. 215), is beautifully camouflaged against a gravelly bottom with its mottled pattern and flattened body; its margin, too, is serrated in a most extraordinary way to obliterate any hard outline. By being all but invisible it greatly increases its chances of capturing unsuspecting prey which may be lured towards its mouth by the play of the moving bait; when it gets older and moves out to deeper and darker water, much of the finer camouflage pattern is lost. The hinges of its jaws are so much at the side that the mouth can be thrown wide open in a flash. The prey is drawn in with the water which rushes in to fill the suddenly enlarged mouth cavity; almost as quickly, the mouth snaps to again, and the backwardly pointing teeth ensure that its prize cannot wriggle out but only pass further in towards the gullet. The teeth are more than simple barbs; they are hinged so that they bend inwards when pushed from the outside and so allow any object to pass easily over them in the inward direction, but spring back to become strong erect barbs when pushed the other way. The angler is certainly a most voracious animal and feeds almost entirely upon fish. Todd, in his studies of 1907, records one of $3\frac{1}{4}$ feet in length with two cod (18 and 20 inches), three haddock ($8\frac{1}{2}$, 9 and 12 inches) and other fish remains in its stomach; while another specimen of close on 3 feet contained as many as thirteen herring. Out of twenty fish he examined, trawled up from eighteen different localities, ten contained food in the stomach. The spawn of the angler is most remarkable; a million eggs or so are laid in a great mucus raft which measures two or three feet across and up to twenty or thirty feet in length, and may occasionally be seen floating near the surface of the sea. The baby angler fish are very attractive members of the plankton and are shown in Fig. 97 *j* on p. 221.

The flatfish on this ground were mainly represented by the large number of long rough dabs, as many as 465 being taken in the fine mesh net as against the 57 in the main trawl; in addition, there were

4 witch, a common dab and a megrim that looked almost like a caricature with its huge mouth. It will be best just to note the flatfish as we meet them and then, a little later in the chapter (p. 200), discuss them altogether as a family so as to compare the different kinds. This completes our first haul. The fish in this and the next three Plates—except for a few in Plate 15—were, of course, all dead when they were drawn, but only just, so that their colours are still as they were in life; I am sorry, however, that they do look so unmistakably dead, and this is obvious when they are compared with the drawings made from living fish in an aquarium, as were those in Plates 3, 4 and 16. Most of these northern fish are just not available in aquaria at the present time.

In my next plates I am drawing the species which we have not met before and leaving out the general background of the commoner forms so as to show up the selected ones more clearly; I have also included some of the representative invertebrates which have come up with the fish. We have now steamed some 60 miles further to the north. Plate 13 (p. 194) is a composite picture of the characteristic fish, apart from the commoner kinds, taken in two hauls from 60 fathoms in a region some 150 miles north-east of Aberdeen. Here we meet more members of the cod family: a fine specimen, just over 4½ feet long, of the almost eel-like ling with large asymmetrical blotches all over it, 5 good-sized pollack and two dark, almost black, saithe or coal fish. Haddock and whiting are also here in large numbers: 257 and 169 respectively in one haul, and 542 and 239 in the other; and there are a few cod. The flatfish are represented by the same species as in the last haul, with fewer long rough dabs, and there is one different one: the beautiful lemon-dab of a rich golden brown marbled with curious round and oval blotches of a darker shade; on account of these marks the fishermen give this fish the less romantic name of smear dab. We shall return to it on p. 202. We now come across a number of gurnards showing a wide range of colour from a very dark grey to a soft rosy pink; but they are all colour varieties of one species: *Trigla gurnardus*, the grey gurnard.

Let us consider the gurnards (Triglidae) in general; they cannot be mistaken for any other fish. Apart from their head, which is very well protected by strong bony plates and spines, they have, as a most characteristic feature, two or, more usually, three of the rays of their pectoral fins separated as long feeler-like, almost finger-like, processes; with these they explore the bottom, turning over stones, in search of food; and at times they can be seen walking with them, stealthily as if on tip-toe. The general form of a gurnard is beautifully shown in

Dr. Wilson's photograph of the streaked gurnard *Trigla lineata* in Plate XXIV (p. 243); this is a southern species and not very common in our waters, but is occasionally taken at Plymouth. The grey gurnard, *T. gurnardus*, which we have just seen in Plate 13, is the commonest British species; it occurs all round our islands feeding mainly on crustacea and reaches a length of about 18 inches. The gunards have characteristic young (Fig. 97g, p. 220).

The tub, latchet or yellow gurnard, *T. lucerna* ( =*hirundo*) is a handsome golden-brown fish with remarkably coloured pectoral fins of a deep blue; curiously, the young forms, known as sapphirine gurnards, have these large pectoral fins even more brilliantly coloured like the wings of some exotic butterfly. A young specimen is shown in Plate 16 (p. 211), note the bright blue margins to its pectorals and the striking round and dark blue areas patterned with light spots like a smart bow-tie. What do these colours mean? Being lost as the fish gets older they cannot be used in sexual display. And, unlike the flash-colourings displayed on the underwings of some moths and grasshoppers, they are not suddenly covered up to mystify a pursuing predator; the fins are often flaunted in all their glowing colours as the fish rests on the bottom. This species grows to be our largest gurnard, reaching nearly 2 feet in length, and feeds mainly on other fish; it is particularly fond of the little solenette (p. 204) and the dragonet (p. 214). It is common to the west and south, but rather rare in the North Sea.

The red gurnard, *T. cuculus* ( =*pini*), is a further handsome species, shown in Plate 15 (p. 210); it, too, is commoner on the west than on the east coast. Two other species, *T. obscura*, the long-finned gurnard, and *lyra*, known as the piper, are more southern forms and only rarely taken in our waters. The gurnards are closely related to the shore-living Cottid family, and also to another attractive little fish, the pogge or armed bull-head, *Agonus cataphractus;* this I shall just mention, and illustrate in Fig. 94 (p. 212), because, while breeding and spending the summer on our shores, it makes a migration to deeper water off the coast in winter and may then often be taken in a trawl.

But to return to the fish on our plate (Plate 13); conspicuous, and shown at the bottom, is a good-sized specimen of the marine catfish, *Anarrhichas lupus*, which is a large fish closely allied to the coastal blennies but inhabiting quite deep water, normally in depths of over 30 fathoms. It is widely distributed in the northern Atlantic and is particularly abundant in the northern North Sea. It is dark grey and usually has a series of darker vertical bands down the sides but sometimes it is spotted. On account of its rather repulsive appearance there is no ready sale for it until it has been skinned; this is usually

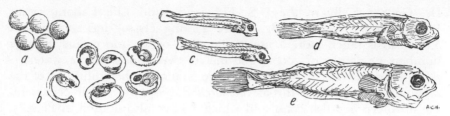

FIG. 89. Successive stages in the development of the viviparous Norway haddock *Sebastes marinus: a,* unfertilized eggs; *b,* developing young (out of a total of some 3,500 taken from one mother); *c,* young taken in act of birth; *d,* and *e,* later young stages from the plankton (all × 5).

done at the fish-docks and the flesh is sold as fillets of "woof" which have become quite popular in the north. It has very powerful teeth—large canine-like fangs in front, and rounded molar-like teeth behind, which are used for crushing the shells of molluscs, crustaceans and echinoderms upon which it feeds. Mammals are not the only vertebrates which have several kinds of teeth to serve different ends! The catfish lays its eggs on the bottom in a remarkable ball-like mass—usually almost a perfect sphere of closely packed eggs of an exceptionally large size, each egg about a quarter of an inch in diameter. Also shown in the plate are the spur-dog, of which close on 300 were taken in the second haul, and the beautiful northern starry ray; but these we have already dealt with (pp. 179 and 186).

We have now steamed north again to fish grounds to the east and north-east of Shetland in depths of 55 to 85 fathoms, and here we have struck halibut. This, the largest of the flatfish, is more often taken by line from regions which are too rough to be trawled; I show both sides of it in Plate 14 (p. 195)—but we will come to it later with the other flatfish. Here, for the first time, I saw the glowing red of our own little *Sebastes: S. viviparus,* which I show at the top of the plate. This is the real British species. The much larger and still more flashy Norway haddock or bergylt *S. marinus* (=*norvegicus*) only occasionally comes into our waters; I show it on Plate 5 (p. 82) because it is some-times taken in deep water to the west of Scotland and often adds a splendid show of colour to the fish docks of Aberdeen and Hull as catches of vessels from Iceland or Norway are laid out for auction. Both species are viviparous[1] and bring forth an enormous number of very small young at one birth—more than a thousand from each ovary (Norman, 1931). In Fig. 89 above I show, natural size, some of the young taken from a single female of *S. marinus* kindly given me by

[1]Among the few examples of internal fertilization in bony fish.

Dr. George Kelly of the U.S. Fish and Wild Life Laboratory at Woods Hole. Recently Dr. Vedel Tåning (1949) has shown that *S. marinus* is much more a fish of the open ocean and occurs in large numbers at depths of 200 to 400 metres over much deeper waters—right across the north Atlantic. There is another beautiful fish of the same family, the blue-throat *Scorpaena dactyloptera*, which occurs off the northern Scottish coast and which I have also figured in Plate 5.

Also featured in these northern hauls were the four smallest members of the cod family which I have figured together in Plate 14: the poor cod, the Norway pout, the blue whiting, and silvery pout; but we shall come to them again in the next chapter. Haddock, whiting, lemon dab, gurnards, and spur-dogs were abundant and there were a few skate and common dogfish, as seen at the bottom of the plate; megrim, long rough dab, cod, ling, saithe, angler, starry rays and argentines were also still being taken.

After a brief call at Lerwick to pick up and draw the rare Opah (p. 75)—what a lucky chance it was that we were so near and got news of it by wireless—we steamed to a position some 100 miles to the ENE and put down the trawl to a depth of 140 fathoms on the edge of the slope dropping into the Norwegian Deep. Here we pulled up no less than 20 of the fabulous chimaeras (p. 189) which I had never seen caught before; each had eyes of an almost luminous green, Plate 2 (p. 19). Other striking fish in this haul were the torsk (Plate 5, p. 82), the blue ling (p. 229) and the greater fork-beard (Fig. 100, p. 230) which we shall come to in the next chapter and the beautiful black-mouthed dogfish already mentioned (Fig. 85, p. 181). Hake, haddock and witches were also present in fair numbers.

We now made our way south and back towards Aberdeen, fishing as we went; but the description of too many hauls will become tedious and in fact we were catching mainly the same species as on the outward path. In the last haul just off Aberdeen came a number of horse mackerel (p. 83) caught on the way up, and the charming little four-bearded rockling (p. 231); they are both shown in Plate 15. In this last haul I had hoped to get plaice and turbot, which are often taken on this ground, to add to my collection; but we were not successful and the paintings of them on this plate were made from living specimens in the Fisheries Marine Laboratory at Aberdeen when we came in. The others on the plate were drawn further south, but they might all have come from a similar ground. Let us now consider the great family of the flatfish together.

All the flatfish (Order Heterostomata) are beautifully adapted for life on the sea-bed. We have already dealt very fully with one example,

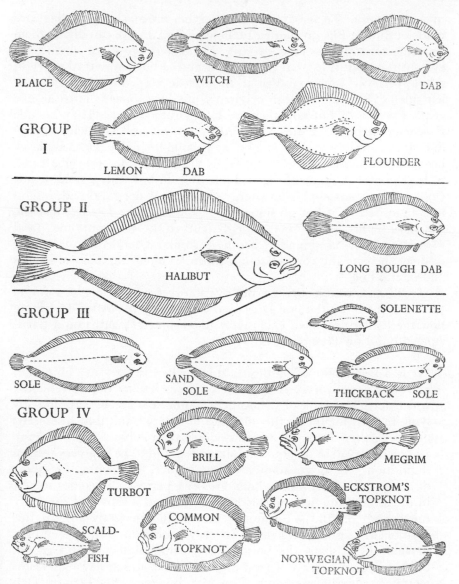

FIG. 90. A diagrammatic guide to the flatfish (for scientific names see text).

the plaice, and have seen the main characters of these fish; space is short and we shall now have to pass all the rest in very rapid review, for there are no less than eighteen species[1] in our own waters, belonging

[1]Omitting a few very rare ones.

to seven genera.  To assist in comparison they are all shown in diagrammatic outline in Fig. 90 overleaf; following Jenkins, we can divide them conveniently into four main groups.  First, there are those which have eyes on the right side (that is, they rest on the bottom with their right side uppermost) but have their teeth most developed on their blind or left side.  These are the fish originally put by Linnaeus into the one genus *Pleuronectes*, but now they are in separate genera.  They include *P. platessa* the plaice (Plates XIX and 15, pp. 222 and 210) with lateral-line almost straight and a spine before its anal fin and a relatively large head; *Microstomus kitt* ( = *P. microcephalus*) the lemon dab (Plate 13, p. 194) similar in regard to lateral line and fin but with a small head; *Glyptocephalus cynoglossus,* the witch, (Plate 12, p. 141) also with lateral line almost straight but no spine before the anal fin; *Limanda limanda,* the dab, with lateral line strongly curved at its front end; and *Platichthys flesus,* the flounder, having a similar lateral line, but easily distinguished by the rows of rough tubercles along the base of its fins and lateral line.

I will here interject a few observations on the feeding of some of these fish made by the late Dr. G. A. Steven (1930).  After describing how the lemon dab feeds exclusively upon annelid worms on a particular ground off Plymouth, he writes:

"It is a frequenter of muddy bottoms where worms are abundant and other organisms correspondingly scarce.  Tubicolous Polychaetes, which form the bulk of the Annelid fauna, cannot be captured by lying in wait for them: they have to be hunted and that discreetly, otherwise they disappear to safety down their tubes.  So the Lemon Dab, if observed in an aquarium tank, is found to be of a very restless disposition.  It is constantly on the move, swimming for short distances with intervening halts for brief periods.  It comes to rest in a characteristic attitude with the head and forepart of the body raised well off the substratum.  Remaining perfectly still in this position, the fish, by means of its very prominent and exceedingly movable eyes, scans the bottom in its immediate neighbourhood.  Should it then observe a food organism—i.e. the anterior end of a worm cautiously emerging from its burrow—the Lemon Dab suddenly pounces upon it like a true hunter with a kind of forward leap, bringing its mouth down almost vertically upon its victim by a strong arching of the anterior part of the body."

In Fig. 91, opposite, I reproduce two drawings from his paper showing this action. Of the dab and plaice he writes:

FIG. 91. The lemon dab, *Microstomas Kitt,* in its characteristic attitude on the look-out for prey and (*below*) about to pounce on a burrowing worm whose head is just showing above the sand. The upper drawing above is by Mr. L. R. Brightwell and the lower by Dr. G. A. Steven from whose paper (1930) they are reproduced with kind permission. Young lemon dabs are shown in Fig. 97*h* (p. 220).

"Both are visual feeders. The former forages in a manner similar to that of the Lemon Dab, but does not raise itself quite so far off the bottom or bring its mouth down upon its prey at such a steep angle. It shoots upon them more from a horizontal direction, and being an active and alert fish it is thus able to capture a greater range of organisms than the Lemon Dab, but is less successful when it comes to Polychaetes alone. The hunting posture of the Plaice is still more nearly horizontal, the head being raised off the bottom even less than that of the Dab. Its food is therefore again more restricted in its range, approaching that of the Sole—i.e. Mollusca, errant Poly-chaetes, and sometimes a few Crustaceans, including an occasional *Upogebia* (a burrowing prawn)."

Next there are flat-fish which also have their eyes on the right side, but have a large mouth, with the jaws similar on the two sides; these are *Hippoglossus hippoglossus* (=*H. vulgaris*), the halibut, (Plate 14, p. 195) a very large fish with a curved lateral line and smooth scales;[1] and *Hippoglossoides platessoides*, the long rough dab, which is a small fish with straight lateral line and scales very rough.

The third group again consists of fish with their eyes on the right, but which have teeth only on the blind side; these are four members of the sole family: *Solea solea* (=*S. vulgaris*), the sole, Plate 16 (p. 211) with pectoral fins well developed and both nostrils on the blind side and not dilated; *Pegusa lascaris*, the sand-sole, with pectorals well developed but only one nostril on the blind side; *Microchirus variegatus*, the thick-back with pectorals very small and body banded on the upper side; and *Buglossidium luteum* (=*S. lutea*) the solenette, also having the pectorals very small, the body dappled on the upper side and with every fifth ray of the fins lined with black. The great William Bateson made a number of observations (1890) on the feeding and perceptions of fish. His remarks about the sole are particularly interesting; after describing how it remains buried under the sand during the day, rarely moving, except at night, he writes as follows:

"In searching for food the sole creeps about on the bottom by means of the fringe of fin-rays with which its body is edged, and thus slowly moving, it raises its head upwards and sideways, and gently pats the ground at intervals, feeling the objects in its path with the peculiar villiform papillae which cover the lower (left) side of its head and face. In this way it will examine the whole surface of the floor of the tank, stopping and going back to investigate pieces of stick, string, or other objects which it feels below its cheek. As already stated, the sole appears to be unable to find food that does not lie on the bottom, and will not succeed in finding food suspended in the water unless it be lowered so that the sole is able to cover part of it with the lower side of its head, when it seizes it at once."

Lastly we come to a large group of flatfish with eyes on the *left* side, i.e. resting on the bottom with their left side uppermost; all these fish have their teeth and jaws equal on both sides. Here we have *Scophthalmus* (=*Rhombus*) *maximus*, the turbot, Plates XIX and 15 (pp. 222 and 210) with a diamond-shaped body, lacking scales, but covered all over on its upper surface with blunt bony tubercles, and *S. rhombus* (=*R. laevis*) the brill (also on Plate 15), with an oval body covered with smooth scales—surely a remarkable difference in two closely

---

[1]In arctic waters these fish may reach an enormous size; I believe the record halibut landed at Hull weighed just on 40 stone.

allied species. How perfectly camouflaged they are, having the power of expanding and contracting their pigment cells to alter their pattern and make it dark or light according to their background. *Lepidorhombus whiff-iagonis*, the megrim (Plate 12, p. 141) has a narrow body compared with the two foregoing, with rough scales and very large eyes and mouth; *Arnoglossus laterna*, the scale-fish, is similar in shape but with much smaller eyes and mouth, and characterised by skin and scales which become easily detached when captured. There remain just three other species: *Zeugopterus punctatus*, the common topknot, having its dorsal fin beginning in front of its eyes, and its pectoral fins united with its pelvics; *Phrynorhombus norvegicus*, the Norwegian topknot, and the rare *Ph. regius*, Eckstrom's topknot, both fish with their pectoral and pelvic fins separate.

Leaving the flatfish for others of very different character, we come to the great conger-eel, *Conger conger* (=*C. vulgaris*) (Plate 16, p. 211). Specimens have been recorded up to 9 feet in length and weighing 160 lbs. The conger occurs all round our coasts, but is more abundant in the Channel and on the west than in the North Sea; it is usually found on or near a rocky ground and, as seen in aquaria, likes to get its body into crevices between rocks. Like the freshwater eel it breeds in deep water in the Atlantic, and has a similar little transparent leptocephalus larva (p. 90); it does not, however, go anything like so far from the European coast to spawn. Like the freshwater eel, too, it is said to spawn only once in its lifetime. The Murry, *Muraena helena*, that large handsome eel of warmer seas—a rich orange-brown mottled with a light buff colour—just comes into the British list as an extreme rarity on the south coast. A fine specimen, 3 ft. 9 ins. in length, was trawled off the Eddystone and brought into the Plymouth Laboratory in 1897. Day had previously recorded two other examples, one, 4 ft. 4 ins., taken on a line at Polperro in 1834 and another caught in a trammel net at Fowey in 1866. The avocet-beaked eel *Nemichthys* was figured, as a deep pelagic fish, in Part I (p. 239).

Talking of extreme rarities being caught near the Eddystone, I may here mention that most extraordinary and charming little creature, the sea horse, *Hippocampus europaeus* (=*H. antiquorum* Day) which occasionally turns up on the south coast. Like its close relatives the pipe fishes, it can scarcely be considered a fish of the open sea; the fact, however, that it has been taken as far from the shore as the Eddystone, surely allows its inclusion, and it is much too interesting a fish to miss. Being such weak swimmers they may be swept away from the coasts by currents and carried considerable distances; no doubt our little sea horses come to us in this way from Brittany. The one which I have included in Plate 2 (p. 19) I painted from a living specimen in the Aquarium of the Zoological Society of London; it had come from Arcachon. While I shall not deal with the several different kinds of pipe fish, I include a sketch of the greater pipe fish, *Syngnathus acus,* in Fig. 92 below, for comparison with the sea horse, for it explains the evolution of the latter from a more normal type of fish. The pipe fishes live among seaweeds and particularly among the waving blades of the sea grass *Zostera* which they closely resemble, as they swim amongst them in a vertical position, moving slowly forwards by undulating the little dorsal fin. This fin, and especially that of the sea

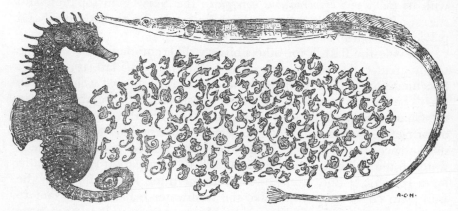

FIG. 92. *Left:* a male of the continental sea-horse, *Hippocampus guttulatus* (*c.f.* the British species in Plate 2, p. 19) with its 142 young taken from its brood pouch (natural size). *Right:* the greater pipe-fish, *Syngnathus acus* ($\times \frac{1}{2}$).

horse, vibrates so rapidly as to have "the appearance of a tiny propeller revolving in the middle of the fish's back;" I take this most apt description from Norman's *A History of Fishes* (1931). The tail of the sea horse has lost its fin and become a prehensile organ for coiling round the branches of weeds and corals; so anchored, these little fish can stem the tidal currents without effort and snap at the small crustaceans and other tasty morsels drifting past.

Perhaps the most remarkable fact about the sea horse relates to its breeding behaviour. The genital opening of the female becomes extended into an intromittant organ for the discharge of the eggs into the male who develops a special brood pouch for their protection and incubation; not only this, the walls of this pouch, like those of a uterus, become richly supplied with blood vessels to give oxygen and nourishment to the embryos. It is almost unbelievable how many little babies one father will carry; in Fig. 92, above, I give a drawing of one complete family taken from the pouch of a male of the closely allied *H. guttulatus* which was kindly given to me by Dr. H. G. Vevers after it had died in the Aquarium of the Zoological Society.

Except for the members of the cod family and other closely related forms which will have the next chapter to themselves, we must now pass the rest of the bony fish in rapid review. *Capros aper,* the boar-fish, of a beautiful coral-pink colour, is a most distinctive fish illustrated in Plates XX and 3, pp. 223 and 34. It is normally only found in our waters at the south-west entrance to the Channel where it lives in rather deep water; very occasionally, however, it comes in fair numbers up towards Plymouth. Dr. L. H. N. Cooper (1952) of the Plymouth Laboratory believes that its normal home is in some of the deep canyons which occur on the edge of the continental shelf, and that its occasional occurrence on the shelf itself is due to a sudden upwelling; he imagines a surge of water (due to unusual winds) passing up the canyon and carrying the boar-fish up to higher levels. Related and not unlike the boar-fish in general form is the larger John Dory *Zeus faber* which is also shown on Plate 3; it is grey in colour and unmistakable with a large black spot on each side—like a bull's eye. It lives at a medium depth, being rarely taken beyond the 50 fathom line, and is quite common in the Channel and southern North Sea, but is very rare further north. It feeds almost entirely on small fish. Norman, in his excellent book which I have just mentioned, describes how its excessive thinness, as it slowly approaches its victim end on, makes it almost invisible until it is within striking distance; suddenly its jaws are shot forward with great rapidity and the little fish is gone. In the deep-water to the west of Ireland lives a rare relative of the John Dory with a similarly compressed body: *Cyttosoma helgae.*

Of the sea perches, the comber, *Serranus cabrilla,* in its bright tartan-like dress (Plate 4, p. 35) and the blue-grey stone-bass or wreck-fish *Polyprion americanus* (Plate XVII, p. 214) are southern forms only met with on our south western coasts in summer. The wreck-fish is so called because it is often found accompanying floating timber; the specimen photographed by Dr. Wilson in the Plymouth aquarium was found, when younger and smaller, swimming inside an empty tea-chest floating on its side off the Devon coast. It is thought that they attend wreckage to feed on the small fish which are attracted to feed on the barnacles and other encrusting organisms. The common bass, *Morone labrax* ( =*Labrax lupus*), comes further up our coasts, to Wales in the west and up the Channel to East Anglia in the east; it comes into brackish or even fresh water to spawn. It is a bright silvery fish (Plate 16, p. 211) and often quite abundant, particularly off the west in summer where it is much fished for by sea anglers; it, too, however, leaves our shores in the autumn.

That delicious fish, the red mullet, *Mullus surmuletus* (Plate 4, p. 35) is another fish rare in our waters except in the extreme south-west, although odd ones are regularly reported up the east coast of Scotland as far north as Orkney, suggesting a migration north from the southern North Sea (Rae and Wilson, 1952–1956). As I painted it in the Plymouth aquarium it kept altering in colour, sometimes blushing red all over, or only in patches, or sometimes going quite pale. I have drawn it with the two barbels under its chin extended and feeling, perhaps tasting, the bottom for food in its characteristic fashion; when not in use they can be folded out of sight into grooves.

The breams are also more southerly fish which are again mainly taken off our south-west coasts. In Plate XXII (p. 227) I show two delightful photographs taken by Dr. Wilson of the black sea-bream or old wife, *Spondyliosoma cantharus*, guarding its nest—an area of slate at the bottom of the Plymouth aquarium cleared of gravel; in the lower photograph it is seen chasing a plaice off the nest. This species should not be confused with Ray's bream *Brama raii* which has also been called the black sea-bream; the latter goes further north and in most years there are records from Scotland. The common sea-bream *Pagellus centrodontus* (Plate 16, p. 211) which is a deeper water species, occasionally enters the northern North Sea as does also *P. bogaroveo*, the Spanish bream; *P. erythrinus*, the pandora, is a Mediterranean species which nevertheless, according to Day, regularly turns up on our south coast.[1]

I was lucky to be able to paint the remarkable red bandfish *Cepola rubescens* (Plate 2, p. 19) in its typical vertical swimming position from a living specimen in the Plymouth Aquarium; they are not infrequently trawled up off Rame Head, but only rarely do they survive capture. It used to be thought that they lived among rocks, but recently Dr. Wilson (1953) has shown that they burrow into the sand; I am also most fortunate in being able to include one of his striking photographs showing it in the act of sucking sand into its mouth in the process of forming such a burrow (Plate XX, p. 223).

The wrasses are generally taken near the coast, but the cuckoo wrasse, *Labrus ossifagus* (=*L. mixtus*), may be caught by trawlers some 20 miles off-shore. The males, especially in the breeding season, are as

[1]There are several fish of another family (Berycidae) and related forms which are sometimes mistaken for bream when they are landed by trawlers fishing for hake in the deep water of the Atlantic slope to the west of Ireland; these include *Beryx splendens*, *B. decadactylus*, *Diretmus argenteus*, and *Hoplostethus atlanticus*.

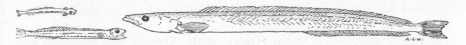

FIG. 93. Raitt's sand-eel, *Ammodytes marinus:* an adult ($\times \frac{1}{2}$) with young stages from the plankton.

brightly arrayed as any tropical fish and during courtship seem able to intensify the colours to an amazing brilliance; the female is very different and used to be thought to be a distinct species. I was able to paint them (Plate 4, p. 35) in the Plymouth Aquarium during the courtship period; I never saw, however, the intense display described and photographed by Wilson (1956) in which the male suddenly blanches to produce a large white patch on the front of the head and back. Two of his striking photographs are reproduced in Plate XXI (p. 226). The ballan wrasse *L. bergylta* ( $=L.$ *maculatus* Day), is re-markably variable in colour and appears to change with age; the specimen shown in Plate 16 (p. 211) is a young one, whereas the very speckled one in Plate 5 (p. 82) is an old one which has lost all trace of the dark bands. Other wrasses are the rainbow wrasse, *Coris julis;* the gilthead or corkwing, *Crenilabrus melops;* the gold-sinny, *Ctenolabrus rupestris;* the scale-rayed wrasse *Acantholabrus palloni* and the rock cock, *Centrolabrus exoletus* (also on Plate 16); they are all handsome fish.

Now let us consider some very small fish which are not often seen, yet, on account of their vast numbers, are of great importance in the general economy of the sea: the sand-eels or Ammodytidae. It used to be thought that there were only three kinds: *Ammodytes lanceolatus, A. tobianus* and *A. cicerelus*—the greater, the lesser and the smooth sand-eels; the first two were known to be common British species and the third was thought to be a more southern Mediterranean form, until what appeared to be one was dredged off Shetland in 1867. In 1928 the Scottish Fishery Research Ship *Explorer* trawled up over 1,600 specimens of this so-called *cicerelus* near the island of St. Kilda and has since found it in a number of localities off the north-west of Scotland and in the central North Sea. This northern form has now been recognised as a species distinct from the southern (non-British) *cicerelus* and called *semisquamatus;* and quite recently it has been found by Mr. P. G. Corbin (1950a) in the Plymouth area. These two species have further been placed in a separate genus: *Gymnammodytes.* I must ask the reader to excuse these somewhat specialized details; I introduce them, not just to show the kind of puzzles which often confront the fishery naturalist, but because they are necessary for an appreciation of the true nature of our sand-eel populations which, as we shall now see, turn out to be still more mixed.

The late Dr. D. S. Raitt (1934), of the Scottish Fishery staff, had now discovered another new sand-eel which he named *Ammodytes marinus* and found it to be quite common round the coast from the Hebrides to the Firth of Forth. Still more recently an examination of the young sand-eels in the plankton off Plymouth revealed a fifth kind of which the parent form was then unknown (Corbin and Vidya Vati, 1949); in the following year Corbin (1950b) discovered the adults and named this further new species *A. immaculatus.* Among the young Plymouth sand-eels were also found those of *A. marinus* which had never been seen as an adult in the area before; it all goes to show how elusive, at any rate to man, these sand-eels are. They are all very much alike: little silvery eel-like fish which occur in large shoals in shallow sandy parts of the sea and escape from their predators by diving like a flash into the sand and becoming completely covered.

---

*Plate 15.*  A MORE SOUTHERLY SELECTION
Painted from freshly caught (1, 2, 3 and 6) or living specimens (4, 5, 7-14) from the various localities mentioned in the key to different species given below.

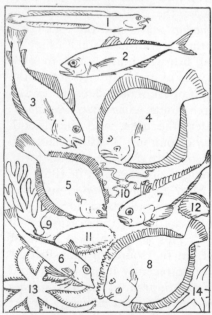

*Fish*

1. Four-bearded rockling, *Onos cimbrius* ($\times\frac{1}{2}$) Aberdeen.
2. Horse-mackerel, *Trachurus trachurus* ($\times\frac{1}{3}$) Aberdeen.
3. Bib or pout, *Gadus luscus* ($\times\frac{1}{4}$) Plymouth.
4. Turbot, *Scophthalmus maximus* ($\times\frac{1}{4}$) Aberdeen.
5. Plaice, *Pleuronectes platessa* ($\times\frac{1}{4}$) Aberdeen.
6. Red gurnard, *Trigla cuculus,* ($\times\frac{1}{4}$) North Shields.
7. Greater weever, *Trachinus draco* ($\times\frac{1}{3}$) Plymouth.
8. Brill, *Scophthalmus rhombus* ($\times\frac{1}{4}$) Plymouth.

*Invertebrates* ($\times\frac{1}{2}$)

9. Sponge, *Axinella polypoides.*
10. Brittle-star, *Ophiothrix fragilis.*
11. Sea-mouse (a bristle-worm), *Aphrodite aculeata.*
12. Queen scallop, *Chlamys opercularis.*
13. Long-armed starfish, *Luidia ciliaris.*
14. Purple variety of the Scarlet Sea-star, *Henricia sanguinolenta.*

Plate 15

Plate 16

Figure 93 (p. 209) shows the new Raitt's sand-eel and its young stages; note that, like all members of the genus, it lacks the pelvic fins—so offering less resistance to slipping into the sand. They are most abundant in the shallow regions round the coast but may also be found on sand banks far out on the continental shelf. The greater sand-eel may reach a length of a foot but the others rarely exceed six inches. The young post-larval sand-eels of almost an inch in length occur in immense numbers in the plankton of the North Sea, often being taken with the young herring of the same size. They form the food of many fish; as I have already said, in spring I have found the stomachs of herrings packed with them. Raitt, after discussing the importance of both young and adult sand-eels in the diet of the haddock, says "other species frequently found gorged with sand-eels include cod, whiting, saithe, gurnards, plaice, sole, flounders, dabs, witches, megrims, turbot and skate." The sand-eels are certainly among the more important fish of our seas; yet we know so very little about them. With the herring and the marine catfish, they are among the very few fish which lay their eggs on the sea-bed. Quite recently the Germans have been fishing for sand-eels with special fine mesh trawls for conversion into fish meal.

*Plate 16.* FISH FROM THE SOUTH-WEST
Painted from living specimens in the Mevagissey Aquarium (Nos. 1-5 and 8-11) and the Plymouth Aquarium (6 and 7). Key to the different species below.

1. Conger-eel, *Conger conger* ($\times \frac{1}{8}$).
2. Common sea-bream, *Pagellus centrodontus* ($\times \frac{1}{4}$).
3. Ballan wrasse, *Labrus bergylta* ($\times \frac{1}{4}$), c.f. other example in Plate 4.
4. Nursehound or greater spotted dog-fish *Scylorhinus stellaris* ($\times \frac{1}{6}$).
5. Bass, *Morone labrax* ($\times \frac{1}{4}$).
6. Rock cock, *Centrolabrus exoletus* ($\times \frac{1}{3}$).
7. Sapphirine gurnard (young form of tub or yellow gurnard) *Trigla lucerna* ($\times \frac{1}{4}$.)
8. Thornback ray, *Raia clavata* ($\times \frac{1}{6}$).
9. Sole, *Solea solea* ($\times \frac{1}{5}$).
10. Spiny spider crab, *Maia squinado* ($\times \frac{1}{4}$).
11. Spiny starfish, *Marthasterias glacialis* ($\times \frac{1}{4}$).

FIG. 94. *a*, the lesser weever *Trachinus vipera; b*, the tompot, *Blennius gattorugine; c*, the butterfly blenny, *B. ocellaris;* and *d*, the pogge, *Agonus cataphractus* (all $\times \frac{1}{2}$).

The lesser weever, *Trachinus vipera* (Fig. 94), is mainly a coastal fish which swims in shallow water with a sandy bottom and feeds largely on shrimps; indeed it is often caught in the shrimp-nets. It does, however, occur at some distance from the coast where there are shallow sandy shoals, as in the southern North Sea; it should therefore be included in our survey, but with a warning to handle with great care—for it stings. The spines on its first dorsal fin and on its operculum are grooved; and these grooves discharge a poison which can be very painful. The greater weever, *T. draco* (Plate 15, p. 210), is a rarer but very handsome fish living in rather deeper water; its striking colours may perhaps be a warning display, for it is even more poisonous. It reaches a length of 17 inches, whereas the lesser weever rarely exceeds 6. Both have the habit of burying themselves in the sand with just their eyes and mouths, which are on the top of their heads, showing above the surface; here they lie in wait for unsuspecting prey.

The gobies in general (Gobiidae) I have left out because they are essentially coastal or shore fishes, but I could not resist the temptation of putting into Plate 3 (p. 34) a striking species which is entirely new to science; so new is it that when I painted it, and indeed now as I write, it has not yet been described and given an official name. I hope and expect that I shall be able to give the name as a footnote before my book is published.[1] It is remarkable that such a novelty could have been living all this time so near to the Plymouth Laboratory and never before recorded; it was discovered swimming in and out of crevices in the rock by Mr. G. R. Forster on one of his "frogman"

[1]It has now been described by Mr. P. G. Corbin (1958), who is naming it after its discoverer, *Gobius forsteri;* it will also be known by the English name of leopard-spotted goby.

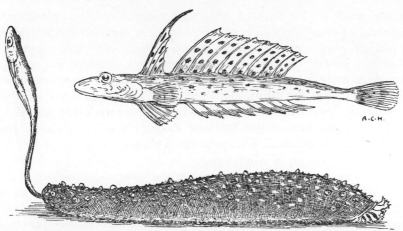

FIG. 95. *Upper left:* a male spotted dragonet, *Callionymus maculatus,* in courtship display. *Lower left:* the fierasfer, *Carapus acus,* just about to enter a sea-cucumber (*Holothuria*) by slipping in tailfirst via the anus (for further explanation see text).

explorations of the sea bottom. All the trawls and nets used so frequently in the area had always failed to catch it.

I have also left out the typical blennies because they, too, are shore fish; two, however, may just be mentioned occurring further off shore: the tompot or gattorugine, *Blennius gattorugine,* which may sometimes be taken in crab pots off the Cornish coast, and the beautiful little butterfly blenny *B. ocellaris,* which is not uncommon to the south west and may be taken on the Eddystone grounds. Both are shown in Fig. 94 opposite. The large and related deepwater catfish has already been mentioned (p. 198) and shown on Plate 13. Then there is the curious little pearl-fish *Carapus dentatus*[1] which until lately has been mainly known in our waters from its young stages being taken in plankton nets; in the last few years, however, a number of specimens have been trawled up from deep water by the Scottish research vessels both to the west and north east of Scotland (Rae and Wilson, 1952, 1953, 1954, 1956). I call it a curious little fish because, like other members of its genus, it has the unusual habit of entering the body of a large sea-cucumber (a soft and sausage-shaped relation of the sea-urchin) by slipping tail first and with great rapidity into its anus. Mr. David Arnold (1953), whilst holding the Oxford Scholarship at Naples, made most interesting observations on the allied species *C. acus.* He demonstrated that the fish is not just seeking shelter inside its host, as was suggested by former writers, but is actually parasitic

[1]=*Fierasfer dentatus.*

upon its gonads. He showed also that *Carapus,* after a planktonic larval stage, passes through a phase when it is completely dependent upon the sea-cucumber and cannot live outside its body; this is followed by the later juvenile and final adult stages when it maintains only an intermittent association with its host. The young fish enters its haven head first, whereas the adult, giving its body a twist to screw itself in, flashes in tail first. Mr. Arnold showed me this remarkable act taking place in an aquarium at the Stazione Zoologica when I visited him there; in Fig. 95, overleaf, I have made a sketch, with the aid of his excellent photographs, of what I saw.

I have kept for the end of the chapter the most beautiful fish of our seas: the dragonets, of which we have three species. At least the males are the most beautiful fish; the females are camouflaged and inconspicuous, perfectly matching their background. Among fish they are the exact counterpart of the peacock or the oriental pheasants among birds: the males, gorgeous in colour and pattern, display in courtship before females of sombre hue. So striking is the difference between the sexes that those of the common dragonet *Callionymus lyra* were for a long time, like the male and female of the cuckoo wrasse, thought to be distinct species; the male in his jewel-like glory was called the gemmeous, and the female the sordid, dragonet. On Plate XXIII (p. 242) are two photographs from a wonderful series of pictures of the courtship of this species taken by Dr. Wilson in the Plymouth Aquarium. The first shows the male displaying before the female. The fins, brilliantly coloured in contrasting bands of canary yellow and vivid blue, are spread to their utmost before the lady, just as is the peacock's train; the first dorsal fin is enormously enlarged and the blue towards the tip passes into shades of violet. I have painted the male displaying before the female in Plate 3 (p. 34). Comparing the two plates, colour and photograph, one should get a good impression of the scene; in the act of display the upper lip is raised up in curious exaggerated pout. The climax comes when the female approaches the male, lies by his right side resting upon his broadly spread pelvic fin and together they rise from the bottom; with the bodies held stiffly together side by side and propelling themselves with their pectoral fins, they sweep upwards in a nuptial swim and the eggs and milt are shed together into the water. Wilson's second photograph has caught them just as they rise from the bottom. Holt (1898) gives a full and most interesting account of the breeding of this species; I cannot resist including the following brief quotation:

"When the two are close together the male gradually raises the fore

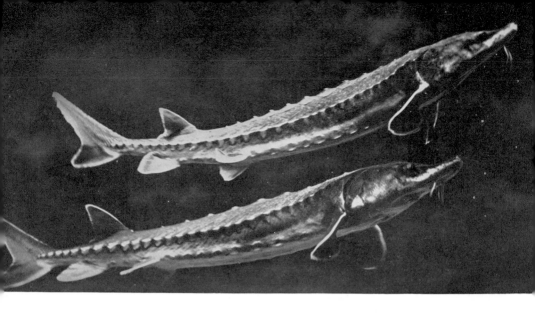

Plate XVII. (*above*) *a.* Two sturgeon (*Acipenser sturio*) photographed with a strong overhead light in the aquarium of the Zoological Society of London (*Hulton Press Limited*). (*below*) *b.* A wreck-fish (*Polyprion americanus*) with a large spider crab (*Maia squinado*), photographed in the Plymouth Aquarium. (*Douglas Wilson*)

*Plate XVIII.* A study in camouflage: a young angler fish (*Lophius piscatorius*) lying on shell-gravel. (*Douglas Wilson*)

part of his body off the bottom by the action of his pectorals, at the same time elevating the hind part of his second dorsal and anal. The female, whose pelvics are rigidly expanded, places one of them on that of the male, and squeezes herself snugly into the hollow between his gill-cover and pectoral and pelvic fins . . . It is impossible to resist the simile of a lady taking a gentleman's arm."

The common dragonet just described is indeed quite a common fish in moderately shallow water all round the British Isles; it is seen in its best courtship colours in spring and early summer. Like the cuckoo wrasse, the male can intensify its colour to a remarkable degree in the actual act of courtship; when not displaying the fins are folded away out of sight and it becomes almost as inconspicuous as the female. The male of the second species, *C. maculatus,* the spotted dragonet, has a pattern of prominent spots on the dorsal fin which, when erected, places the spots into horizontal bands as seen in Fig. 95 (p. 213); whereas the third species, *C. reticulatus,* has a different system of spots on the corresponding fin so arranged that they produce vertical bands when the fin is raised in display, as shown in Fig. 3 of Plate 3. These two species are much rarer than the common *lyra,* in fact the last has only recently been recorded as a British fish since H-W. Chang (1951) published an account of it in the English Channel: another surprising addition to our fauna.

CHAPTER 11

# HAKE, HADDOCK, COD AND CO.

THIS chapter, which completes our survey of the bony fish—indeed of all our fish—deals with the British representatives of one large and notable group: the Gadiformes or cod-like fish (sometimes called the Anacanthini—the fish without spines). It includes those commercially very valuable species like the cod, haddock, hake, ling, saithe and whiting. The first three at least deserve a consideration like that we gave the herring and the plaice, on account of their ecological as well as economic importance; space, however, is so short that we must be content with a briefer treatment. Three families are generally recognised: the deepwater grenadier fish (Macruridae), the hake family (Merlucciidae) and then all the rest (Gadidae).[1] We will leave the unusual and specialized grenadiers till the last and begin with the hake.

The hake, *Merluccius merluccius,* is a large fish reaching a length of 4 feet, but smaller specimens of 2 or 3 feet are more usual on the market, especially at the present day when fishing is so intense. Its general appearance, with the number and arrangement of fins, is shown in Fig. 100 (p. 230) and its colour in Plate 12 (p. 141); we see that it lacks the barbel which distinguishes so many of the cod family, but, like most members, its pelvic fins have moved forwards to be in front of the pectorals. It has a large mouth and its prominent sharp teeth have elastic hinges like those of the angler; they turn over to allow objects to pass inwards, but at once spring back to form sharp barbs if there is any movement outwards. It is a swift and voracious hunter feeding upon small fish and oceanic squids over the deepwater of the continental shelf, and along its edge, from Norway in the north to Madeira in the south; it is found also throughout the Mediterranean.

The world distribution of the hake genus *Merluccius* is interesting. There are distinct species one on each side of the North Atlantic, two other species one on each side of the South Atlantic, separate species on the Pacific coasts of North and South America and yet another around New Zealand. They are all fish of the continental shelf isolated from one another east and west by the deep oceans or land masses, and north and south by temperature barriers; none of them enters the tropics. Dr. J. T. Hart (1948) has given us a valuable review of the general biology of the whole genus.

Our own hake (*merluccius*) gives rise to a very important trawl fishery from the two west coast ports of Milford Haven and Fleetwood; in earlier days they were caught largely by line, but now, taking the United Kingdom as a whole, some 500,000 cwt. are landed in a year by trawlers as compared with only some 9,000 cwt. caught by line. The great advances in our knowledge of this species and the state of its fishery are almost entirely due to tireless researches carried out by Dr. C. F. Hickling when he was a naturalist on the staff of the Ministry of Fisheries Laboratory;[2] the results from his more technical papers are brought together for the general naturalist in his excellent *The Hake and the Hake Fishery* (1934). To gain this knowledge he sailed with the English trawlermen on some 60 voyages, as well as making many

---

[1] Dr. Tucker tells me that a recent and important work by Dr. A. N. Svetovidov of Leningrad is likely to have a very drastic effect on our naming and classification of the Gadiform fishes.

[2] He is now Fisheries Adviser to the Colonial Office.

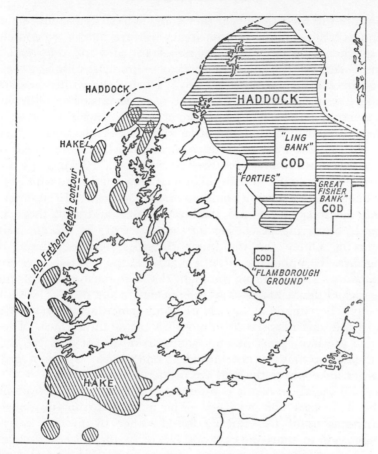

FIG. 96. A chart showing the approximate areas of the spawning grounds of the haddock (horizontal shading), hake (oblique shading) and cod (open rectangles). Re drawn, omitting some detail, from *Sea Fisheries: Their Investigation in the United Kingdom* (Graham, 1956).

special cruises in research ships; referring to his life with the fishermen he says "he has never experienced anything but comradeship, hospitality and help from them in conditions at all times difficult, and occasionally rough."

The main catches of hake are made by trawlers in the daytime, very much smaller ones being taken during the night. They are fish which feed at night in mid-water—some indeed come very nearly up to the surface—and then they all go down to the bottom to rest during the day. In the first year or two of their lives the young hake feed mainly on planktonic crustaceans, particularly upon the krill (euphausiacean shrimps), but in their third year they come to feed almost entirely upon fish and oceanic squids. Bottom living fish are hardly ever found in their stomachs; by far their most important prey are the small blue whiting *Gadus poutassou* which must occur in immense numbers over the edge of the continental slope (p. 229). During the winter and spring the hake live in deep water from 90 to 300 fathoms or more down the slope, swimming up each night to feed on these blue whiting, on younger members of their own kind and upon squid. It is somewhat surprising to be told that the hake is so much a cannibal that 21 per cent of its food consists of its younger brethren; "but", says Hickling, "I do not see why a hake should see any difference between a blue whiting, say, and a smaller hake, when it comes to making a meal." In summer and autumn the hake move into shallower water and feed more upon mackerel, horse mackerel, herring and garfish; or in the Minch, between the Outer and the Inner Hebrides, Hickling found them feeding heavily upon the little pollack-whiting (or Norway pout), *G. esmarkii* (p. 228). During the night the hake must scatter through a wide range of depth in search of prey for in the old days of line fishing they might be caught at any depth; and sometimes they have been taken in trammel nets set for salmon just below the surface. The fish on which the hake prey, like the young hake themselves, feed largely upon the krill so that it is not unusual to find concentrations of medium and larger hake where the krill are particularly abundant.

Like all members of the cod family and most other bottom-living fish the hake lays floating eggs. The main spawning-grounds and breeding-seasons of fish can be found either by making extensive townet surveys to chart the eggs and fry, or by the less costly means of examining vast numbers of mature fish to find out when and where those with roes just ripe for discharging their eggs are found. Dr. Hickling followed the latter course and, after examining and weighing the reproductive organs of over 12,000 fish, found that the main spawning period was from April to July and the principal regions those shown in Fig. 96 overleaf. A good sized female may produce from a half to two million eggs a year. During spring and summer he found that there were peaks of higher landings of fish at regular monthly intervals suggesting that the hake has a monthly breeding period when the fish come together in greater concentration; these periods, however, do not show a lunar periodicity, for in some years they come with the full moon and in others with the new. At the end of the breeding season, the catches of large and medium fish decline.

To return, however, to the floating eggs, the tiny fry hatch out and drift eastwards with the moving waters into shallower regions; and as their yolk is used up they must begin to feed on the plankton. This, as we have already seen (p. 166), is one of the most critical phases in a fish's life; they begin to feed on the very small crustaceans, small copepods and larvae in the plankton (Lebour, 1920). They reach a length of 4 inches in 12 to 15 months and at the end of their second year go down to the bottom during the daytime like the adults. The age of a hake can be told from its otoliths as already explained for the plaice (p. 168). They increase in length at an average of 3½ inches a year; but weight is more important: from the third to the seventh year the hake roughly doubles its weight every year. At 10 years old the hake has grown to a length of 2½ to 3 feet. Since the early days of the century there has been a marked decline in the proportion of larger fish in the catches; this is a sure sign of intensive fishing, and most likely over-fishing, but that is the subject for a later chapter (p. 247).

Now we come to the great cod family, the Gadidae, which, even after leaving out five extreme rarities from the Atlantic deeps to the west of Ireland, are represented by upwards of nineteen species in our waters. The general form of such fish is familiar to everyone, and is well shown in the photograph of the cod in Plate XXIV, (p. 243). Let us first take the members of the genus *Gadus*, to which the cod belongs. They can be distinguished from those of other genera in the family by having *three* dorsal and *two* anal fins; there are ten species, which we will briefly distinguish before discussing any features of their biology. I am following the convenient arrangement of Jenkins. Six of the ten possess a barbel, a sensory process which hangs down, or may be extended forwards, from the lower lip. Four of these species have the upper jaw larger than the lower; they are the cod, *Gadus callarias*,[1] green-yellow with a number of dark spots and a white lateral line (Plate 12, p. 141); the haddock, *G. aeglefinus*, grey with a prominent black blotch on the shoulder and a black lateral line (also Plate 12); the bib or pout, *G. luscus*, very deep in the body and copper-coloured, with some dark irregular bands (Plate 15, p. 210) and the poor cod, *G. minutus*, similar to the last, but smaller and not so deep in shape and brownish-yellow with no bands (Plate 14, p. 195). Then come the two species which have a barbel but whose lower jaw is larger than the upper one: the coal-fish or saithe, *G. virens* (Plate 13, p. 194) with skin very dark on top, almost black, but lateral line white and the teeth in the upper jaw all about the same size; and the pollack-whiting, or Norway pout as it is sometimes called, *G. esmarkii*, with the teeth on the outer margin of the upper jaw stronger than the others—a little fish of a beautiful golden colour (Plate 14). Now we come to those members

[1] =*G. morrhua*.

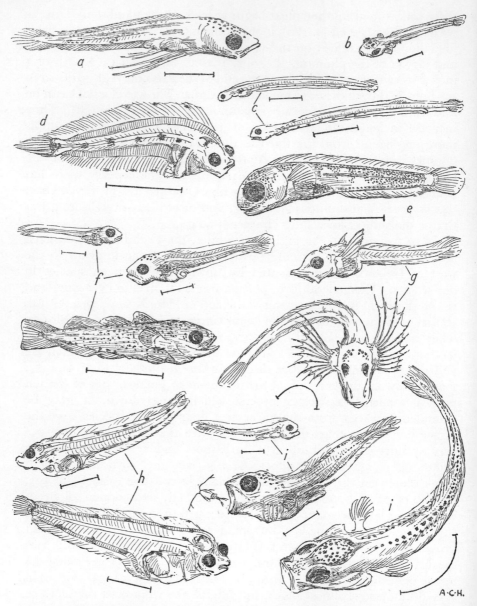

FIG. 97. Young fish from the plankton, with lines showing natural size: *a*, ling; *b*, mackerel; *c*, herring; *d*, witch; *e*, catfish; *f*, haddock; *g*, gurnard; *h*, lemon dab; *i*, cod. Drawn from specimens kindly given me by Mr. Alan Saville of the Scottish Marine (Fisheries) Laboratory at Aberdeen. (For Fig. 97*j*, see next page).

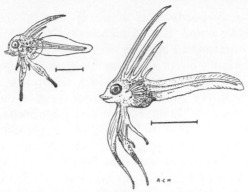

FIG. 97j. Young stages of the angler fish (*Lophius piscatorius*).

of the genus which have no barbel: the whiting, *G. merlangus,* with silvery sides and a black spot at the root of the pectoral fins (Plate 12); and the pollack, *G. pollachius,* dull green with a lower jaw longer than the upper (Plate 13); the blue whiting, *G. poutassou,* which is like a whiting, but has a very long first anal fin, and is smaller (Plate 14); and the silvery cod, *G.* ( =*Gadiculus*) *argenteus,* which lives in deep water over the edge of the continental shelf (Plate 14).

The cod is undoubtedly the most important demersal food-fish of our seas, and not only round the British Isles, but in the Arctic waters of Iceland, Northern Norway and Bear Island; then, of course, on the western side of the Atlantic the great line-fishery for cod on the New-foundland Banks has been an attraction since the end of the sixteenth century for fishermen of many nations, particularly the French. Tagging experiments with fish in different areas show that extensive migrations may on occasion be made; journeys have been recorded, for example, linking the stocks of Newfoundland and Greenland with those of Iceland and again those of Iceland and Bear Island with those of northern Norway. There is evidence, however, as Graham (1948) shows, that our North Sea cod are to a large extent separated from other populations. Just as Dr. Hickling gave us our knowledge of the hake, so has Mr. Michael Graham, also of the Ministry of Fisheries and now its Director of Research[1], given us most of our natural history of the North Sea cod; in more recent years he has made many voyages to the north leading the Ministry's investigations into the biology of the Arctic cod. Here we will only be concerned with the North Sea stocks and what I am now writing comes largely from his work.[2]

[1] Just retired, and succeeded by Mr. R. S. Wimpenny.
[2] Graham *et al.* (1924); Graham, Carruthers and Goodchild (1926); Graham 1934, 1948).

A large cod may produce as many as four million eggs at one spawning. We have noted that all members of this family lay floating eggs; their little transparent spheres drift with the moving waters and develop into the young fry in the same manner as those of the plaice and hake which we have already followed. February to April is the spawning period and the principal areas are those of the Great Fisher and Ling Banks, and the Long Forties and Flamborough grounds as indicated by the rectangles in Fig. 96 (p. 217); these have been determined by the charting of eggs and fry caught in plankton nets and from the landings of ripe and spawning fish. The fry, which are only $\frac{1}{4}$ of an inch long when they hatch, spend about $2\frac{1}{2}$ months as members of the plankton, and are subject to the same hazards of shortage of food or excessive abundance of predators as are the young of other species; they feed almost entirely upon the small crustaceans (copepods) of the plankton. The fry of the cod and some other planktonic young fish are shown in Fig. 97 overleaf. During this period the circulating currents keep them within the North Sea and when they are just over $\frac{3}{4}$ inch long they seek the bottom. Once on the sea-bed, they are extremely difficult to catch, especially as the nursery regions contain a good deal of rough ground. To illustrate the labours of the marine naturalists in piecing together the life-story of a fish, let me quote from Graham regarding this phase:

"Our direct catches of cod at this stage have been meagre. Three voyages of the *George Bligh* only yielded eighty specimens from many hauls, although we were working in the area where the work on the pelagic stages showed that countless numbers of little cod must have made bottom. One way of catching them was to bring on board quantities of "sea-mat" (*Flustra*) or "curly weed" (*Alcyonidium*) and pick it over by hand,[1]"

Still feeding upon crustacea, but now the bottom-living amphipods, isopods and little crabs, the young cod grow quickly on the typical nursery grounds and begin to be caught by the commercial trawlers when they are $1\frac{1}{2}$ to 2 years old and from 12 to 14 inches in length; in some deeper regions of the North Sea, however, growth is slower and they may not enter the fishery till they are 3 years old. The age of a cod is generally told from its scales and not its otolith; the annual rings on a scale are clearly shown in Fig. 15 (p. 34). Cod do not begin breeding until they are about five years old and have reached a length of some 27 inches. To give an idea of the abundance and

[1]*Flustra* and *Alcyonidium* are not plants but polyzoan colonies (p.99).

Plate XIX.  More camouflage:  (above) a.  The plaice (Pleuronectes platessa).
(below) b.  The turbot (Scophthalmus maximus) (Douglas Wilson)

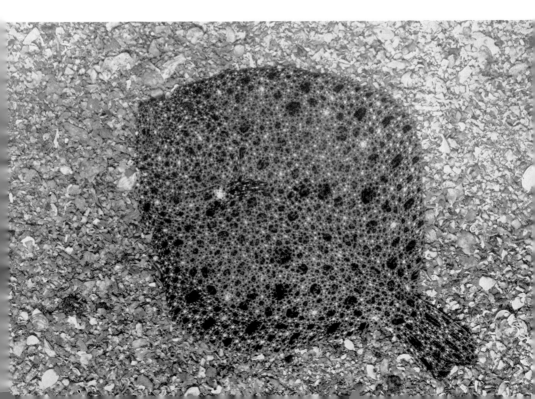

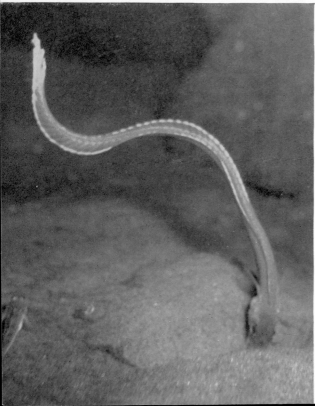

Plate XX. (above) a. The boar fish (Capros aper). (below) b. The red band-fish (Cepola rubescens) sucking sand into its mouth in the process of making a burrow.     (Douglas Wilson)

distribution of the cod in the North Sea, I reproduce, overleaf, in Fig. 98, charts showing the quantities caught per 100 hours fishing by steam-trawlers in different areas.

Adult cod feed mainly upon fish, particularly herring, mackerel, small haddock and sand-eels, but they also take molluscs, crustaceans and bristle-worms to a lesser extent. There is a marked contrast between the feeding of the cod and that of its very near relative, the haddock. This is interesting in view of the well-established rule that two closely allied species cannot remain competing with one another in the same habitat; one, if only slightly the more efficient, will surely eliminate the other. The cod and haddock exist together on the same grounds, but have distinctly different food-preferences. Whereas the cod takes mainly fish, the haddock, except for sand-eels, feeds almost entirely upon invertebrates: bristle-worms, crustacea, molluscs and particularly brittle-stars and small sea-urchins. Haddock also, it will be remembered (p. 51), collect in numbers to gorge themselves on the masses of herring-spawn deposited on the sea-bed.

Homans and Needler (1946) writing of the haddock in Nova Scotian waters make some interesting remarks on its feeding. "It is evident", they say "that to obtain much of their food haddock root around in the bottom somewhat in the manner of a pig" and they refer to the frequent presence of mud, gravel and sand in their stomachs. They then make an interesting comparison of hake, cod and haddock in the matter of feeding. I quote them as follows:

"We have seen that haddock food is limited to rather small slow-moving animals found close to or burrowing in the bottom . . . Cod and hake taken in the same trawls eat larger and more quickly moving animals—even considering only fish of comparable size. The nature of the mouths of these three species is significant. The mouths of hake and cod are much larger than those of haddock and practically if not absolutely terminal. They are provided with sharp teeth and all the mouth parts are strong. Haddock, on the other hand, have small mouths placed ventrally to quite a degree. Their mouth parts are soft and teeth ordinarily dull. They are, however, provided with better developed muscular lips. Cod and hake are well provided for the capture of large or fast-moving objects. But haddock with their smaller ventrally placed mouths are . . . best fitted for picking small animals off or out of the bottom . . . In addition, the heaviest built portion of the haddock is the anterior part of the body and it may be that this helps them to remain more easily in a forwardly tilted position while feeding."

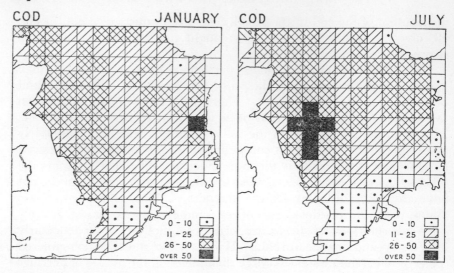

FIG. 98. Distribution of cod in the North Sea: charts showing the average quantities, in hundredweights per 100 hours fishing, caught in these standard rectangular areas during January and July (1920-1935) by steam trawlers landing at British ports, compiled from statistics published by the Ministry of Agriculture and Fisheries.

The haddock (Plate 12, p. 141) is perhaps commercially second in importance to the cod among the trawl-caught fish. It is very abundant in the North Sea, particularly in the northern half, and further north to the Faeroes, Iceland and Barents Sea; but it does not go as far north towards Spitsbergen as does the cod. On the western side of the Atlantic the haddock is also abundant on the coastal banks from Cape Cod to the Cabot Strait, and large concentrations are found on the southern half of the Grand Banks of Newfoundland. The charts of the catches of haddock given in Fig. 99, opposite, may be compared with those of the cod (Fig. 98) and the earlier ones given for the plaice (Fig. 79, p. 169) to show the relative abundance of these three species in the bottom-living community of the North Sea.

It is the naturalists of the Scottish Fishery Department's Laboratory at Aberdeen who have given us our natural history of the haddock: notably Dr. Harold Thompson (1923, 1928, 1929), the late Dr. D. S. Raitt (1936, 1939) and Mr. Basil Parrish (1949, 1950). My information is from these sources and the Buckland Lectures recently given by Mr. Parrish; these lectures, which will be published

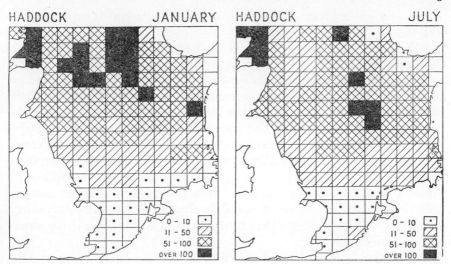

FIG. 99. Distribution of haddock in the North Sea, charts from data similar to those for cod in the previous figure.

shortly, will most conveniently bring together the information from many papers. The main spawning period, like that of the cod, is from February to April. The haddock is smaller than the cod, becomes mature much earlier, when only 2 years old, and is less prolific; a two-year old fish of about 10 inches will produce some 30,000 eggs, a three-year old (a foot long) some 100,000 and a six-year old (only about 16 inches) some 280,000. Haddocks in the trade category "extra large", over 2 feet in length, are to-day rare; occasionally, however, much larger "jumbos" are caught and Day cites a remarkable specimen of 37 inches taken in Dublin Bay. For both cod and haddock there is quite a marked difference in the growth rates of fish from the northern and southern halves of the North Sea; in the north a 5-year old haddock will have an average length of only $12\frac{1}{2}$ inches, whereas in the south one of the same age will measure $15\frac{1}{2}$. The sea-bed to the south is a good deal warmer than that of the north not simply on account of the difference in latitude but because of one in depth. The deeper water of the north is cut off in summer from the warmer zones by the formation of a discontinuity layer;[1] in the much shallower south, where the water is more disturbed, no marked separation of

[1]As explained in Part I, p. 59.

upper and lower layers takes place and so the sea-bed is kept warmer and the fish grow more quickly.

The main spawning grounds of the haddock are shown with those of the cod and hake in Fig. 96 (p. 217); spawning takes place at various points in the very large area shown over the northern North Sea and in a much smaller isolated patch just north of the Outer Hebrides. It is still not known to what extent the Hebridean spawners are linked to the main North Sea stock. The positions of spawning within the large area are not fixed; their centres shift from place to place in different years. While we do not yet know the causes of these movements, they may well be linked with the year to year changes in the influx of Atlantic water. Then again there is a northern movement among haddock as they get older; if the spawning stock is relatively young, spawning will be concentrated further to the south than if the stock were an older one.

Until the little embryo fish begin to produce their characteristic pigment it is exceedingly difficult to distinguish the eggs of the haddock from those of the cod, and they are often found floating together. They drift and develop as do those of the cod but the fry stay up in the plankton longer and so do not seek the bottom till they are over 2 inches long. The young stages of both are shown in Fig. 97 (p. 220). As with the cod, the great North Sea eddy normally keeps the haddock fry from being carried out of the area and off the continental shelf. Since the young haddock are larger than the young cod when they first settle down to a bottom-living life they can be caught more easily. By using special small mesh trawls or standard trawls with their ends covered with small-mesh shrimp netting, Harold Thompson, in the early 1920's, began to make surveys of the relative abundance of the young fry on the sea-bed in different years. He found most striking fluctuations and was able to show that the years of good broods were not necessarily those in which there were good stocks of spawning adults. Once again, as with other fish, there was good evidence that the success or failure of the broods was determined by something happening during their drifting life as eggs or larvae. From his surveys of the quantities of the newly-settled young he was now able successfully to forecast the state of the stocks of older haddock and so the success of the fishery a year or two in advance. This has been continued and is a notable practical result from research; trawler owners, warned ahead of the coming good or poor years of haddock fishing, can adjust the deployment of their vessels accordingly. Very wide fluctuations have been found; for example, 1920, 1923, 1928, 1931, 1935 and 1945 were all years in which the brood survival was

*Plate XXI.* The courtship of the cuckoo wrasse (*Labrus ossifagus*). (*above*) *a*. A male biting and worrying a female in his attempt to attract her attention and lead her to the nest; the blanched area of the male only slightly developed. A second female looks on in top right-hand corner. (*below*) *b*. The male displaying above the nest (blanched area fully developed) while the female looks on. Coloured drawings of these fish are shown in Plate 4 (p. 35)                                   (*Douglas Wilson*)

*Plate XXII.* The nesting behaviour of the black sea-bream (*cautharus spondyliosoma*). (*above*) *a*. The male guarding the " nest " which is the area of slate cleared of gravel; thousands of eggs stuck to the slate form a large whitish patch below the fish. (*below*) *b*. The male chasing a plaice off the " nest ". Photographed in the aquarium at Plymouth.　　　　　　　　　　　　　　　　　　　　　　　　　　　　(*Douglas Wilson*)

far above the average whereas in 1922, 1937 and 1946 it was very low.

Can we explain these fluctuations? For many years now Dr. J. N. Carruthers has been considering the possibility of variations in the wind influencing the brood survival of fish. Changes from year to year in the strength and direction of the wind over several months, before or at the time of larval drift, may, he believes, so affect the water movement as to carry the eggs and larvae sometimes into conditions that are better for their survival and sometimes into those that are worse. He and his collaborators have written a number of papers showing some apparently remarkable correlations between wind and brood survival for a number of fish including herring, haddock, cod and plaice;[1] their results, however, have come in for some criticism and have not yet been generally accepted. Now, Dr. K. M. Rae, who until recently directed the plankton recorder survey from the Edinburgh Oceanographic Laboratory,[2] has published some new and independent evidence (1957). Using a particular species of plankton animal, the copepod *Metridia lucens*, as an indicator of the flow of Atlantic water down the western side of the North Sea, he shows how its distance off the Scottish coast in late autumn from year to year can be correlated on the one hand with the strength and direction of the wind which may be deflecting the water from the coast, and on the other with the success or failure of the haddock broods. For some years now he has successfully predicted the state of the haddock broods before they have settled down on the bottom and been surveyed. This, if confirmed, will be a great step forward. For one thing it will enable us to make the prediction of the state of the future haddock stocks a year earlier than Thompson could from his survey of the newly-settled fish and, secondly, it will link the brood survival with some factor in the Atlantic water which can be indicated by the plankton and that in turn with the wind which influences its movement. Several pieces of our ecological puzzle look as if they were about to fall into place.

We must turn now to the other members of the genus *Gadus*. The bib or pout *G. luscus* (Plate 15), is small, rarely over a foot long, and not an important commercial fish, although by no means uncommon round our coasts. It is a more southern species and is said to be more abundant on the coasts of France and Spain. The poor-cod (Plate 14), as its name *G. minutus* implies, is the smallest of all our gadoid fish, rarely exceeding 8 inches in length; it is common all round the British Isles but rather more so in the south. Off Plymouth it is

[1]Carruthers (1950); Carruthers, Lawford and Veley (1951).
[2]Described in Part I, p. 309.

said to be "probably the commonest gadoid on the trawling grounds".[1]
The coal-fish, or saithe, *G. virens* (Plate 13) is a large gadoid reaching
some 3½ feet in length, common in the North Sea and extending its
range up the coast of Norway, but not going so far north as the cod.
The young fish tend to congregate along the coasts, but the adults
spread widely over the sea-bed. It is thought more of in Scandinavia
than in this country, but is now becoming increasingly popular in our
fried fish shops. The pollack-whiting, or Norway pout, *G. esmarkii*,
(Plate 14) is a small northern fish, very common off the north-west of
Scotland, the Faeroes and the coasts of Norway.

Among the four members of the genus *Gadus* which lack the barbel,
the whiting, *G. merlangus*, (Fig. 9, p. 27; also Plate 12) is the most
notable. It forms a considerable part of the catch of North Sea trawlers
and seiners and is also abundant in the Channel and Irish Sea;
indeed it is the most important demersal species for the fishermen of
Northern Ireland. Comparatively little has been written about this fish
so that a recent paper by the Scottish workers, R. W. Ellis and R. Jones
(1956), is particularly welcome. The catches in the North Sea have
indeed been increasing since the war and in 1952 it has been estimated
that the total European catch for human consumption from this area
was 73,000 tons with, in addition, some 20,000 tons of smaller fish taken
for fishmeal. The whiting spawns principally in April and May
throughout the northern North Sea, but mainly within the 50 fathom
line. In their pelagic phase, after reaching ¾ inch in length, the young
whiting, as described in our earlier volume (p. 128), associate with jelly-
fish, particularly *Cyanea*, which become very abundant in June; they
shelter under the bell and appear to swim among the tentacles without
coming to any harm.[2] When almost 2½ inches in length they go down
to the bottom. In their first two years they are found in greatest
numbers between the latitudes of 55° and 57°N. In some of the older

[1] *The Plymouth Marine Fauna* (1957).

[2] Large numbers of the amphipod *Hyperia galba* also live under jellyfish of several
kinds, probably robbing them of their food. In writing of the young whiting in
Part I I have said that I wondered if perhaps they came to the jellyfish to feed on
these amphipods and went on to say "but this can hardly be so, for they have been
observed swimming round the medusae and darting underneath for shelter." I have
now heard from Mr. A. K. Nagabhushanam, who is making a study of the feeding
of gadoid fish at Port Erin in the Isle of Man, that he finds *Hyperia* indeed forming
a substantial part of the food of such young fish and that, on one occasion, he has
taken as many as 59 young whiting and 3 young cod from under a single jellyfish
(*Rhizostoma*) of some 17 inches diameter (43 cm.). He also picked 22 *Hyperia* from it.
It may be that the young whiting also rob the plankton-feeding jellyfish of their
food, for he also finds them with the copepods *Temora*, *Pseudocalanus* and *Calanus* in
their stomachs. They normally take planktonic crustacea, but here may be a
concentrated supply being collected for them.

books the whiting was said to be a shallow water species, and to be more abundant in the southern North Sea; more recently, however—certainly since the middle 1930's—the heavier catches of adult fish have been made in latitudes to the north of Aberdeen. Like the hake and cod, the whiting feeds largely upon smaller fish, but at times may also take large quantities of the more active swimming crustaceans, such as shrimps, prawns, mysids and euphausiids. Jones (1954) from an examination of a great many stomach contents places sand-eels and the small pollack-whiting as their most frequent prey in the northern North Sea. He contrasts the habits of this fish with the more benthic feeding of the haddock.[1]

The pollack, *G. pollachius*, (Plate 13), is more a coastal fish than any other member of the genus and sometimes it may be taken near the surface when fishing for mackerel; it is common all round Britain but is never important commercially. The blue whiting, *G. poutassou* (Plate 14), lives over the deep water off the edge of the continental shelf; it is rarely taken in trawls, but is clearly present in very large numbers for it forms, as we have seen, the principal food of the hake. Further evidence of its great abundance to the west has come from the plankton recorder survey to which I have just referred; lines run to the west of Ireland have revealed heavy concentrations of the fry of this species (Henderson, 1957). The adults must mainly inhabit the mid-water layers; when fast pelagic trawls are successfully developed to fish at various depths, this species may well become of direct economic value. The little silvery pout *G. ( =Gadiculus) argenteus*, (Plate 14) is an even more deep-water species and relatively rare immediately around our islands.

Fish in the next cod-family group have two dorsal fins of which the first is short and the second very long; and they have one long anal fin. Three genera come into this category. In one the fish have very long bodies and minute scales: the lings, *Molva molva*, the common ling (Plate 13), and two close but rare relatives.[2] The common form is a species reaching a large size, up to 6, and occasionally nearly 7, feet in length; it inhabits deep water from 50 to 100 fathoms to the west of the British Isles and off the continental shelf of Norway. Commercially

---

[1] As I was revising this chapter for the press I was particularly pleased, when acting as external examiner at the University of Aberdeen, to find a student, Douglas Raitt, the son of the late Dr. Raitt (referred to on pp. 210 and 224) following in his father's footsteps by making, when still an undergraduate, an excellent comparison of the food taken by whiting and haddock caught in the same trawl hauls. He shows again, as with the cod and haddock, that there is no competition between the two on the same ground, because their food is so different.

[2] *Molva byrkelange*, the blue ling in deep water off the west of Britain and off Norway, and *M. elongata*, the Mediterranean ling in deep water south-west of Ireland.

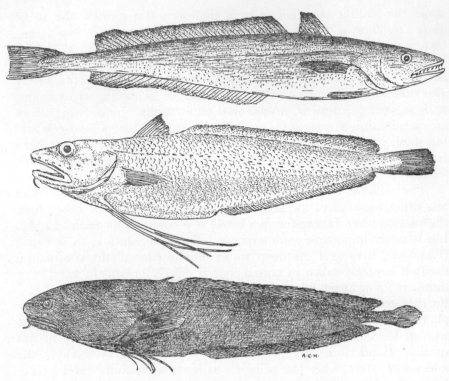

FIG. 100. *a*, the hake *Merluccius merluccius* (for colour see Plate 12, p. 141); *b*, the greater fork-beard, *Urophycis blennoides; c*, the lesser fork-beard, *Raniceps raninus.*

it is a valuable fish and is caught as much by long-lining as by trawling. The second genus in this group is represented by the greater fork-beard, *Urophycis blennoides* which is seen in Fig. 100 above. It is easily distinguished by its pelvic fins which are very far forward, long and divided, so that each forms a conspicuous double filament; these are no doubt sensory and used for searching the bottom for food as are the barbels of many other fish. It is a deep water Atlantic species, only occasionally being taken in our waters, but may sometimes enter the North Sea in winter.[1] In the third genus the first dorsal fin is quite rudimentary; there is only one member, the lesser fork-beard *Raniceps raninus,* also in Fig. 100. It has a somewhat flattened and fleshy head. It occurs off rocky coasts, but is not very common.

Next in the cod family is a group characterized by having two dorsal fins of which the first is very narrow and sunk in a groove, and

[1]The much rarer *U. chuss* (see Goode and Bean, 1895) has also been recorded.

by having barbels on their upper lip as well as on their chin; these are the rocklings, and we shall only just mention them because they are coastal fish. There are three species[1] *Onos tricirratus*, *O. cimbrius* (Plate 15) and *O. mustelus*, being the three-, four- and five-bearded rocklings having two, three and four upper barbels respectively, in addition to a lower one each. To end this family there is a genus with one species which has only one dorsal fin and one anal one, both being very long: this is the torsk or tusk, *Brosme brosme*, shown in Plate 5 (p. 82). It is a northern fish occurring in the waters round the Faeroes, Shetland and north of Scotland, and is frequently fished for by line. When the specimen I painted came up in the trawl on the edge of the Norway deeps (p. 200) I was astonished to see its colours. I made a very rapid colour sketch straight away and it was lucky I did so; within twenty minutes almost all trace of the blue had gone and the yellow was but a faint impression. The thin outer margin to the fins was quite a bright, almost sky, blue, whereas the broad bands between the yellow on the body were of a much more delicate lavender shade.

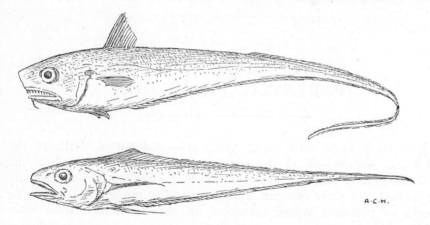

FIG. 101. Deepwater grenadier fish (Macruridae): *Malacocephalus laevis* with *Bathygadus melanobranchus* below it, (both × ⅓). Drawn at the British Museum (N.H.)

Finally we come to the curious deep water grenadiers or rat-tailed fish of the family Macruridae which live down on the lower parts of the continental slope. *Malacocephalus laevis*, which is shown in Fig. 101 above, is often taken in large numbers in the deepest trawl-hauls. when fishing for hake to the south west of Ireland. *Bathygadus melanobranchus* is another allied form from the same region. The

[1]Dr. Tucker tells me that he is at present engaged upon a revision of the British rocklings and that considerable changes will almost certainly be made.

macrurids all have the same curious tapering body which is very characteristic of bottom-living fish of the abyssal regions; their shape reminds us of *Chimaera* (p. 189) which also extends far down the slope. In the deep water of the Arctic Ocean, which is separated from that of the Atlantic by the Wyville-Thomson Ridge (referred to in Part I, p. 220), we get no macrurids but their place is taken by species of the genus *Lycodes*,[1] which are really members of the family Zoarchidae, and these too have the same tapering form. We do not know the reason for this curious shape so peculiar to deep water fish, but, because of its prevalence, it must have some special significance. Dr. Hickling, who found many specimens of *M. laevis* when studying the hake out on trawlers to the west, described a gland on their underside, between the pelvic fins, which secretes a luminous fluid (1925); Harvey, in his book *Bioluminescence* (1952), quotes Osorio (1912) who says that Portuguese fishermen rub fragments of dogfish on the belly of this fish and so obtain a bait which remains luminous for many hours.

CHAPTER 12

# PARASITIC PROFUSION

WE HAVE been considering three great categories of life in the sea: the worlds of the plankton, of the benthos and of the swimming fish; there is, however, another category perhaps equally important, yet more obscure and consequently much less known: the world of parasites whose members are mostly hidden from view within their hosts.

A test sometimes set in an examination in practical zoology is to ask the candidates to investigate a given animal for parasites, to report on the various kinds found and make mounted preparations of them for microscopic study. The animal provided might be a frog or a fish. A candidate who could find only four different kinds of parasite would be unlucky. In a frog he might have found three different species of flukes (trematode flatworms): one kind in its lungs, another in its intestine and yet another in its bladder; he should also have found

[1] By this I don't mean to imply that the genus *Lycodes* is confined to the north polar basin.

thread worms in the lungs and at least two or three kinds of protozoa in the intestine and rectum, with perhaps another protozoan (a trypanosome) in the blood. These are just the commoner kinds. There must be very few adult animals of the size of a small fish (or larger) which do not harbour at least two or three different kinds of parasite. When we consider this, and that every host may carry several of each kind, we begin to realise a fact of nature which at first seems to us most extraordinary: the number of animals we see living freely in the world—making up what we call the typical fauna of this and that habitat—is actually far smaller than the number living tucked away in their insides.

The Hon. Miriam Rothschild and Dr. Theresa Clay in their brilliant *Fleas, Flukes and Cuckoos* (New Naturalist Series, 1952) show us the wealth of parasites of birds, and in doing so, give us an excellent introduction to parasitism in general. I cannot resist quoting the following paragraph, for it is such a striking illustration of what I have just been saying:

> "Their feathers are eaten and sometimes completely destroyed by lice and mites. The superficial layers of their skin and its waxy exudation are devoured by certain flies. Mites and tongue-worms also invade the nasal cavities, the bronchial tubes, air sacs and lungs and feed upon their secretions. Fleas, lice, mosquitoes, midges, bugs, leeches and ticks suck their blood from outside. Protozoa (one-celled organisms), such as the malaria parasite, destroy the red blood corpuscles from inside the body. Other Protozoa, the trypanosomes, are found in the bone-marrow and lymph vessels, and flagellates swarm in the crop and mouth. Varieties of worms are located in almost every organ of the body, the subcutaneous tissues, the muscles, the eye, the brain, the trachea, liver, kidneys, gall-bladder, bile-duct, reproductive organs and the alimentary canal. Leeches fix themselves inside the vent and sometimes in the throat-pouches of pelicans."

All these creatures are not, of course, carried by every bird, but the numbers of just a few kinds found on one bird may be very great. These authors, after recording striking examples of over 10,000 nematode worms being taken from the intestine of a grouse and more than 1,000 feather lice from the plumage of a curlew, quote a saying about birds made by the late Sir Arthur Shipley, who was so impressed by the variety and number of their parasites; "They are not only birds" he exclaimed, "but aviating zoological gardens."

But to return to the sea, it is not only the fish and other vertebrates which carry so many parasites. Dr. H. A. Cole, in his excellent chapter on "Benthos and the Shellfish of Commerce" in *Sea Fisheries: their Investigation in the United Kingdom* (edited Graham, 1956), gives lists of those found in some of the edible molluscs; these include eleven different kinds, mainly fluke larvae, found in the common cockle (*Cardium edule*) and fourteen in the mussel (*Mytilus edulis*). He says little is known of the parasites of the whelk (*Buccinum undatum*) but goes on to record two species of larval flukes, another kind of flatworm (a rhabdocoele) in the gut and a protozoan in its kidneys. It is only the commercial species of mollusc which have so far received attention; we may be sure that all the other molluscs, in fact most invertebrates, are similarly infected.

Those who regard parasites as loathsome, exceptional and inexplicable blots on the fair pages of Nature's creation must, if they face the facts, come to recognise that their thinking is badly out of line with reality. Parasites, indeed, show us some of the most remarkable and beautifully adjusted adaptations in the whole of Zoology. They are creatures as much in their own right in Nature as any others. We think of them as loathsome either because we mix up their way of living with standards and values of human behaviour, or because one of them may have brought about the death of a dear friend. Some parasites do kill their hosts, but the great majority do not; should the latter be worse in our eyes than the predators who live by ending the lives of others? When next we enjoy our lamb and mint sauce—and how I adore it—we might ask ourselves if we are any better in relation to that beautiful animal than the flukes in its liver. We must not, of course, mix moral values and natural history. The lives of parasites present as fascinating a field of study to the naturalist as any other; lack of space unfortunately, will only allow the briefest introduction to the subject in a book devoted to the whole of the open sea.

'Live and let live' is the motto of the well-established parasite; most of those that kill their hosts are still in the evolutionary experimental stage. If the host dies, the parasite has lost its home and food; evolution automatically works towards an adjusted balance between the two.

A consideration of parasitism, perhaps more than any other aspect of nature, brings home to us the magnitude of the pressure on space and of the competition for food between animals. Life, by its prodigious powers of multiplication, is forced into every nook and cranny that can support it. We often marvel that creatures, even if tiny, can get a living at all in some of the places in which we find them

on mountain crags or in barren desert and arctic wastes; they have
been forced to live in such poverty by the pressure of competition.
The larger animal bodies are full of nourishing food, flesh and blood,
which might be tapped if only a means of entry could be found; and
once inside, the invader might lead a life of comparative security
sheltered from the hazards of the outside world. But what a remarkable
step to take: for one animal to force itself into the body of another and
to live there. It is this pressure of competition which supplies the force,
coupled with the all-important variability of nature; it has not been
done all at once, but by the long slow succession of an almost infinite
series of steps of selective evolution.

The majority of these internal pests have probably passed inside
their hosts by a gradual process of adaptation from ancestors which
were originally parasitic on the outside. External parasites, like lice,
ticks and leeches, may be as numerous as the worms and flukes inside,
but some are only temporary. Mosquitoes and leeches, which take
occasional drinks of our blood, are temporary parasites; whereas lice
and skin mites which live all their lives on the body of their host are,
of course, permanent. It is easy to see how small animals might, under
the pressure of competition, come to colonize the outer surface of larger
animals and pass from being temporary parasites to become permanent
ones. Some blood-sucking insects are clearly descended from ancestors
which originally sucked the juices of plants. Again, some parasites may
have begun as quite harmless partners. We see many examples of a
co-operative association between two different species for their common
good, as that of hermit crabs and sea-anemones already quoted (p. 134);
one may then have begun to live at the expense of the other and so
changed the relationship.

Once external parasites are well established we can easily imagine
how they might enter the cavities of the body; invading first the mouth
and then, evolving varieties which would be immune to the digestive
juices of the host, they would pass into the alimentary tract to wallow
in and share its partially digested food. Then, from being inhabitants
of the gut, anchoring themselves to its wall to avoid being carried
through the system, it would be but a small step for them to wriggle
through into the true interior of the host and come to live in the
blood and other body fluids rich in the products of digestion. A few
may have entered the body from the outer surface by just burrowing
into the skin; then passing deeper and deeper into the host tissues they
may have reached the blood vessels as a means of transport.

Parasitism has clearly been going on for many millions of years. It
must have been, for there are several large classes of animals which

live by no other means and exhibit adaptations to this mode of life—
and particularly for getting from one host to another—as elaborate as
any of the specialisations seen in other groups of animals; and most of
these other groups we know to have been well defined in the days when
the early palaeozoic rocks were laid down some five hundred million
years ago. Prominent among these parasitic groups are two large
classes of the flat-worms—members of the phylum Platyhelminthes
(Gk. *platys*, flat; *helmins, helminthos*, a worm); these are the trematodes
or flukes and the cestodes or tapeworms. When flatworms were first
found in the liver of the sheep in the sixteenth century, and seen to
look something like tiny flatfish, they were called liver-flukes because
'fluke' was then the name commonly given to fish like dabs and
flounders; in later days, however, the term has seldom been used for
fish and is now widely applied to all similar parasites of the class
Trematoda (Gk. *trema, trematos*, a hole, hence *trematodes*, perforated).
Tapeworms of the class Cestoda are those whose bodies look like long
coiling ribbons in the intestines of many animals: ribbons which
fragment into countless segments, each potent with tremendous powers
of reproduction; the name comes from the Greek *kestos*, a girdle.

Then there are the round or thread worms of the phylum
Nematoda (Gk. *nema, nematodos*, a thread); some of these are very small
and free-living, some are parasites in plant tissues, but the larger ones
are parasites of animals. The spiny-headed worms, the Acanthocephala
(Gk. *acantha*, a thorn, *kephale*, a head) are quite a separate group and
entirely parasitic, mainly in aquatic vertebrates: fish, whales, seals and
water-birds. Again all the members of one great division of the
Protozoa, the class Sporozoa (Gk. *spora*, a seed or spore; *zoon*, an
animal), are entirely internal parasites.

A great many of these uninvited guests, both worms and protozoa,
do not spend all their lives in one host; they spend their early childhood in one animal, usually an invertebrate, and their maturity in
another, often a vertebrate. There is no special virtue in the in-
vertebrate-vertebrate part of the story beyond one of size and con-
venience; the invertebrate, which is first attacked by the parasite, is
usually smaller than the second host. In some cases the first host is
eaten by the second and so it serves, as did the wooden horse of Troy,
to carry the invaders into the citadel of their later life. But we will
come to these remarkable adventures a little later, and find that there
are some invaders which reside in three hosts in succession.

Before we pass from this brief general introduction we should
mention another very important class of marine parasites: certain
members of the crustacea. Just as on the land there are many insects

which have forsaken the freedom of the open spaces to become fleas and lice on the bodies of larger animals, so in the sea many crustaceans have followed the same course. The copepods are those which have taken more particularly to this mode of life; and, as among the insects, we see some which are permanent and others which are only temporary parasites.

I shall deal mainly with the parasites of fish, partly because they are better known than those of the invertebrates and partly because of their importance in fishery economy; for this latter reason I have placed this chapter after those dealing with the fish themselves. Before, however, passing to these, let us look at just a few of the more interesting examples of those infesting invertebrates. Rothschild and Clay (*loc. cit.*) refer to a minute worm which "lives relatively safely in the groove on the arms of certain starfish and when the host is feeding it wriggles up to the vicinity of its mouth and surreptitiously catches a few stray morsels." In this way, they say "it obtains free board and lodging." So we see parasitism arising in a simple association. Some other little worms show us the process carried a stage further. Look closely at two or three specimens of the beautiful feather-star *Antedon* (p. 108 and Plate 11) and on one of them you are almost certain to find a little round and brown object stuck to one of the ciliated grooves carrying the collected food towards the mouth. This is *Mysostomum*, a much modified bristle-worm robbing the host of some of its food on the way to its mouth and fixed to it with special hooks and suckers.

Among the more remarkable parasites of marine invertebrates are the curious barnacles, *Sacculina* and *Peltogaster* which infect certain crabs. The first may often be seen as a large orange growth on the underside of the abdomen of the shore-crab *Carcinus* or the spider-crab *Inachus,* and the other attacks hermit crabs. At first sight we should never suspect that they were barnacles at all; they show themselves to be so, however, by having the typical barnacle nauplius and cypris larval stages which were described in the first volume (p. 165). We often see, as in Plate 13 (p. 194) many acorn barnacles stuck to the shell of a crab; these, of course, are not parasitic, but just accidentally attached, as they might be to a stone or dead shell, and so carried about. We might perhaps imagine that some such barnacles, becoming fixed to the thinner folds of the chitinous armour on the underside of a crab, penetrated the skin with their roots of attachment and so began to draw nourishment from the body fluids of their host. Such a simple beginning, however, is very difficult to reconcile with the extraordinary story of *Sacculina's* entry into its host as we see it in its life-cycle of to-day; it is worth looking at.

The free-swimming cypris larva of *Sacculina* attaches itself by its first pair of antennae to a 'hair' on the leg of a crab, and then one of the antennae penetrates the thin cuticle at the base of the 'hair'. Now a little bulb-like structure is formed round a group of un-differentiated (embryonic) cells within the body of the larva and a tube from the neck of the bulb passes down the antenna. Next, the body of the larva disintegrates and falls away, leaving the little bulb hanging to the base of the hair; and *hey presto!*, like a hypodermic syringe, it suddenly injects its contents—the little cluster of cells—into the blood stream of the crab. Once inside it is carried round in the blood until it reaches the wide spaces below the intestine in the thorax; here it attaches itself and sends out long root-like processes in all directions to absorb nourishment from the blood. It grows in this rich medium and its swelling mass begins to press down against the plates forming the underside of the crab at the junction of thorax and abdomen. This causes the crab's skin at this place to break down and thus, when next it moults, a little hole is formed through which the body of the *Sacculina* pushes to the outside. Its roots penetrate to the remotest corners of the crab, even to the ends of its limbs.

*Sacculina* has no gut; it simply absorbs the already digested food from the blood in which it bathes. It becomes just a large mass of reproductive organs; eggs and sperm are produced and the story repeats itself again. Incidentally this infection brings about the castration of the crab, so that the male *Inachus* comes to resemble the female, but that is too long a story to be included here; it should be followed in the account of its discoverer, Geoffrey Smith (1906). Another parasite of crabs, but living in the gill chamber, is the isopod crustacean *Portunion* which, as regards the female, undergoes almost as complete a loss of its ancestral form as has *Sacculina;* it has lost all sign of segmentation and is distorted into a twisted fleshy mass by the enormous development of the ovaries and brood pouch.

We have space to include only one more parasite of an invertebrate host, before passing to those of fish, and for this I choose a copepod crustacean which is free-living as an adult, but, as such, never feeds; it builds up a big food reserve during development when living in the blood system of a bristle-worm. The copepod is *Haemocera* (one of the Monstrillidae) and the worm is *Salmacina*[1] (a serpulid). The eggs of the copepod develop into little swimming nauplii which are without mouth or gut; they must find the right kind of worm very quickly or perish. As soon as one comes in contact with the worm, it bores its

[1]Other closely related monstrillid copepods parasitise other worms such as *Polydora* and *Syllis* in the same way.

way through the integument with its sharp knife-like mandibles; and once inside, casting off its limbs and cuticle, it becomes a mere mass of embryonic cells, very reminiscent of *Sacculina*. Indeed, I have chosen this example because of this remarkable parallel. Then, by a kind of amoeba-like movement, so it is said, it passes into the main longitudinal blood-vessel and there develops a chitinous (horny) envelope; now two long processes grow out, which serve, again like those of *Sacculina,* as organs of absorption. The chitinous envelope is shed and replaced by a remarkable elastic one which expands as the animal grows and gradually differentiates into the perfect adult copepod; it reminds one of a butterfly being built up within its chrysalis. And like the butterfly, when fully formed, it bursts from its prison, a male or female which goes off to find a mate. They never feed, but only breed, and start the race again.

Having come to the copepods, we pass naturally to the parasites of fish, for, as already said, these small crustacea play a part in the sea similar to that played by insects, as the lice and fleas of vertebrates, on land. Thomas and Andrew Scott, in their monograph *The British Parasitic Copepoda* (1913) list no fewer than 114 species; and these they obtained from the examination of 91 different kinds of fish.

The commonest of these fish lice belong to the large family of the Caligidae, one of which, *Caligus rapax*, is shown in Fig. 102 overleaf. After passing through the free swimming nauplius stage, the young copepod attaches itself to the surface of its host by a sticky thread secreted from a special gland at the front of the head and, during this phase, cannot free itself; later, however, when adult, it can run about the surface and swim from one host to another, and so may be taken in the plankton nets. This species is found on various fishes, but perhaps most frequently on members of the cod family. The adults cling to the fish by little suckers at the base of the first antennae and by the maxillipeds (first thoracic limbs) which form powerful hooked claws. The mouthparts are adapted for piercing the skin and are placed in a proboscis-like tube through which the juices of the fish are sucked from the wound into the mouth. The females produce long egg-sacs like strings stretching backwards from either side of the abdomen.

The majority of fish lice have life-histories very similar to that just described, but a more remarkable one is that of *Lernaeocera* (=*Lernaea*) which has two hosts and comes, at the end, to look like anything but a crustacean; it is also illustrated in Fig. 102. Starting as a typical nauplius, it becomes a young copepod and attaches itself by its second antennae to the gills of a flatfish such as a flounder or a plaice and sucks nourishment from the highly vascular respiratory plates. It now becomes fixed by a cement secretion; its legs degenerate and it becomes known as the pupa stage. From this pupal case the male or female eventually breaks out to lead a free-swimming life for a short time. After pairing the male dies, but the female, whose body has lengthened enormously, now attaches herself to the gills of quite another kind of fish—a cod, haddock or whiting—and here undergoes a radical change.[1] It now loses not only its legs but all signs of segmentation and comes to look like a bloated swollen worm. Its head, buried in the flesh of the gills, sends out three branching absorptive processes and towards the lower end of the now twisted body there arise a pair of exceedingly long and coiled thread-like egg-sacs. No-one, if he did not know its story, would guess it was a copepod.

In the same family (the Lernaeidae) are two forms deserving special mention. One is *Lernaenicus*, often found attached to the eye of the sprat with its long egg-sacs reaching more than halfway to the fishes tail as shown in the sketch opposite; it may also be fixed to other parts of the body and its head is entirely buried in the tissues of its host. The second is *Pennella* of which one species, *P. orthagorisci*, parasitises a sun-fish (*Orthagoriscus Mola*) and another, *P. balaenopterae*, is found on whales. It is the whale one which surprises us; like its host among mammals it is gigantic compared with other copepods, for it can exceed a foot in length. I was given the fine specimen shown in Fig. 102 while at the whaling station at Horta on the island of Fayal in the Azores; it measures 9 inches and was taken from a sperm whale. They are also found on rorquals and right whales. A good description of this species will be found in the paper by Sir William Turner (1905); its head buried deep in the blubber is anchored by three horny barbs at right-angles to the body.

What effect do parasites of this kind have upon their hosts and so upon the fisheries? Z. Kabata (1955), who is making a special study of this problem found that on an average 15 per cent of the haddock and 5 per cent of the cod of the North Sea are carrying *Lernaeocera*. "If it caused", he writes, "each infected haddock to lose 1 oz. in weight, almost certainly an understatement, it would mean a loss of 30 ozs., almost 2 lb., on one box of 'seed' haddock. On the same basis the loss to Aberdeen landings of haddock in 1954 would have been about 9,200 cwt. and to the total Scottish haddock catch about 19,600 cwt."

[1]The name *Lernaea* has recently been changed to *Lernaeocera* and Mr. Z. Kabata of the Scottish Fishery Laboratory has now discovered that there are two species: the old *L. branchialis* which attacks the plaice, flounder, cod and whiting, and a new species *L. obtusa* which attacks the lemon dab and haddock. The drawings in Fig. 102 were made from specimens of this new species which he kindly gave me.

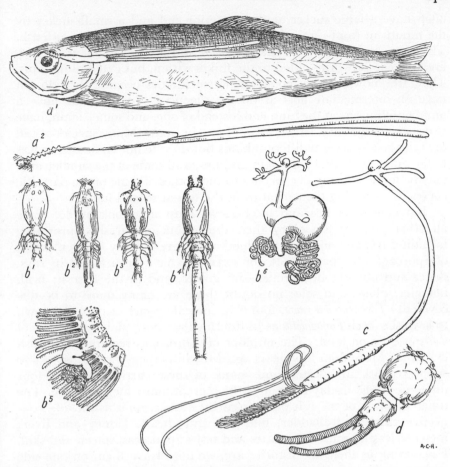

FIG. 102. Some crustacean parasites (Copepoda) of fish and whales. $a^1$, $a^2$, *Lernaenicus* attached to the eye of a sprat and also shown enlarged. $b^1$–$b^6$, *Lernaeocera*: $b^1$, young larval stage attached to gills of a flatfish; $b^2$ and $b^3$, free-swimming male and female; $b^4$ the female elongates and attaches itself to the gills of whiting, haddock or cod and becomes as $b^5$ with long coiled egg-sacs; $b^6$, the last stage enlarged. *c*, the whale parasite *Pennella; d*, the common fish-louse *Caligus rapax* (it is figured in colour in *Plate 11* of the first volume, p. 160).

In addition to copepods there are marine blood-sucking leeches, such as *Ichthyobdella* and *Pontobdella,* to be found on the bodies of fish; the latter genus is commonly found on dog-fish, sharks and rays. They differ but little from the typical leeches familiar to us in fresh water. Then on the gills of many fish are to be found little creatures which might at first sight be thought to be very small leeches, for they

often have a large sucker at the posterior end and a small sucker by
the mouth in front—and they suck the blood of the fish like a leech.
They are, however, flatter than a leech and are not segmented; they
are, indeed, flatworms allied to the flukes within, but external in habit.
They are known as the monogenetic trematodes because they do not
have an intermediate host as do the digenetic flukes. Some have a
number of suckers at the hind end instead of one, and some, again, have
two suckers right and left, instead of one in front. Many species of fish
are attacked by several different kinds but they do not all fix themselves
to the gills; some attack the skin and fins, and some of the smaller ones
may be found sticking like leeches to the bodies of some of the parasitic
copepods, receiving their meal from the fish at second hand.

But enough of lice and leeches, we must now look inside. Like
all other animals fish carry their due quota of parasitic protozoa,
including trypanosomes in the blood and a great many different kinds
of Sporozoa. Trypanosomes, for example, have been found in rays,
skates and dogfish, in blennies and gobies, and in the flatfish: brill,
flounder, plaice and sole; no doubt there are many more to be discovered. *Trypanosoma raiae,* found in several species of rays, is known
to have the leech *Pontobdella* as its intermediate host, playing the part of
the tsetse fly on land. The number of sporozoans recorded from fish
is legion. More than fifty years ago Minchin (1903) gave a list of 130
species of fish so infected and many of these carried three or four
different kinds; to-day there must be a great many more known. The
different parts of the fish parasitised by these organisms include con-
nective tissue, gall-bladder, gills and gut; heart, kidney and liver;
mesenteries and muscles; ovaries and testes; pancreas, spleen and skin.
Fascinating as their life-histories are, we must leave them on one side
and pass on to those masters of parasitic adaptation, the flukes and
tapeworms.

Before we discuss the flukes of fish, let us recall in the briefest outline
the well-known life history of the liver-fluke of the sheep so that we can
use it for comparison. It can only attack sheep living in wet marshy
pastures. The adult fluke living in the bile-duct produces a vast
number of eggs which reach the intestine and pass out of the sheep
with its dung. If they fall on to wet ground they hatch out into little
ciliated larvae which swim about and are attracted towards a particular
species of water snail (*Limnaea truncatula*) which lives in wet grass. On
reaching the snail the larva (the miracidium) bores into its flesh by
means of a sharp piercing organ and, once inside, degenerates into
a hollow sac (the sporocyst) containing a number of embryonic cells;
these now divide like eggs and develop into other little larvae, called

*Plate XXIII.* The courtship of the dragonet (*Callionymus lyra*) (*above*) *a.* The male displaying before the female, fins raised and mouth pouted downwards; the female has raised her head and is preparing to join him. Note how the female is marked and coloured like the shelly sand so that she is often almost invisible until she moves; so, too, is the male, except in courtship posture. The colours of male and female are shown in Plate 3 (p. 34). (*below*) *b.* The actual pairing. The female, nearest us, rests on the broadly-spread right pelvic fin of the male and together they leave the bottom, bodies held stiffly, breast fins beating to propel themselves upwards; as they sweep upwards the eggs of the female and the milt of the males are shed together into the water.

(*Douglas Wilson*)

Plate XXIV. (above) a. The cod (*Gadus callarias*) with a plaice and ray on the bottom below it. (below) b. The streaked gurnard (*Trigla lineata*) (*Douglas Wilson*)

rediae, which live in the liver of the snail.  Each redia may, from further embryonic cells within it, produce another generation of rediae; but eventually, by similar means, a redia produces a batch of little tadpole-like creatures, the cercariae, which break out from the snail and swim again in the wet grass.  Each swims in the water film to the top of a blade of grass and there loses its tail and secretes a hard covering round itself; now in a state of suspended animation it awaits the chance of being eaten by a grazing sheep.  If it is lucky enough to reach this promised land, the hard covering is dissolved away and the cercaria makes its way up the bile duct to become an adult fluke.

It is indeed an adventurous life.  What are the odds against the miracidium finding a snail, or the cercaria being eaten by a sheep? They must be very large.  To suggest a human parallel, it is almost as if the people of some overcrowded Pacific island put their children into barrels with a month or two's food supply and cast them into the sea in the hope that some, before it was too late, would reach some other, and perhaps less crowded, island; to ensure that some of them survived they would have to send out a very large number.  It is to meet this risk that the fluke has developed such a remarkable power of reproduction.  This is a notable characteristic of parasites of this kind; but the flukes and the tapeworms achieve it in quite different ways.  The flukes accomplish it not only by the adult producing a vast number of eggs, but by the young stages so produced each having a further means of multiplication; not all flukes have redia stages as well as the universal cercariae, but all have some such means of reproduction during development.

In our marine fishes there are a great many different kinds of flukes which, as adults, may infest different parts of the body: oesophagus, stomach, duodenum, pyloric caeca, intestine rectum, coelom and blood vessels.  B. Dawes in his monograph *The Trematoda* (1946) records that there are seven families of these digenetic flukes each with many species in British fishes and four other families less frequently represented.  The commonest flukes of our marine fishes belong to the Hemiuridae.  In this family one species (*Derogenes varicus*) occurs in more than 40 kinds of fish, another species (*Hemiurus communis*) in more than 30, two other species each in more than 20, and another (*Zoogonoides vivipara*) in more than a dozen of which 8 are flatfish.  In nearly all these species the first hosts are molluscs, either marine snails or bivalves—and we have already seen (p. 234) how many different kinds may be found in the cockle and the mussel; not a few of these flukes have another host as well: a fish which in turn gets eaten by a larger fish which so becomes the final adult host.

Looking from another angle, Dawes (1947), in his *Trematoda of British Fishes*, records the number of kinds of fluke, both monogenetic and digenetic, found in various species of fish. Here are some examples: cod, 13 species; haddock, 6 species; whiting, 14; conger eel, 12; sturgeon, 11; thornback ray, 8; herring, 5; catfish (*A. lupus*), 12; yellow gurnard, 14; grey gurnard, 12; dab, 12; plaice, 9; flounder, 10; and sunfish (*Mola*), 20.

We come now to the cestodes or tapeworms, those animals which are apt to fill us with disgust because one of their kind, if we are not sufficiently careful as to the pork we eat and how well it is cooked, may come to reside in our own inside. There are many which are common parasites of fish. As with the flukes, it will be well to introduce them by the summary of a typical life-history. Because it is well known, relatively simple and, unfortunately, of special interest to us, we may as well take for our example the *Taenia solium* of man. Let us begin with the adult firmly hanging on to the wall of the intestine by its so-called 'head' or scolex—anchored by a ring of sharp hooks and four suckers. It is still a nice point, by the way—and one which was keenly debated when I was an undergraduate student—as to whether this scolex represents the head of the animal or is really the tail end as some zoologists have maintained; it has no mouth to guide us, for it has no alimentary system at all, and it also has no eyes or brain. The absence of a gut is an extreme specialisation of the parasitic life. The animal lies bathed in well-digested food and just absorbs it through its outer skin, instead of through an inner alimentary surface; not only may it be back to front but, in function, it is, as it were, inside out.

The tapeworm grows into a flat ribbon of prodigious length: a ribbon which is seen to be divided into innumerable little segments. As it grows new segments are continually being budded off from the scolex in a manner rather similar to the way young jelly-fish are budded off from the base of their polyp stage (as described in Volume I, p. 123). If we should liken the scolex and its ribbon of segments to a railway engine and a train of trucks, then the train gets longer and longer by new trucks being budded off from the back of the engine; the 'trucks' themselves also increase in length as they grow older and get further and further away from the 'engine'. Close on a thousand of these segments may be formed and the worm, coiled up in the intestine, comes to be eight or nine feet in length.[1] This great production of

---

[1]Another tapeworm of man, *Bothriocephalus latus*, coming from uncooked river fish, has as many as 3,000 segments and reaches a length of 20 to 30 feet (Benham, 1901).

segments is the tapeworm's method of increasing its powers of multiplication, for each segment has a complete reproductive system. As one
passes along the animal from the scolex to the other end, one sees the
segments becoming filled with eggs and eventually all their other parts
degenerate; finally, when fully ripe, the end segments drop off and pass
out of the body.

In country districts, where sanitation is primitive, the tapeworm
segments may reach the open ground and disintegrate. Now their
mass of eggs, in hard resistant shells, will lie dormant for a time, dry up
and be scattered by the wind; and eventually a few lucky ones may be
swallowed by pigs when rooting for their food. Again we see the need
for this tremendous power of reproduction; only those producing a
vast number of eggs are likely to have any offspring surviving. Once
in the pig an egg will hatch out into a tiny larva armed with six little
knife-like blades to cut its way out of the intestine into the main body
cavity; and then from there it cuts its way to its resting place within the
muscles of the main bodywall. Here it grows into a spherical cyst,
and presently, at one point on its surface, a curious infolding occurs
to form a deep pouch; this is a pocket of sinister significance, for in its
lining appear four suckers and a ring of curved hooks, reminiscent of
something we have seen before. Here it remains in a state of suspended
development waiting to be eaten with the pig by unsuspecting man;
its cyst can withstand considerable heat and so may withstand poor
cooking. If it survives, its resistant coat is dissolved away as the pork
is digested and suddenly the pocket turns inside out to form the fore-
shadowed (hooked and suckered) scolex which soon attaches itself to
the intestinal wall; its bladder-body shrinks to nothing, little segments
begin to appear, and the whole adventure starts all over again.

A similar story, or rather a part of it, goes on in nearly every fish
in the sea; many adult and many larval stages are known, but few are
linked to one another with certainty. The late Professor James
Johnstone, of Liverpool University, was a pioneer in recording many
species of tapeworms from fish in the Irish Sea (Johnstone 1905-12);
relatively little, however, has been done since. Space will only permit
the briefest impression of their importance and this I will try to give by
just a few quotations from Johnstone. Referring to *Bothriocephalus*
(=*Dibothrium*) *punctatus* Rudolphi., he writes (1906) "Every turbot and
brill examined has so far proved to be the host of one or more of this
cestode . . . One turbot was greatly infested, and I counted over 60
*Dibothrium* in the gut . . ." Then after describing a number of other
species, mainly in various rays, he refers to *Tetrarhynchus erinaceus*, van
Beneden, as "one of the commonest tapeworms of Irish Sea fishes;" he

gives as its main hosts five species of rays and as its intermediate hosts: plaice, cod, haddock, hake and gurnards. The next year (1907) he writes of another species *Abothrium rugosum* (Goeze): "About a dozen large cod were dissected . . . and this cestode was invariably found; sometimes there were as many as a dozen large worms in each fish." Again (1909) "when trawling to the southwest of the Calf of Man . . . a small hake was caught which contained, in its intestine, about a dozen cestodes which I refer to the species *Dibothrium crassiceps*, Rudolphi." And so the record goes on: fish after fish, tape after tape, but any more of it may be tedious; I have quoted enough to illustrate that there is indeed a profusion of them.

As for the nematodes or round-worms, I will quote Johnstone, Scott and Smith (1924) writing on the parasites of the cod: "The nematodes of the cod (and other edible fishes) are very imperfectly known and there are doubtless many more species than are recorded here." After referring to specimens found in the flesh, the body cavity, the intestine and the stomach, they say "many (indeed most) of the forms usually seen are larval and this adds immensely to the difficulty of identification." Then they add—and this applies as much to-day as when they wrote—"a thorough investigation of the nematode parasites of fishes is badly wanted." Again this is equally true for the spiny-headed worms (Acanthocephala); the same authors (in the same paper) refer to one, *Echinorhynchus acus*, as being "fairly common (in the cod) occurring in the intestine."

Here we must end our parasite parade and point, as did Johnstone, Scott and Smith, to the need for more research in this fascinating, but difficult and much neglected, field of natural history in the sea.

CHAPTER 13

# THE OVER-FISHING PROBLEM

W̲E̲ M̲U̲S̲T̲ now come to an important matter which we left over from our account of the fisheries: the problem of over-fishing and how best to avoid it. There can be no doubt that it occurs in many areas; there was abundant evidence of it in the North Sea before the first world war. The average size of the plaice landed became smaller and smaller, year after year, as the larger fish tended to be trawled up more quickly than the younger ones could grow to replace them. Further, it was found that in some of the tagging experiments up to 70 per cent of marked fish were recaught within a year; thus at least this proportion of the stock was being destroyed annually in these parts of the sea.

Various suggestions were made to close certain areas of the North Sea for a time, to give the stocks a chance to recover; but the different nations could not agree as to which areas, or for how long. Then came the first world war and the closure was automatically brought about by the extensive mine-fields and the operations of naval craft. This enforced experiment gave a simple demonstration of the previous effect of Man's fishing. After 4½ years' respite the stock of fish had increased enormously and, instead of there being a vast number of small unprofitable fish as in 1914, there were plenty of the very large fish which used to mark the fishery in the early days of the century. During the twenties, however, the landings of fish fell away again, and once more the average size of fish became smaller. The second world war repeated the experiment of closure and again, even more strikingly, demonstrated the evil effects of over-fishing. Fig. 103, overleaf, is an interesting chart taken from a paper by Mr. Michael Graham given to the United Nations Economic and Social Council in 1949. It shows, for the different fisheries round Great Britain and Iceland, the improvement in the yield for 1919 expressed as a percentage increase of that of 1913, and similarly the yield of 1946 as a percentage of that of 1938. The results are indeed striking.

Certainly no one can deny that over-fishing exists; we must find

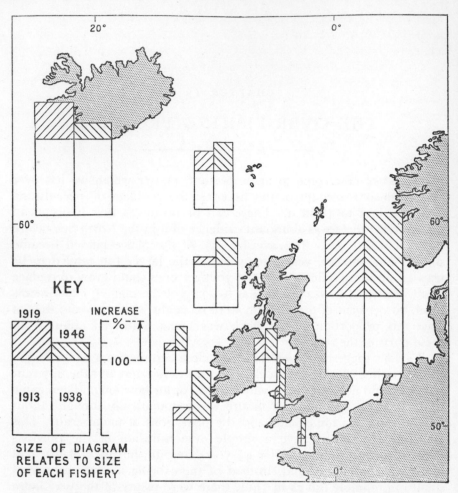

FIG. 103. Histograms (from Graham, see text) showing the increase in the catch of fish in various regions round the British Isles immediately after the two World Wars (i.e. in 1919 and 1946) expressed as percentages of the catches just before the wars (1913 and 1938). The effect of the reduced fishing during the wars is clearly seen. The size of each diagram gives a measure of the relative yield of each fishery.

the best way to remedy it. A great deal of discussion has taken place on the question since the beginning of the century. Because people have looked at it from different points of view, and have so often stressed some particular aspect without seeing the matter as a whole, there has often been misunderstanding. The late Dr. E. S. Russell, who wrote the pioneer book on the subject in 1942, cleared the air very much in an earlier paper (1931) when he represented the various factors by a simple algebraic expression. Normally I would think it quite unsuitable to introduce such a formula into a book of this character, but here I will make an exception because this way of summarising the problem, whilst at first appearing somewhat technical, will actually bring the different sides of the question into their proper perspective better than many pages of writing. He expressed it as an equation written thus:

$$S_2 = S_1 + (A+G) - (C+M)$$

$S_1$ represents the weight of the catchable stock of fish at the beginning of the year;—this means those big enough to be caught by the particular trawls or other nets, used in the fishery (i.e. leaving out those small enough to be able to escape through the meshes). $S_2$ is the weight of the catchable stock at the end of the year. A represents the addition of catchable fish from the younger recruits growing up during the year and G is the added weight by growth of both $S_1$ and A (i.e. after A have come in). C represents the weight of fish caught during the year and M is the weight of fish dying by natural mortality, *i.e.* by any means other than man's destruction.

Looking back at the equation we see that $S_2$ will be greater than, equal to, or less than $S_1$ according to whether $(A+G)$ is greater than, equal to, or less than $(C+M)$. A will tend to vary in different years according to fluctuations in the broods; we have seen, for several species, that in some years there are many more young fish surviving than in others. G will also tend to vary according to the quantity of food available and to some extent with temperature. We have already seen how plaice may grow very much more on the Dogger Bank than on the over-crowded regions of the Dutch coast (p. 172); and how haddock in the deeper and more northerly waters grow more slowly than those in more southerly and warmer waters (p. 225). The rate at which the catchable fish A come into the stock during the year depends partly on the number growing up, but also on their rate of growth whilst they are still below catchable size. The factor G, which is the added weight by growth, must of course be expressed in terms of weight and, strictly speaking, the other factors should also be expressed in weight, but it will be easier for the moment to discuss and think about A, C and M in terms of numbers. If we were going, then, to make the whole thing into a strictly quantitative equation, we would have to convert these numbers into weights and we shall do this in an example given a little later.

Let us now consider what happens with different rates of fishing—

keeping in mind the simple equation. As a first example let us suppose $(C+M)=(A+G)$—*i.e.* the fish caught, and those dying naturally, equal by weight those coming into the stock plus their increase in growth—then of course $S_2$ (the weight of the stock at the end of the year) must be equal to $S_1$ (that at the beginning).

For a second example let us suppose that the numbers of A and M remain constant and the growth rate is just as before, but C *decreases, i.e.* there is less fishing. Now $(C+M)$ in this case will be less than in the first example and G will be greater because the number of survivors is greater. Therefore, of course, $S_2$ will be greater than $S_1$. Similarly if C *increases,* $S_2$ will be less than $S_1$ *provided that the growth rate G remains the same.* The growth rate, however, may alter. If C is increased very much there might be more food available for the remaining fish, so G might increase. We will refer to this matter presently; so much depends upon the age and the growth rate of the fish.[1] A big increase or decrease in A would clearly affect $S_2$ although such an increase in A would, to some extent, reduce G because food is limited. If G (the growth-rate) increases and the rate of C and M remain constant, C and M would increase in weight; but $S_2$ would also increase, because the number of survivors would be the same and they too would be increased in weight.

Now let us consider the conditions on what is usually termed a virgin ground, *i.e.* one which has never been fished. C will be nil, and so our equation will become:

$$S_2=S_1+(A+G)-M$$

Now there must be a maximum value for S, depending upon the food available in the area. Therefore, under normal conditions, $S_2$ must equal $S_1$. This being so $(A+G)$ must equal M. Now if M (natural mortality) is very small it means that *the addition to and growth of the stock must also be very small.* Here is a very important point. Young fish put more food to growth than older fish; old fish put more food to maintenance. If the old fish succeed in getting more food than the young fish, then these young fish may tend to be starved out and die. So it comes about that the stock on a virgin ground, when it is first fished, is so often found to consist of very large old fish in poor condition. This was very clearly illustrated by G. T. Atkinson (1908), who made a voyage on one of the first trawlers to visit the Barents Sea in 1907. In Fig. 104 opposite, we show two graphs based on his figures:

[1] Increase in C will actually diminish M slightly on arithmetical grounds. i.e. there will be fewer to die naturally but it does not affect $(C+M)$ together.

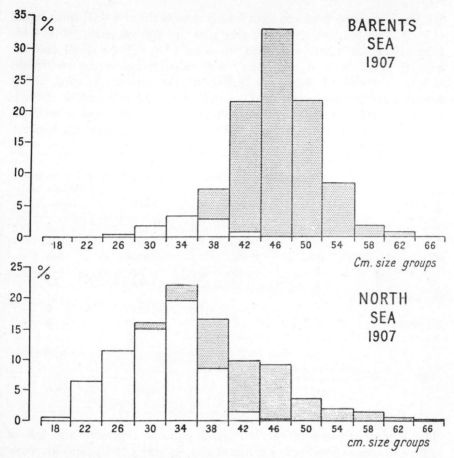

FIG. 104. Histograms showing (above) the relative numbers of female plaice of different sizes (in '4 centimetre' groups) expressed as percentages of the total sample taken during the fishing in the Barents Sea in 1907 when that fishery was just beginning. Compared with this we see a similar treatment of the data for female plaice sampled in the North Sea during the same period. The graphs are redrawn as percentages from the original figures of Atkinson (1908); the unshaded and shaded parts represent immature and mature fish respectively.

one representing the relative numbers of immature and mature fish in the Barents Sea and the other showing similar figures for the North Sea.

An increase in fishing up to a point may thus improve a fishery and give an increased yield, but if carried too far there is over-fishing and the fishery is damaged. The proper exploitation of a fishing ground means, of course, a stabilised fishery where $S_2 = S_1$. In other words

the stock must be kept constant which means that (A+G) must equal
(C+M), but this equality may take place at *different levels*. If (C+M)
is small (as on a virgin ground) then (A+G) will be small and the
annual production of the fishery will be well below the maximum
possible. Rational fishing is *fishing at the optimal intensity*. Most
fisheries are grossly over-fished, so that the yield per unit of effort is
much less than it might be. Let us illustrate this with a few very simple
figures as shown in the following Table taken from Russell's book:

| Age | 80 PER CENT RATE OF FISHING | | 50 PER CENT RATE OF FISHING | |
|:---:|:---:|:---:|:---:|:---:|
| | *Stock* | *Withdrawals Annually* | *Stock* | *Withdrawals Annually* |
| I | 1,000 | — | 1,000 | — |
| II | 200 | 800 | 500 | 500 |
| III | 40 | 160 | 250 | 250 |
| IV | 8 | 32 | 125 | 125 |
| V | 2 | 6 | 62 | 62 |
| VI | — | 2 | 31 | 31 |
| VII | — | — | 16 | 16 |
| VIII | — | — | 8 | 8 |
| IX | — | — | 4 | 4 |
| X | — | — | 2 | 2 |
| XI | — | — | 1 | 1 |
| | 1,250 | 1,000 | 2,000 | 1,000 |

The Roman figures in the left hand column represent the fish of
different ages in the stock: i.e. fish of 1, 2, 3, and 4 etc. years old. Now
at the left-hand side of the table we will suppose that there is a very
heavy fishing-rate, capturing 80 per cent of the catchable stock, but on
the right-hand side of the table we have a fishery capturing only 50
per cent of the catchable stock. In the two columns under each type of
fishery we see to the left the number of fish left in each age-group from
1,000 fish going into the catchable stock at 2 years old (i.e. A in our old
equation). In the heavier fishing we see that a stock of 1,000 fish will
be fished out in five years. When 1,000 fish have been caught, assuming
that 1,000 fish are coming into the stock each year, the catchable stock
compared with the 1,000 caught will be 1,250; whereas with the
lighter fishing for every 1,000 fish caught the catchable stock will be
2,000. The significance of this table lies in the fact that there are so
many more fish in the older age-groups left by the lighter fishing,
than by the heavier, because with each year of age there is a big increase

in growth and so weight of fish. This is seen in striking fashion in our next Table:

| Age | Weight at end of year | Average weight per year class | WEIGHT OF YIELD | |
|---|---|---|---|---|
| | | | per 80 per cent reduction | per 50 per cent reduction |
| I | 40 gms | — | | |
| II | 124 | 82 | 65,600 | 41,000 |
| III | 227 | 175 | 28,000 | 43,750 |
| IV | 339 | 283 | 9,056 | 35,375 |
| V | 460 | 400 | 2,400 | 24,800 |
| VI | 586 | 523 | 1,046 | 16,213 |
| | | | 106,102 | 161,138 |

The first column of Roman numbers represents, as before, the age of the fish in years; the second represents the average weight of each fish in grams at the end of the year. The third column represents the average weight per year-class taken in the fishery; all the fish are not taken at the end of the year when they have grown the full amount, so that although (for example) a two-year-old fish will weigh 124 grams at the end of its second year, the average weight of a two-year-old fish taken in the fishery is only 82 grams. Now in the next two columns we are converting the figures given in the other table for the numbers of fish caught by the two different rates of fishing into *weight, i.e.* in the fishery of 80 per cent reduction we have multiplied the 800 for the second year by the average weight of 82 giving 65,600. Similarly for the 50 per cent fishery we have multiplied 500 by 82 giving us 41,000. Down the table we have made similar multiplications for the next four years. When we add them up, we see that the yield for the heavier fishery is 106,102 units of weight and that for the lighter fishery is 161,138 units of weight. This means, of course, that for a greatly reduced effort in fishing (fishing at only 50 per cent rate instead of 80 per cent rate) the actual yield of fish obtained is nearly 50 per cent higher than that of more intensive fishing. Over-fishing means reduced yield for increased effort. The remedy of course is to reduce the rate of fishing until the optimal level of the equation $(A+G)=(C+M)$ has been reached. It is very difficult at present to get the industry to reduce C, the catching rate, because there are so many different nations on the same ground. If we would agree to fish less on the Dogger Bank with our trawlers would other nations agree to cut down their fishing with their seine nets? We have a long way to go yet before such international agreement may be established; but it must come in the end, if the populations of the world are to get all the food that nature could provide. In the meantime, however, there are some other things we can do.

C could clearly be allowed to be bigger if we could increase G, the growth rate. In our story of the plaice (p. 173) we saw an example of how this might be done, by the large-scale transplantation of young fish from the coastal region to the Dogger Bank, giving a greatly increased growth-rate; that again must depend upon international co-operation but it should not be so difficult as limiting fishing effort. Is there anything we can do about A, the addition to the stock of catchable size? We could allow the fish to grow a little more before we caught them, if we adjusted our nets to catch them only when they were a little larger; we should catch less fish just at first, but in a year or two, since weight increases by the cube of the length, the value of A in weight would be very much higher. If we can, by international law, regulate the size of mesh used by trawlers, so that more of the very young fish can escape through the meshes of the net, then we shall have done just this.

When such a proposal was first put to the industry the answer was that they were convinced that such a change in mesh would be useless, because they thought that the young fish could not escape from the trawl as it was being pulled along. They thought that the meshes, under the strain of towing, would close tightly together at the cod-end and make any escape impossible. However, the ingenious experiments of Davis and Goodchild (Davis, 1934) conclusively proved that in fact vast numbers of young fish do escape unhurt from the trawl. They attached to the trawl an outer fine-mesh net which formed a long bag trailing behind the cod-end, and then by a special mechanism they closed it with a noose when the trawl was ready for hauling up; in this way they proved that all the young fish they caught had escaped whilst the trawl was actually being towed on the bottom. The wonderful ciné photographs taken by the late Commander Hodges, swimming as a frogman round a seine net working, have also clearly shown that not only young round fish, but young flat fish, can escape through the meshes of the cod end; this is seen in the photograph in Plate XIV (p. 163) taken from the film specially made for this demonstration by the Fisheries Division of the Scottish Home Department.

Just before the last war, largely through the efforts of the British fishery departments, international agreement was achieved on the use of a wider mesh, saving the destruction of vast quantities of young fish which were too small to be of economic value. The first step towards a more rational exploitation of the sea has been achieved; but it is only a small step compared with what might be done.

Actually the over-fishing problem has received in recent years a much more detailed mathematical treatment. I will not however, attempt to carry the reader any further into this highly elaborate field, partly because it would mean becoming far too technical, and also because I should myself be getting well out of my depth. The simple formula provided by Russell gives us the essence of the over-fishing problem in a nut-shell; those who wish to go further should read Michael Graham (1935) and the chapter by R. J. H. Beverton and S. J. Holt on the theory of fishing (Chap. IX) in *Sea Fisheries, their Investigation in the United Kingdom,* edited by M. Graham (1956).[1]

CHAPTER 14

# MARINE REPTILES—FACT AND FANCY

LEAVING the fish, and passing higher up the scale of vertebrates, we find no amphibians in the sea. These newt- and frog-like animals, which were evolved from fish in the freshwater swamps of far off palaeozoic times, have never, apparently, in the whole of their long career, succeeded in invading the sea. No fossil amphibians have ever been found in marine deposits except a very few in estuarine beds into which they were almost certainly carried from the rivers when in flood. As, of course, their name implies, they live in two worlds, aquatic and terrestrial, but hardly make the best of both.

The Amphibia began the vertebrate conquest of the land which was completed by the reptiles; and these in turn gave rise, through two distinct branches, to the birds and mammals. All the higher vertebrates of the sea have been evolved from these three terrestrial stocks, no doubt driven back to the water by the severe competition for food on the land. In the mesozoic age, some hundred million years back, our seas abounded with large reptiles which had become as

[1]Since going to press Beverton and Holt have produced a *magnum opus* on this and related subjects: 'On the Dynamics of Exploited Fish Populations.' *Fish. Invest. Lond., Ser. II, 19,* 1–533, 1957.

well adapted to the water as have the mammalian whales and seals of to-day. There were three great groups of them: the whale-like ichthyosaurs, the long-necked plesiosaurs and the large sea-lizards or mosasaurs; in addition, though less important, were the marine crocodiles or geosaurs. Like the dinosaurs of the land, these huge saurians of the sea all became extinct at the end of the cretaceous period; that would be about fifty million years ago.

Our present-day reptiles are but a remnant from their glorious past, and only the turtles and sea-snakes have become adapted to go far from land; they are tropical or sub-tropical in distribution, but, occasionally, a few turtles may accidentally get carried out of their way to be stranded on our shores. But before coming to these, let us look for a moment at the larger reptiles of the past, for, judging by the number of fossils found, they must at one time have been very prominent in the life of our British seas.

Our knowledge of these creatures began in the second decade of the last century with a surprising discovery made at Lyme Regis in Dorset by Mary Anning, aged eleven. Even at that early age she was an ardent collector of fossils, for she had been taught how to go about it by her father who, in addition to his trade as carpenter, collected and sold fossil shells and other natural curios to visitors to the town. He died when she was only ten, whereupon, in spite of her age, she resolved to continue his natural history business and did so with results that he could never have dreamed of. In the very next year, 1811, this little girl noticed some bones sticking out from the face of the cliff not far from her home; after tracing the position of the skeleton with her hammer, she hired men to cut it out of the limestone: a skeleton 30 feet long which is now in the British Museum. Rarely has a fossil excited so much scientific interest; only after long controversy was it named *Ichthyosaurus* and its true position in the animal kingdom understood. But that was only a beginning; she went on finding many different kinds and in 1823 discovered the first *Plesiosaurus*. This wonderful lady continued to unearth these reptiles with devoted skill and care until she died of cancer in 1847; we must not forget her when we talk about the past she found for us. Since her day, of course, a great many specimens of these animals have been dug up in various parts of the world; the beds of the Oxford clay have been very productive, particularly in the Peterborough district where Mr. Alfred Leeds and his family made a large collection and a very thorough study of them.

Of all reptiles the ichthyosaurs were the most perfectly adapted for life in the sea; they were rightly named the fish-like saurians (Gk.

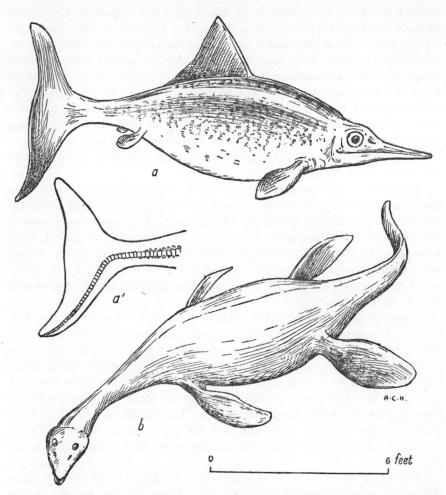

FIG. 105. How the more typical of the marine reptiles of the Mesozoic Age most probably appeared in life: sketches of reconstructions in the British Museum (Natural History). *a*, the ichthyosaur *Ophthalmosaurus icenicus* (13 feet 6 in. long) from the Oxford clay, with *a'* the tail vertebrae in relation to tail fin; *b*, the plesiosaur *Macroplata tenuiceps* (15 feet 3 in. long) from Harbury, Warwickshire.

*ichthys*, a fish) for they had evolved a graceful stream-lined shape and the more advanced types had a powerful vertical fish-like tail as seen in Plate XXV, overleaf, and Fig. 105 above. In a series of specimens we can see the evolution of this tail from the more usual reptile type which is found in the primitive forms in the Triassic; it is interesting to note, as in Fig. 105, that the backbone bends downwards into the lower lobe of the tail, whereas in fish it does the opposite. Of course all such aquatic reptiles must come to the surface to breathe air as whales do. The ichthyosaurs were able to become so very fish- or whale-like because they had left the land for good; they became viviparous, like a mammal, bringing forth their young in an advanced stage of development instead of having to go ashore to lay eggs in the sand as do the turtles. We know this because fossils have been found which were certainly mothers with a number of well developed young inside them. With their pointed jaws and sharp teeth they must have been voracious hunters of fish; they ranged in size from little ones of only a foot long to leviathans of 30 feet.

The plesiosaurs were much less fish-like and probably used their paddles for rowing themselves along as turtles do, instead of using mainly tail-propulsion as did the ichthyosaurs; they were clearly much slower animals. While some of them reached a length of 40 feet, they would not be so bulky as a large ichthyosaur because so much of that length would be a long thin neck and tail as seen in this Plate XXV and Fig. 105, overleaf. Dean Buckland, the celebrated Oxford geologist of the early nineteenth century, picturesquely likened a plesiosaur to "a snake threaded through the shell of a turtle". They were also fish feeders, but instead of depending upon speed of body for capturing their prey, they probably used the great flexibility of their long necks to flash their heads this way and that to snap at fish on either side. The mosasaurs were true lizards which took to the sea after fish and modified their limbs into paddle-like flippers; some of them reached a gigantic size of 50 feet (Swinton, 1954). The marine crocodiles of the Jurassic also became well adapted for swimming; some such as *Geosaurus* actually developed a tail-fin not unlike that of an ichthyosaur, only smaller.

We must come now to the turtles of to-day. Four species have definitely been recorded for Britain. They belong to the order Chelonia (*chelone,* a tortoise), and are marine tortoises with their limbs beautifully adapted as paddles. They are not completely aquatic, but almost so. They only come ashore to lay and bury their eggs in the warm sand of a tropical beach (just above high water) and hurry back again to the sea, leaving them to be incubated by the heat of the sun. They may be met with far out into the ocean, hundreds of miles from land. Like the tortoises, they have their trunk region encased in a box of bony plates, forming the carapace above and plastron below; most species, but not all, have these dermal bones covered by horny shields called tortoise-shell.

An examination of the "shell" will tell us what species we have

*Plate XXV*. Marine reptiles of the past. (*above*) *a*. One of the most perfect known fossil remains of an ichthyosaur (*Ichthyosaurus acutirostris* from the Upper Lias) preserving the actual outline of the dorsal and tail fins, photographed from the specimen in the Oxford University Museum. Length 6 ft. 5 in. (*below*) *b*. A photograph of an accurate cast of the fossil skeleton of a plesiosaur (*Plesiosaurus dolichodeirus*) from the Lower Lias of Lyme Regis, Dorset, also in the Oxford University Museum. Length 5 ft. 7 in. Much larger specimens of allied forms are known, e.g. an ichthyosaur of 30 ft. and a plesiosaurus of 40 ft.

found. If there should be no outer covering of tortoise-shell, but a soft skin raised into longitudinal ridges—then it is the leathery turtle or luth (*Dermochelys coriacea*); below the ridges, we can often make out, at any rate on the younger specimens, rows of small bones representing those of the carapace above or plastron below. This is the largest of the turtles, and is said to grow to a length of six feet or more and a weight of more than half a ton. There are only a very few records of leathery turtles reaching the British Isles, and all are confined to their southern shores. If we find a turtle having tortoise-shell plates which overlap one another, like the slates on the roof of a house, then it is the hawksbill turtle (*Eretmochelys imbricata*); it is smaller than the former species, about four feet long, and has (indeed) a very hawk-like head as seen in Plate XXVI opposite. The horny plates of this species provide the true tortoise-shell of commerce. The hawksbill has been recorded on all our coasts, including even the north of Scotland. The other two species to reach our shores have tortoise-shell plates which do *not* overlap; they are so much alike that they are often mixed up: they are the common loggerhead, *Caretta caretta*, and the Kemp's loggerhead *Lepidochelys* (=*Colpochelys*) *kempi*. In size they are both about midway between the hawksbill and the leathery turtle. Most of the British records are of these species but owing to the confusion between them many of the earlier records of one or other cannot be taken as certain unless the specimens have been kept for examination. They can best be determined by looking at the arrangement of the so-called "inframarginal" plates of the plastron, i.e. those on the underside just behind the fore-limbs; the difference between the two is clearly shown in the drawing in Fig. 106, overleaf. The turtle of "turtle soup", the green turtle (*Chelonia mydas*), has occasionally been 'reported' from British waters but never confirmed by expert examination.

The stranding of turtles at all, so far from their natural habitat is something very remarkable; however, the green turtles are vegetarians, feeding on seaweeds and sea-grasses, and so are less likely to stray as far from their native coasts as are the others, which are predators feeding upon fish or crustacea and other invertebrates. Recently a

---

*Plate XXVI.* (*above*) *a.* A small loggerhead turtle (*Caretta caretta*) photographed swimming in a pool at Bude, north Cornwall, where it was stranded by the tide in August 1945. Note the tufts of an alga (filamentous weed) growing on it which prove it to be of trans-Atlantic origin. (*below*) *b.* A hawksbill turtle (*Eretmochely imbricata*) together with two remora (*Remora remora*) one of which is attached, and another just about to attach itself to the underside of the turtle (see p. 92). This photograph was taken in the aquarium at Miami, Florida, but both the turtle and fish occasionally come into British waters.                    (*Douglas Wilson*)

clue has been found which may help to explain the mystery of these turtle journeys to our colder waters, in which they cannot for long survive. Dr. P. E. P. Deraniyagala of Ceylon (1939) first drew attention to the fact that some of the turtles reported from our coasts as common loggerheads were really the other species, Kemp's loggerhead; he had found this to be so for two in the National Dublin Museum which had been stranded on the west of Ireland in 1928 and

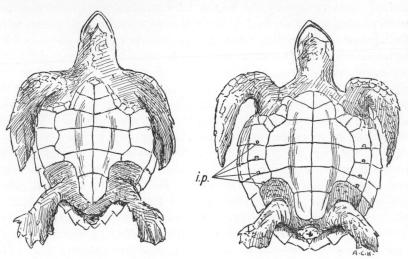

FIG. 106. A comparison between the common loggerhead turtle, *Caretta caretta* (left) and *Lepidochelys* (=*Colpochelys*) *kempi*, Kemp's loggerhead (right). They are drawn from specimens in the British Museum (Natural History) arranged to show the distinguishing inframarginal plates on their undersides: three on each side in on and four on each side in the other; those of the latter are perforated by small pores *i.p.* whereas those of the former are not.

1934. He pointed out that as Kemp's loggerhead is a native of the Gulf of Mexico and adjacent waters, and not an eastern Atlantic form at all, they must have drifted right across the ocean. He further suggests that if *kempi* can so drift, why not also the common loggerhead which is also taken off the west of Ireland? "It is very probable" he writes "that the presence of *Caretta caretta* in European waters is mainly if not entirely due to currents, for no definite breeding grounds exist on the European coast as on the American side of the Atlantic." He believes that turtles may be used as ocean current indicators.

Very soon afterwards Dr. H. W. Parker (1939) reported the stranding of ten turtles on our south-west coasts during December and January 1938–39; four of these were the common loggerhead, three were Kemp's loggerhead and the other three were not identified. As both species came together, he believed it "more probable, but by no means certain, that the turtles have crossed from the American shore"; there was still the doubt that our knowledge of the distribution of Kemp's loggerhead might not be complete. Deraniyagala's view, however, that both species may originate in the Caribbean region has now been confirmed by a nice little piece of detective work. The remarkable invasion of our waters in the autumn of 1945 by armadas of the Portuguese Man-of-war, *Physalia,* driven by the wind, was referred to in the earlier volume; Dr. D. P. Wilson, who recorded this invasion, also reported at the same time from August 1945 to February 1946, the stranding of nine common loggerhead turtles. This again suggests that the turtles, like the *Physalia,* were driven before the wind, at any rate at the end of their journey. It is supposed that they started on their drift across the Atlantic by being blown into the ocean by local storms and were then carried by currents from the American side to the region of the Azores. At times turtles are certainly there in very large numbers. In early September 1952, when on a cruise on the R.R.S. *Discovery II,* we passed a great many on our way home; all afternoon and evening of the day after leaving these islands we were passing turtles at an average rate of ten or so an hour within a span of some 150 yards on either side of the ship. This would be almost 250 to 300 miles from the Azores and would mean, at our speed of some 9 knots, roughly a turtle a mile. Now on the carapace of one of the turtles stranded in August 1945 at Bude, North Cornwall, was found the clue to which I have referred: a little tuft of weed, an alga, which might be a national 'flag'. It was; it has been identified by two specialists as *Ectocarpus mitchellae* Harv., an American species, giving proof of Deraniyagala's view. This actual specimen, photographed by Dr. Wilson as it swam in a pool at Bude, is shown on Plate XXVI (p. 259). There are a few systematic botanists who will not agree that the American *E. mitchellae* and the closely related European form *E. virescens* are really two different species; however, they must be at least subspecies—separate geographical races.

Here, next to the reptiles, is perhaps as good a place as any to refer to the legendary sea-serpent. All the marine snakes that are known are of modest proportions, whereas the sea-serpent, if real, must, according to all accounts, be at least some twenty feet in length; indeed, in most such stories it is estimated to be much longer. The name 'serpent' for such an animal is a mere descriptive term to imply a long and sinuous form; it is rarely suggested that it is a true snake or even a reptile and those who claim to have seen it are not usually qualified zoologists.

References to the occurrence of such a creature go back to the middle
ages or even to classical times; one of the earliest of the collections of
these stories is to be found in the *Historia de gentibus septentrionalibus* ...
published in Rome in 1555 by the Swedish historian Olaus Magnus
(brother of Johannes Magnus, Archbishop of Upsala) and from here
they and their illustrations passed, with some scepticism, into Gesner's
great *Historia Animalium*.  It was however the account of Erich
Pontoppidan, Bishop of Bergen, in his *Natural History of Norway* of 1755
which first made some of the more modern naturalists take the sea-
serpent story seriously.  Since then there has been a long series of
reports; they are mostly fantastic, being due either to incorrect
observation or to definite hoaxes, but a very few remain which appear
to be well attested.

Before referring to the accounts which seem more worthy of
attention, let us consider some of the possible explanations for the
great majority of stories.  A school of dolphins or porpoises in line may
appear when seen from a distance to resemble a monstrous snake
with its body thrown into a series of undulations; a giant squid, itself
a most unusual sight, if seen swimming at the surface with its long arms
trailing behind it might well be called a serpent.  A whale or two
breaking surface in the distance, a flock of birds, ducks in line, large
masses of seaweed half awash or even the effect of wind upon the water,
perhaps seen in a poor light, may appear to a highly imaginative
traveller to be the fabulous monster he has always hoped to see.
Nearly all the dead remains of so-called sea-serpents reported in the
daily papers as washed up at some outlandish point on the Scottish or
Irish coasts have proved on examination by a zoologist to be those of a
basking shark; when decomposition sets in the enormously enlarged
gill slits of these fish (see p. 71) cause the lower jaw and all the underside of the throat to fall away and so leave a fantastic creature, perhaps
25 feet long, with a strange head and long serpentine neck (the
cartilaginous 'backbone').  It is little wonder that such a monster,
which cannot be found in any orthodox natural history, is heralded as
the "sea-serpent at last found in the flesh".

Perhaps the most authentic account of a sea-serpent is that from
H.M.S. *Daedalus* which was first reported in *The Times* of October
10th 1848 as follows:

"NAVAL INTELLIGENCE: Plymouth, Oct. 7.—when the Daedalus
frigate, Captain M'Quhae, which arrived here on the 4th instant,
was on her passage home from the East Indies, between the Cape of
Good Hope and St. Helena, her captain, and most of her officers

FIG. 107. A drawing copied from the engraving of the 'sea serpent' seen from
H.M.S. *Daedalus* and published in *The Illustrated London News* of Oct. 28, 1848;
the engraving is said to be accurately done from a sketch made at the time by the
officer of the watch.

and crew, at 4 o'clock one afternoon, saw a sea-serpent. The creature
was 20 minutes in sight of the frigate, and passed under her quarter.
Its head appeared to be about four feet out of the water, and there
was about 60 feet of its body in a straight line on the surface. It is
calculated that there must have been under water a length of 30
or 40 feet more, by which it propelled itself at the rate of fifteen
miles an hour. The diameter of the exposed part of the body was
about 16 inches; and when it extended its jaws, which were full of
large jagged teeth, they seemed sufficiently capacious to admit of
a tall man standing upright between them . . ."

This might have been dismissed as just another 'story' had not the
Captain, a few days later (*The Times*, October 14th), published the full
report which he sent to the Admiralty showing that this animal,
described in considerable detail, was seen at close quarters by several
officers and that a sketch was made of it immediately after it was seen.
In general his account agrees with the newspaper report but makes no

reference to its open mouth and jagged teeth. He later gave a good defence of his account against the scepticism of the great Sir Richard Owen. The officer of the watch, Lieutenant Drummond, wrote an independent but confirmatory statement in the *Zoologist* (December 1848). In Fig. 107, overleaf, I have made a drawing, from an engraving in the *Illustrated London News* of October 28th, 1848, which is said to be accurately redrawn from the Officer's sketch made at the time; unfortunately it proved impossible to reproduce the fine lines of the engraving in a text figure, but, if my officers on the poop are sketchy, I can vouch that my drawing of the animal itself follows the outline in the engraving exactly.

In 1892 Dr. A. C. Oudemans, a Dutch zoologist, published a large treatise on *The Great Sea-Serpent* (London, Luzac & Co.) in which he reviewed all the reports up to this date and from his analysis of them concluded that the mysterious animal was a very large and at present undescribed seal with a very long thin neck and tail. A year later came some support for this view in the account of Captain R. J. Cringle, master of the S.S. *Umfali*, of a creature seen off the west coast of Africa on December 4th, 1893. He writes "I saw full 15 ft. of his head and neck on three several occasions . . . The base, or body, from which the neck sprang, was much thicker than the neck itself, and I should not therefore call it a serpent".[1] Space will permit a mention of only one further report: that which appeared in the *Proceedings of the Zoological Society of London* for 1906 (pp. 719–21) from two naturalists, Mr. E. G. B. Meade-Waldo and Mr. J. Nicoll, who accompanied the Earl of Crawford on his yacht *Valhalla* and saw their 'sea-serpent' while cruising off the coast of Brazil. This animal also had a head on a long slender neck rising from a larger body in the water and there was a big oblong fin showing above the surface. The head was described as being shaped like that of a turtle "and it moved its neck from side to side in a peculiar manner". I am deliberately not discussing the so-called Loch Ness monster. If there is some strange creature there it is clearly not a sea-beast bigger than a seal which might make its way up the shallow River Ness; a suggestion has been made that there may be a large subterranean connection between the bottom of the loch and the sea, but this, of course, is quite untenable because the surface of the loch is 50 feet above sea-level.

It is difficult to believe that there can be in existence so large a mammal, or a reptile for that matter, that is so little known, and this for at least two reasons. Firstly such a large air breathing creature must surely show itself at the surface much more often than the 'sea-serpent'

[1]Quoted from *The Case for the Sea-Serpent* by R. T. Gould, London (P. Allen) 1930.

appears to do from the extreme infrequency of reliable accounts. Secondly there are no fossil remains of so large a seal-like mammal; and the reptilian plesiosaurs, which, with their long thin necks and tails, and total length of some 50 feet, would answer the descriptions well, all became extinct in the Cretaceous. It is true that the recently discovered coelacanth fish was thought to be extinct for a still longer period—but compared to a plesiosaur it is small and apparently very confined in its distribution; and being a fish need not come to the surface.[1] Perhaps after all the 'sea-serpent' is a fish—a gigantic eel—which shows itself only on very rare occasions; a very large leptocephalus eel-larva has been caught for which as yet no adult is known. Lieutenant Drummond in his account of the *Daedalus* animal in *The Zoologist* (December 1848, p. 2306) writes "In fact it gave one quite the idea of a large snake or eel". It would, however, be a very unusual fish to swim with its head out of water for as long as the *Daedalus* animal appeared to do. The late J. R. Norman of the British Museum in his *A History of Fishes* (1931) writes:

"The Sea Serpents of Aristotle, Pliny, and other classical authors seem to have been nothing more than gigantic eels. The monster described as having the head of a horse with a flaming red mane is the Oar-fish or Ribbon-fish [our p. 76], a species which probably grows to more than fifty feet in length, and may sometimes be seen swimming with undulating movements at the surface of the sea. The famous Sea Serpent, measuring fifty-six feet in length, that was cast up on the shore of Orkney in 1808 was almost certainly this fish."

Some 'sea-serpents' may well be the oar- or ribbon-fish, but here Norman was evidently unaware of the reference which Sir Richard Owen made to the Orkney example in his criticism of the *Daedalus* account. I quote from his article in *The Times* of November 14th, 1848:

"The vertebrae of the sea-serpent described and delineated in the *Wernerian Transactions*, vol. I, and sworn by the fishermen who saw it off the Isle of Stronsa (one of the Orkneys), in 1808, two of which

[1]The interesting case of the false killer whale (*Pseudorca crassidens*), discussed on p. 288, might be referred to in this connection; before 1927 it was only known to Britain as a sub-fossil, whereas since then many have been stranded on our shores. If so large a creature (up to 18 feet in length) remained elusive for so long, why not also the sea-serpent? The false killer, however, may often have been seen before from ships without being correctly identified.

(vertebrae) are in the Museum of the College of Surgeons, are certainly those of a great shark, of the genus *Selache,* and are not distinguishable from those of the species called 'basking shark', of which individuals from thirty to thirty-five feet in length have been from time to time captured or stranded on our coasts."

And here we must leave this riddle of the sea.

# CHAPTER 15

# WHALES, WALRUSES AND 'WILD' MEN

HIGHER than the reptiles in the scale of vertebrates are the birds and mammals. The sea-birds form too big a subject to be included in a book dealing essentially with life below the surface and fortunately they have already been treated in a splendid volume in this series: *Sea-birds* by James Fisher and R. M. Lockley (1954). Among many other fascinating themes these authors clearly show the impact of these birds on the marine community by their predations upon fish and planktonic animals.

Had the great auk *Alca impennis* not been massacred to extinction— the last being killed in 1844—I should have been much tempted to include it; like its southern counterpart, the penguin, it was indeed an underwater bird. Swimming fast after fish and plankton it was beautifully adapted to aquatic life; its wings, like those of the penguin, were modified for aquatic locomotion and no use for aerial flight. Indeed a penguin swimming under water is really going through the motions of flying; it propels itself swiftly forwards by a quite slow and graceful flapping of its flipper-like wings which reminds one of a film of a flying bird projected in slow motion. In the southern ocean I have seen large schools of penguins swimming more than a hundred miles from land; they looked more like porpoises than birds—only breaking surface at intervals for air. While the other members of the auk family swim and hunt fish and plankton below the surface, none have become so completely aquatic; and they can still fly in the air. But there, I *am* bringing in the birds; and I must now stop and refer the reader to Fisher and Lockley's chapter on the auks.

We come now to the whales. The Cetacea (Gk. kètos, a whale), which also include the porpoises and the dolphins, must certainly come into a book on the open sea; here, however, they will only be treated briefly because they again have already been so well dealt with in this series of volumes—by my friend Dr. Harrison Matthews in his *British Mammals* (New Naturalist, 1952). In addition to describing our various species, he has written an excellent account of those peculiar anatomical and physiological characters by which these originally terrestrial animals have become so perfectly adapted to a completely aquatic life. I shall mainly summarise those features distinguishing the different kinds, so that they may be recognised if seen, and then discuss some aspects of their natural history and general mode of life to link them to the rest of our marine community. There are, however, some important discoveries regarding the adaptation of whales which have been made since the publication of Matthews's book, and these I shall presently mention.

Before the war it was not unusual to find, among a group of otherwise well-educated people, a number who thought that a whale was just a particular kind of exceptionally large fish. To-day, however, there can be few who have not, at any rate once, tried a whale steak for dinner and, finding it not unlike beef, have learnt the fact (at first most astonishing) that whales are just as much warm-blooded red-fleshed mammals as are oxen and sheep; and that long ago their ancestors walked the land as quadrupeds. The seals show us mammals well on the way to becoming aquatic animals but not yet completely so; they must come to land to have their young. In the whales the hind limbs are so reduced as to be invisible outside the body; they are only represented within by tiny vestigial thigh and pubic bones. The similarity of the general form of a whale to that of a fish—or an ichthyosaur—is one of the more obvious examples of an adaptational parallel or convergent evolution. Apart from its being a lung-breather and so forced to the surface at intervals for air, the most striking feature which distinguishes a whale from a fish is the fact that its tail-fin is horizontal instead of vertical. The nostrils have been moved to the very top of the head where, as the 'blow-hole' (in many whales they open together as a single aperture) they enable the whale to breathe without raising more than the smallest part of its body from the water; to bring this about there has been a considerable modification in the form of the front part of the skull. The blow-hole is in fact, in function and position, the counterpart of the snorkel on the conning-tower of the submarine. Many people imagine that typically a large fountain of water appears when a whale 'blows' for so it is often shown in the old

whaling pictures.  Usually, however, only a little water is shot out of
the blow-hole, just that which was filling the nasal passages; what is
usually seen looks like a puff of steam as is beautifully shown in the
aerial photograph of a school of fin whales in Plate XXVIII (p. 275).
Until quite recently it had been thought to be just the moist warm
breath condensing in the cooler air, as does our breath in winter; there
was, however, always a most inconvenient fact which was hard to
reconcile with such a view: the blow of a whale is just as visible in the
heat of the tropics as in the cold of the polar seas.   The reason has now
been discovered; there is a curious oily emulsion which is discharged
with the breath, but the reason for this we shall come to a little later.

The whole body of the whale is as beautifully streamlined as that
of any fish, and it has a smooth surface devoid of the usual mammalian
coating of hair.[1]  Its head and trunk region merge together without a
trace of the neck or shoulders of a terrestrial quadruped; this is achieved
by an extreme shortening of the neck vertebrae or by their fusion into
one mass, and the perfect curves of the body are helped by the great
development of fat below the skin.  This thick layer of blubber serves
both as an insulation to maintain the body heat in the cold polar seas
and as a food reserve, particularly for plankton-feeding whales, when
in waters where food is not abundant.  The external ears, which would
clearly obstruct the streamline flow, have disappeared; all that can be
seen, and seen with some difficulty, is a minute hole on each side of the
head, a little astern of the eye, leading into the inner organ of hearing.
This does not mean that the whales' hearing is poor; as we shall see, it
has recently been shown to be very acute.  The forelimbs are modified
as the so-called 'flippers'—a poor name because it suggests that they
are used, like the limbs of a turtle, to paddle the animal along; on the
contrary, they are elevating planes for steering up or down or to right
or left.  During the course of development the five-fingered 'hand' of
the young foetal whale is gradually converted into the 'flipper' as
shown in Fig. 108 opposite.  The whale swims by an oscillation of its
tail and the hind part of its body, in a similar style to a fish but in
another plane: its horizontal tail moves up and down instead of from
side to side.

Some whales are much larger than any terrestrial animal could
possibly be; they are in fact the largest animals of which we have any
knowledge either in the present or from the past, far larger than the
gigantic dinosaurs of the Mesozoic.  While *Brontosaurus* and *Diplodocus*
measured some eighty feet in length, a great deal of this was made up

[1]Actually most whales have a few hairs on the snout and the edge of the lower jaw,
especially young specimens.

of a very long thin neck and an even longer and more slender tail; the actual bulk of the body would be much less than that of a whale of the same length, and there are whales which are longer, reaching up to close on a hundred feet. The largest whale measured during the Discovery Investigations was a female blue whale of 98½ feet;[1] the largest whale to be weighed was an 89 foot member of the same species which scaled just over 120 tons (Mackintosh, 1942). This, as Dr. Mackintosh has said, equals the weight of some forty Indian elephants. It seems that mechanically there is no limit to the size that an aquatic animal might reach, whereas an elephant is near the limit of bigness for a terrestrial quadruped. The body of a whale is supported

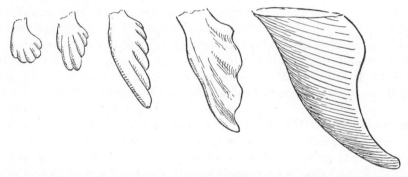

FIG. 108. Stages in the development of the flipper of an embryo porpoise showing how the typical five-fingered hand becomes modified into a plane-like flipper as the animal grows. Drawn from models in the British Museum (Nat. Hist.).

by the water all round it and its mass is no greater than that of the water it displaces. The mass, and consequently the weight, of the body of a land animal increases as the cube of linear dimensions, whereas the cross-sections of the legs which support it increase only as the square of these dimensions; this means that, with every increase in size, its legs, in order to support its weight, must become thicker in proportion to the length of the body. A terrestrial animal much larger than an elephant would have to have legs so thick that it could not walk with efficiency. It is generally believed that the Brontosaurus and similar very large dinosaurs were semi-aquatic, living in swamps so that much of their mass was water-borne.

What advantage has a whale in being so large, apart perhaps from being less vulnerable to attack simply on the grounds of bulk? It appears that the larger an aquatic animal is, the faster it can swim.

[1] I believe the Norwegians have measured one just over 100 feet.

This rather surprising conclusion is again one of those queer results of surface-volume relationships which we discussed in the first volume (p. 37) when considering some of the very small planktonic organisms; the larger the animal the greater is its volume in relation to its surface area. Since the power of swimming is dependent upon the quantity of muscle available and the hindrance to swimming is dependent very largely on surface resistance, it follows that the larger the animal the greater is the power developed in proportion to the frictional resistance to be overcome. Gawn (1948) refers to what he regards as reliable observations made in the Antarctic in 1946–47 to show that a "blue whale can attain a speed of 20 knots for a short burst of about 10 minutes and a speed of $14\frac{1}{2}$ knots for two hours and probably longer." He then estimates that 520 horsepower would have to be developed to drive a 90 ft. blue whale at 20 knots. Professor J. B. S. Haldane in one of his fascinating essays, 'On being the right size', (1927) refers us to the other end of the scale and explains why we can't have a whale the size of a herring. Whales range in size from the hundred-foot Blue Whale to the smallest dolphin of a few feet in length; but there is none as small as a hare, let alone a mouse. Again it is a question of volume and surface area. Mammals are warm-blooded animals and lose heat from their surface. The smaller an animal is, the larger is its surface in proportion to its volume, and thus the greater will be the loss of heat per unit of volume. A very small aquatic mammal would be unable to maintain its body temperature over a long period.

How long does a whale live? That is a question which has not been easy to answer. For years scientists have been on the lookout for some feature of the whale's anatomy which might give an indication of age as do the scales and otoliths of a fish. From the study of the ovaries it is possible to know how many young a whale has had, and, since they normally breed every two years and have one calf at a time, it is possible to get a rough indication of the age of a female whale. Exceedingly fine ridges in the baleen plates of plankton-feeding whales were then shown to be arranged in a manner so as to show annual growth zones; but unfortunately, as the whale gets older, the plates wear away at their edges and so a complete record of the past years of life is lost. At last a new method has been discovered in a most unexpected place, but to explain it we return to the ear of the whale.

Because their external ear holes are so small it used to be thought that whales had poor hearing; we know now, however, that they are sensitive to a wide range of sound-wave frequencies. And further, by listening with hydrophones, they have been heard to emit a great variety of sounds "from a low rattling to high pitched whistles." In the large whalebone whales there has been found superimposed upon the eardrums a long waxy plug which has excellent sound-conducting properties. When a longitudinal section of this was examined it was seen to be formed in a series of layers and these are now shown to be formed annually so that they can indeed be read like the rings on the scale of a fish (Purves, 1955, and article in *The Times,* May 25th, 1957). In the last-mentioned account the known life-span of a whale is said to be 50 years, according to the oldest specimen examined.

The studies by Dr. F. C. Fraser and Mr. P. E. Purves on the hearing of whales made at the British Museum (Natural History) have had another most unexpected outcome. They had shown that the organs of hearing in whales are separated from the rest of the skull and surrounded by a sound-insulating layer of a fatty foam contained in large recesses connected with the middle ear; such an arrangement prevents interference in the whale's determination of the direction of the origin of any sound. They have now shown (Fraser and Purves, 1955) that this foam also occurs in the lungs and suggest that, as fat has a nitrogen absorptive capacity six times greater than blood, this fatty foam emulsion is ideal for the absorption of this gas, and so serves yet another purpose, linked to a further one-time puzzle.

As Matthews has so clearly explained a whale does not suffer from caisson sickness when coming up from a deep dive because it has not been breathing air continually supplied under pressure as a diver has. Caisson sickness is, of course, caused by nitrogen, dissolved into the blood *under pressure,* coming out in the form of fine bubbles (like those in sodawater) if the diver is brought to the surface, i.e. to a lesser pressure, too quickly. The lungs of the whale contract under pressure and the air is forced into rigid sinuses like those just mentioned surrounding the ear. It now seems likely that a fresh fatty emulsion is continually being formed which absorbs the nitrogen as the lungs contract and so prevent it going into the blood. Fraser and Purves also believe that it is some of this emulsion which is exhaled with the breath as the whale blows and that it is this which is seen in the tropics when it is too warm for normal breath to condense and show. "If the oil-nitrogen absorption idea is correct", they say, "it would be expected that an animal of the size and deep-diving capacity of the sperm whale would require a very considerable reservoir, such as the spermaceti organ, of liquid oil for emulsification, to replenish that lost at each exhalation."

As to the different kinds of whales, no fewer than twenty-four species have been recorded from British waters. There are two sub-orders: the Mystacoceti, or Mysticeti of some authors, (Gk. *mystax,*

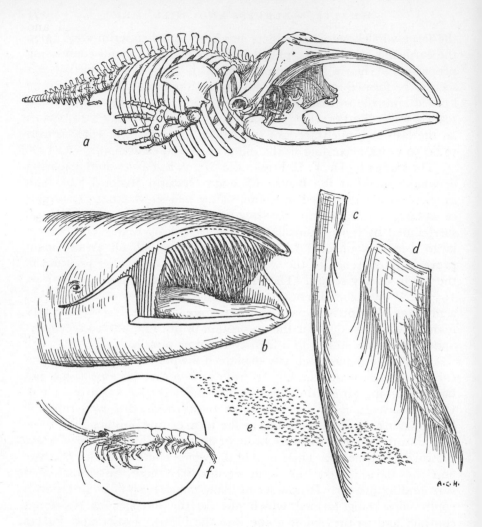

FIG. 109. The feeding of a 'whalebone' whale. *a*, the skeleton of an Atlantic right whale drawn from the right front to show, in relation to *b*, the huge jaw bones which provide the frame for the capacious mouth; note, in passing the massive ribs and, behind them, the tiny pair of pelvic-bones which are all that remain of the hind limbs of their long past terrestrial ancestors. *b*, model of the mouth of the same whale with the right side of the lower jaw cut away to show the tongue and baleen plates of which some from the right side have been removed to show the full set opposite. *c* and *d*, single baleen plates of a right whale and a rorqual respectively, with *e* a swarm of krill or euphausiacean 'shrimps' (their food) to scale and *f* one greatly enlarged, on that scale, but actually life size. (*a–d* are drawn from exhibits in the British Museum of Natural History).

*mystakos,* moustache; and *kètos,* a whale) or whalebone whales; and the Odontoceti or toothed whales (*odons, odontos,* a tooth).  The whalebone whales are all relatively large and have no teeth;[1] instead their mouths are furnished with a remarkable series of horny plates, the so-called whalebone or baleen, which project downwards along the inside of the margins of their upper jaw.  These plates are frayed out into a fringe of fibres like a vast moustache—but inside the mouth—hence the name Mystacoceti; they form a tremendous filtering system as shown here in Fig. 109.  The whalebone whale's mouth is enormous.  Great quantities of water are taken in and then forced out sideways through the filters by the piston-like action of a gigantic tongue; all the larger plankton animals contained in the water are now left as a deposit upon this huge moustache and are thought to be wiped off and passed to the gullet by a further movement of the tongue.  The fact that there are no small whalebone whales, corresponding in size to the porpoises and dolphins among the toothed whales, is no doubt due, as Harrison Matthews points out, to there being a size below which such a filtering mechanism, for the larger plankton animals, ceases to be efficient.  We have seen that there are plenty of *very small* filter feeders catching the micro-plankton.

There are two main families of the whalebone whales: the right whales or Balaenidae, and the rorquals or Balaenopteridae.  The *right* whales were so called by the early whalers to distinguish them from other kinds which for the 'fishery' were the *wrong* ones, either because of their lacking certain qualities or being more difficult or impossible to catch.  Only one species of right whale may be met with off the British Isles: the rare Atlantic right whale (*Balaena glacialis*) shown in Fig. 110 (p. 277).  It was once much more numerous, being often called by its Dutch name, nordkaper, and was the quarry of the first whale fishery in Europe.  The Basques in the Bay of Biscay in the tenth or eleventh century are usually referred to as being the earliest whalers; there seems, however, little doubt that the same species was being hunted by the Norwegians about the same time, for Ottar mentions such whaling in a report he made to King Alfred on his voyage of discovery to the White Sea in about 890.  The now familiar story, of great success, followed by overfishing and failure due to the collapse of the stock, has marked the history of all the different whale fisheries in northern waters down the centuries.  The nordkaper was fished out from one area after another, as was later the more northern and larger Greenland right whale (*Balaena mysticetus*).  There was a time when the nordkaper was thought to be extinct; but when a whaling station was

[1]Little vestigial teeth come and go during early development.

operating in the Hebrides before the First World War, *glacialis* was not infrequently taken; of sixty-seven specimens measured, the largest went to fifty-nine feet.

A right whale is usually black all over and may be distinguished from the rorquals by having no fin on its back, by the much shorter and more rounded flippers, by the more arched appearance of the jaws and the much greater length of the baleen plates. These horny baleen plates, which can measure up to nine feet in length, were of great value in providing the 'whalebone' of former days, when it might fetch a price of over £2,000 a ton; but that was the time when it was much in demand for those almost forgotten objects of ladies' wear—the corsets of yesterday. A single Greenland right whale might produce as much as one and a half tons of whalebone as well as nearly thirty tons of oil. The small sailing vessels going whaling in those days cost little to maintain, so that the capture of a single whale might save a serious loss, two would give a profit, and three a handsome dividend. A multitude of such small expeditions reduced the Greenland right whales almost to the point of extinction in one area after another, just as they had done with the nordkaper further south. The great whaling fleets built up during the seventeenth and eighteenth centuries at Hull and Dundee, and a number of smaller ports, such as Peterhead and Whitby, dwindled; the last northern whaling ship from Hull, the *Truelove,* sailed in 1868. Just at that time, in 1865 to be exact, a Norwegian named Sven Foyn invented a gun which fires a large harpoon with an explosive shell at its head; this, together with the introduction of the fast steam whale-catchers, enabled the larger, more powerful and faster rorquals to be fished for the first time. The right whales by comparison are relatively sluggish animals, easily approached by a rowing boat and attacked with the hand harpoon; the rorquals could never be hunted by such means.

The fishing for rorquals in the north followed the same sad history of overfishing in area after area as had that for right whales, but much more quickly. At the turn of the century, just when it began to look as if whaling in the world was rapidly nearing its end, reports of enormous numbers of rorquals in the Antarctic seas began to be received. That enterprising Norwegian whaling captain, C. A. Larson, who had already made several sealing voyages to the south in the eighteen-nineties, went in 1902 with Nordenskjold's Swedish expedition; indeed he captained the *Antarctic,* which was crushed in the ice of the Weddell Sea. He came back convinced of the great possibilities of whaling in the south and tried to raise the capital to found a station at South Georgia, that mountainous island some 800 miles east by south of

Plate XXVII. (above) a. Fin whales (Balaenoptera physalus) at the surface.
(below) b. A large blue whale B. musculus drawn up on the plane of a whaling station.

('Discovery' Investigations)

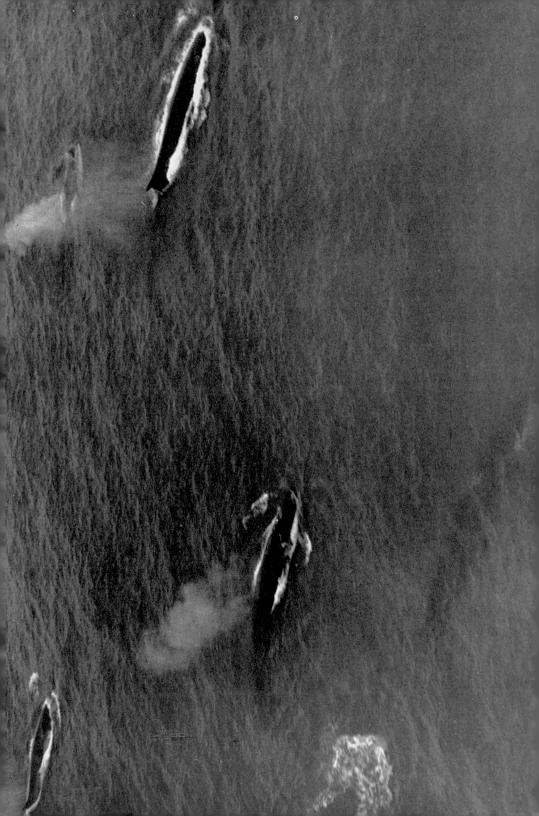

Cape Horn; he failed to get the money in Europe but was successful in South America. The first whaling station in the south was founded by an Argentine company at South Georgia in 1904. It was an instant success. By 1911 there were no fewer than eight whaling stations established there and twelve 'floating factories' visiting the South Shetlands further to the south. The so-called floating factories of those days were mostly old ocean liners saved from the breakers and converted to carry all the equipment of a whaling station; they steamed south to anchor for the season in certain natural harbours among the Antarctic islands of the South Shetlands and South Orkneys, and were each served by a small fleet of whale-catchers just like a shore station.

Never before had whaling been carried on on such a scale. It is of interest here to recall the remarkable prophecy of Dr. George Forster (1777), who accompanied Captain Cook on his voyage in the *Resolution* when he discovered and laid claim to South Georgia in 1775. He wrote in his account of the voyage as follows:

"If the northern ocean should ever be cleared of whales by our annual fisheries, we might then visit the other hemisphere where these animals are known to be numerous. However, there seems to be little necessity to advance so far as New Georgia in quest of them,

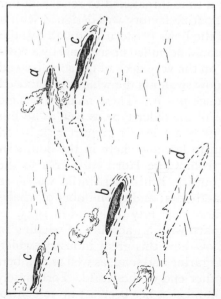

*Plate XXVIII.* A school of fin whales (*B. physalus*) photographed from the air, showing all stages in the process of surfacing and 'blowing': *a.* breaking surface and beginning to blow; *b.* exhalation finished and inhalation beginning; *c.* blow-hole just submerging at end of breathing and dorsal fin showing; *d.* whale completely submerged after blowing. The photograph was taken from a helicopter in the Antarctic by Mr. M. Vardy, a whale spotting pilot attached to the Floating Factory Ship *Southern Harvester.*

F &F—T

since the Portuguese and North Americans have of late years killed numbers of them on the coast of America, going no farther than the Falkland Islands. It should therefore seem probable, that though Southern Georgia may hereafter become important to mankind, that period is at present so far remote and perhaps will not happen, till Patagonia and Tierra del Fuego are inhabited and civilized like Scotland and Sweden."

The whales which Forster was referring to as being fished off South America and the Falklands were the southern right whales which are very similar to the northern Atlantic right whale; these, also like those of the north, were almost exterminated in the early part of last century.

South Georgia, the South Shetlands and South Orkneys, together with that sector of the Antarctic mainland, are Dependencies of the Falkland Islands and so part of the British Empire. Realising that if nothing was done the southern stocks of whales would suffer the same fate as those of the north, the Colonial Government limited the number of whale-catchers; they further levied a tax on the industry to finance research into the biology of the southern whales so that any further restrictive legislation might be based on scientific fact. It was this fund which paid for the series of Discovery expeditions which sailed to the south between 1925 and the second World War. Just as these investigations were giving us the required information a change occurred in the industry which for a time threatened to render all our efforts of no avail. A new type of floating factory was designed with a large mouth-like opening, either in the bows or stern; through this the whales, harpooned by the catchers, could be pulled up a tunnel by a powerful winch and cable to be flensed on the very deck of the ship, instead of alongside as hitherto. The ship now swallows the whale; it is indeed "Jonah avenged", as a journalist once put it. These modern pelagic factory ships rapidly replaced those of the older type as well as all but a very few of the shore stations; they no longer required sheltered waters in which to work and began to fish anywhere in the Southern Ocean along the edge of the ice from Cape Horn eastwards to the Ross Sea. They thus now fished outside British territorial waters so that we lost any control over their activities; and the number of whales killed per year increased to somewhere near fifty thousand in 1935.

But I must not take up more space with an account of whaling in the far south; I merely want to show how this great industry, which produces the valuable oil for our margarine and soap, as well as numbers of by-products, has shifted to the other end of the world. Fortunately now the International Whaling Commission has been set up to control

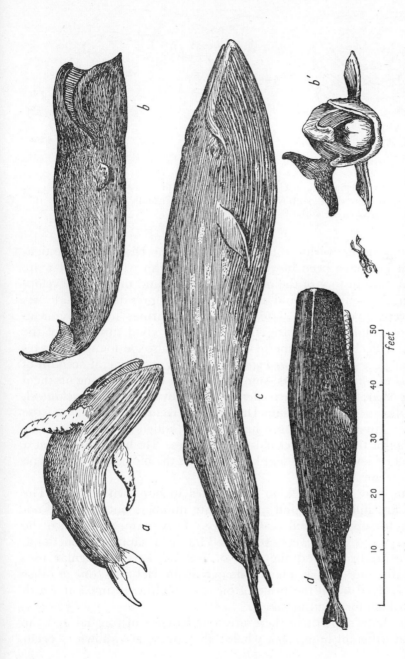

FIG. 110. A group of large whales, and a 6 ft. frogman, drawn to the same scale (shown below them in feet). *a*, the hump-back, *Megaptera novaeangliae*; *b* and *b'*, side and front views of the North Atlantic right whale, *Balaena glacialis*; *c*, the blue whale, *Balaenoptera musculus*; and *d*, the sperm whale *Physeter catodon*. Sketched (except the frogman) from scale models in the whale gallery of the British Museum.

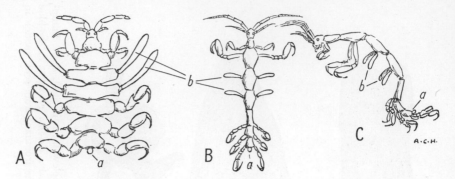

FIG. 111. A, the whale-louse *Cyamus* compared with *Caprella* (which feeds on hydroids) seen viewed from above (B) and, as more usually, from the side (C). *a*, the reduced abdomen; *b*, the branchiae (gills).

the whaling of the world, so that the work of the Discovery Investigations will not have been in vain. For those who wish to read more about the past history of the northern whaling and the early developments in the south I would recommend two presidential addresses which were given by the late Sir Sidney Harmer to the Linnean Society of London (1928, 1931). A short but vivid summary of the course and decline of northern whaling will also be found on pages 436–40 of James Fisher's *The Fulmar* (1952). For a general account of the stocks of southern whales, summarising all the work done on them up to the War, there is the excellent account by Dr. N. A. Mackintosh (1942) who succeeded the late Dr. Stanley Kemp as Director of the Discovery Investigations and has himself added so much to our knowledge of these huge yet elusive creatures. He has also written a very good review of our present knowledge of the biology of whalebone whales in general (1946).

Let us now come back to the whales in our own waters. The rorquals are still to be found in moderate numbers but there are not sufficient to support a full scale fishery. It is many years since the whaling stations which were established for their capture at Shetland, the Outer Hebrides and the west of Ireland were in regular use; occasionally, however, as a few years ago at the Hebrides, one or other may be revived when the price of oil is so high as to make it worth while working for small numbers.

In the Balaenopteridae there are four species[1] of rorqual and the somewhat different humpback whale; all of these are known to occur

[1]Bryde's whale (*Balaenoptera brydei*) is sometimes distinguished from the sei whale (*B.borealis*) as a fifth species which appears to be confined to South African waters.

Plate XXIX. Humpback whales (*Megaptera novaeangliae*) photographed from the air. (*above*) *a*. A mother with a newly-born calf; note the very long flippers (as shown in Fig. 110, p. 277) (*below*) *b*. two humpbacks sounding; flippers pressed back against body. Photographs taken by Mr. S. Fowler from a plane during fishery exploration flights off the coast of Australia (see fuller acknowledgment on p. XII in Author's Preface)

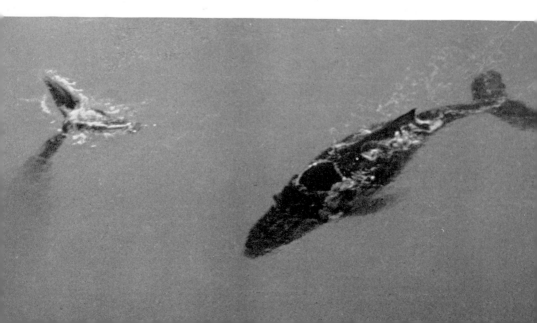

in our waters. They all have a small fin on their backs at about two thirds of the way down the length of the body; and they all have a large number of parallel grooves along the underside of their throats. These grooves are generally thought to serve as 'pleats' to allow for the fullest expansion of the mouth cavity when a great gulp of water is taken in in feeding, but it has also been suggested that they may have a stabilizing effect like the bilge keels of a ship. Let us look first at the humpback, *Megaptera novaeangliae*, which we see in Plate XXIX and Fig. 110 (pp. 277 and 278). It has rather a robust body tapering markedly towards its tail; it is black above, white below and particularly characterized by extremely long, slender and slightly curved flippers nearly a third of the length of the whole animal. Humpbacks at times, as if in play, make extraordinary manoeuvres in the water, sweeping this way and that and rolling over at the surface, and sometimes waving their long flippers in the air. The front edges of their flippers bear a number of irregular knobs and these, together with a copious growth of large white acorn-barnacles (*Coronula*), which infect the flippers as well as the head regions, give this whale a unique if somewhat untidy appearance. Growing on the acorn-barnacles in turn may often be found clusters of the stalked-barnacle *Conchoderma* which add to the Caliban-like effect. The remarkable whale-louse *Cyamus* (or *Paracyamus*), which is shown in Fig. 111 (p. 278) is also particularly common on the humpback as well as on the right whale.

This little crustacean is—though you would hardly believe it—an amphipod; it is as a matter of fact a close relative of those extraordinary caprellid amphipods which, as described in our earlier volume (p. 170) are specialized for feeding upon hydroids. *Cyamus* has the same comically reduced abdomen and an exactly similar arrangement of limbs; it is a curiously flattened and shortened version of the slender *Caprella,* such as might be seen if that creature were to disport itself before the appropriate kind of distorting mirror. How is it possible that the members of this one family of very aberrant crustacea should have become specialized to live upon two such very different organisms as the delicate little sedentary hydroids of our coasts and shallow seas, and the great fast-moving monarchs of the open ocean? Did ancestral

---

*Plate XXX.* An unusual view of a male sperm whale (*Physeter catodon*). This is one of two which, after being stranded on the coast of Holland, were towed to Rotterdam and lifted out of the water onto the quay for dissection. (A photograph kindly supplied by Professor H. Boschma of the University of Leiden). The belly of the whale is facing us; note the following: relatively small lower jaw, the sockets in the upper jaw into which the teeth of the lower jaw fit when the mouth is closed, the very small flippers and the penis further back.

whales, perhaps slower than those of to-day, once carry fringes of hydroids growing upon them as well as barnacles? It is a mystery whose solution may well be buried for ever in the past; the one I have just suggested, however, seems to me the most feasible. It is not difficult to imagine that the original hydroid browsers changed their habits when they found by chance that their usual diet was growing, not on stones, but upon a bed of food as rich as butter.

We must pass now to the true rorquals belonging to the genus *Balaenoptera*. They all have very much the same shape of body—longer, more slender, more truly stream-lined than that of the humpback; they also have much shorter flippers and very many more of the parallel grooves on the throat and chest. The four species differ mainly in size, colour and habits. The blue whale or sibbald's rorqual,[1] *Balaenoptera musculus*, Plate XXVII (p. 274) and Fig. 110 (p. 277) is the largest and measures up to a hundred feet, although eighty-five feet is a more usual size. It is a dark bluish grey all over its body and is more or less (in different specimens) mottled with pale oval spots. The fin whale or common rorqual, *B. physalus,* on Plates XXVII and XXVIII, comes next in size, reaching up to eighty feet but more usually about seventy; it is dark grey above and white below. The sei whale or Rudolphi's rorqual, *B. borealis,* is again smaller, growing to sixty feet, though often only about fifty feet; it is bluish grey on the back but grades off to a lighter shade on its belly. It differs further from the blue whale in being without the lighter mottling, and from the fin whale in never having the white underside to the flippers. Lastly comes the small lesser rorqual or pike whale, *B. acutorostrata,* which never exceeds about thirty feet and is in proportion somewhat stouter than the other species; it is coloured not unlike the fin whale except for a most striking distinguishing badge: a white patch on the outer surface of its flipper, as if it were wearing an arm-band.

The blue, fin and sei whales, like the humpback, are world-wide in distribution; and like those in the Antarctic, the northern members migrate towards the equator to breed in winter. These four species pass along the western coasts of the British Isles, going south in the autumn and north again in the spring; so they were taken by the whaling stations on the Hebrides or west of Ireland, and today are still occasionally stranded on our shores. Whether there is any interchange between the stocks of the southern hemisphere with those of the north we do not know, but it seems unlikely, for the stocks which were

[1]It has also been called the sulpher-bottom whale on account of a yellowish scum of diatoms which these whales usually carry when they first return to polar waters again after visiting warmer latitudes for breeding.

reduced so much by overfishing in the north at the beginning of the century do not appear to have been made up by any influx from the south. It is surprising that so far no character differences, except perhaps size, have been found between examples of the same species from the two poles. We might have expected the formation of distinct geographical races; Dr. Mackintosh tells me that there is now some evidence that the average length at sexual maturity of the northern rorquals is a little lower than that of the southern ones, but that may simply be due to richer supplies of food in the south. The blue whale feeds almost entirely upon the shrimp-like planktonic Euphausiacea, known to the Norwegians as *krill,* which occur in immense swarms (of different species) in the polar seas both north and south. The fin whale and the humpback also take krill, but may, in addition, supplement their diet by taking shoaling fish such as the herring.

I spent two years of my life studying the distribution of the krill and other plankton animals in relation to the movements of these three species of whale in the Antarctic when on the 1925–27 *Discovery* Expedition. The immense swarms of the krill there have to be seen to be appreciated; it is likewise very impressive, when a whale-stomach is cut open on the flensing platform, to see a cartload or so of these little shrimps come gushing out. At the time when we were making our survey of the distribution of the krill round the island of South Georgia we got the whalers to record on charts just where they caught their whales so that we could map their concentrations as well; we found a close correspondence between the contours of abundance for the whales and those for the krill during the same period (Hardy and Gunther, 1935).

The sei whale has a finer sieve of baleen fibres which enables it to collect still smaller plankton animals—such as the copepods, like *Calanus,* that often swarm in enormous numbers. The lesser rorqual, in addition to catching plankton, takes fish—particularly herring—perhaps more than any other of the whalebone whales; it comes into the North Sea round the north of Scotland, and follows the movements of the different shoals of herring as they come in in sequence further and further to the south as the autumn advances, and may often be seen on the East Anglian grounds in October and November. The lesser rorqual is thought to be world-wide in range like the other species, but little is known of its distribution because it is too small to be worth hunting commercially for its oil; recently, however, it has been taken extensively by the Norwegians for meat. It can often be seen close against the coast in Scottish waters, whereas the larger species tend to keep to deeper water.

It was during the *Discovery* Investigations that Mackintosh and Wheeler (1929), while working at the Grytviken whaling station at South Georgia, and also at others on the African coasts, made their remarkable discoveries as to the rates of growth of young whales. Most whales produce only one calf at a time, although occasionally twins have been recorded. The blue whale calf is born at a length of about twenty-three feet, a little over a quarter of the length of its mother, and it grows to this huge size in but eleven months of gestation; this must be a record rate of growth, showing how rich in nutriment the krill must be to supply the mother with the necessary material. In the southern stock the calves are usually born in May (but a few may be earlier or later) and accompany their mothers until they are weaned some six months later, by which time they have travelled to the rich krill feeding grounds around South Georgia or along the edge of the ice, and their baleen plates have grown large enough to form effective collectors. The teats of the mother, when not in use, lie hidden in grooves on either side of the reproductive aperture, but in suckling they are protruded to be taken by the calf. At weaning the blue whale calf has reached a length of some fifty-two feet—as big as an adult humpback or a sei whale—and by the time it reaches its first birthday it will have added ten more feet to its length. At two years old it may be up to seventy-five feet long and reaches sexual maturity; it goes on growing, however, till it reaches a length of some ninety to one hundred feet. With the fin whale the story is very similar but the size reached is not so great.

In 1913 Sir Sidney Harmer, then Keeper of Zoology and later Director of the British Museum (Natural History), started a scheme with the Board of Trade for the reporting to the Museum of all stranded whales, dolphins and porpoises; this has been continued ever since, giving some most valuable information. From time to time reports are published giving the results[1] which have added much to our knowledge of the cetaceans in our seas, particularly regarding some of the lesser-known and smaller toothed whales to which we shall now be referring. Much of the information given here regarding these species is obtained from this source. The British Museum has also published a most useful *Guide for the Identification and Reporting of Stranded Whales, Dolphins, Porpoises and Turtles on the British Coasts* by F. C. Fraser and H. W. Parker (1953) with excellent illustrations and clear descriptions of all the species.

The toothed whales or Odontoceti are characterized by the absence of baleen plates and, of course, by the presence of teeth. Unlike those of

[1] S. F. Harmer (1914–27) and F. C. Fraser (1934 and 1946)

nearly all other mammals, the teeth of whales cannot be distinguished as incisors, canines, molars and premolars; they are all alike, and there are far more of them than in a typical mammal. The sperm whale or cachalot, *Physeter catodon*, Plate XXX and Fig. 110 (pp. 279 and 277) is the largest, but being a warm-water species is only very rarely seen round our coasts. Those that are seen are nearly always males and it was thought that they were the old ones that tend to wander off on their own from the rest of the stock: Clarke (1954a) now finds some evidence that they are not necessarily old, but no doubt adult males. Nine have been reported since 1913. The males reach a length of sixty feet, double the length of the females. No other whale could be mistaken for the sperm whale with its enormous square-fronted head and relatively short and narrow lower jaw very much 'underslung' beneath it. This huge head forms a reservoir of a liquid wax—that curious substance Spermaceti—which is just fluid at body temperature. Its real function has always been a puzzle and I had thought that it might perhaps be concerned with buoyancy, like the 'balloon' of lighter oil which enables the bathyscaphe to rise from the depths; but now, on p. 271, we have seen a new and more feasible suggestion. There is evidence, as we shall see, that the sperm may go a good deal deeper than other whales and so may require this greater store of oil for nitrogen absorption. The lower jaw bears numerous large pointed teeth which fit into sockets in the seemingly toothless upper jaws when the mouth is closed; actually there are small rudimentary teeth in the upper jaws which usually remain covered by the gums, but may occasionally be exposed. It is a dark bluish grey and has a small hump-like fin about two-thirds of the way down its body and a number of secondary humps between this and the tail. The world-wide fishery for sperm whales carried out by the New England whalers in the warmer seas, and immortalized by the story of *Moby Dick*, has long been over. It ended not by overfishing, but because the oil of the sperm whale is so much less valuable than the rorqual oil and usually cannot compete with the mineral and vegetable oils. In the Azores, however, there is still a sperm whale fishery carried out from open boats with hand harpoons, a remarkable survival from earlier days; this has recently been so well described by Dr. Robert Clarke (1954a) who has accompanied the whalers in the chase. Actually, since the last war, there has been some increase in the taking of sperm whales by the large factory ships in the off-season of rorqual fishing.

In Part I (p. 288) I dealt with the importance of the oceanic squids in the diet of the sperm whale. After referring to some of the instances of the really giant kinds being taken, I quoted a personal communication from Dr. Clarke telling me that of the 112 squids which he had taken from sperm stomachs in the Azores, the largest measured only 8 feet (i.e. body and arms, but excluding the long tentacles) while the average length was just on 3 feet. Since then (1956b) he has, also at the Azores, recovered from the stomach of a 47 foot sperm whale a complete and intact giant squid, *Architeuthis sp.*, measuring 34 ft. 5 ins. from the tail to the tip of the tentacles, or 16 ft. 3 ins. excluding the long tentacles; it is interesting to know that these whales can swallow so large a mouthful whole. Clarke has also lately published (1956a) his full report on the biology of the sperm whales of the Azores. He finds, as already quoted in Part I, that various fish may also be taken from time to time and among these he now includes a young 8 foot basking shark. In addition, however, and more surprising, he quotes other naturalists occasionally finding benthic animals such as spider-crabs, skates and octopus in sperm whale stomachs; so at times they must actually visit the sea-floor in search of food. More recently there has come further striking evidence that this indeed is so. B. C. Heezen (1957) has brought together no fewer than fourteen instances of sperm whales being found entangled in submarine cables. Six of these were from depths of about 500 fathoms and one as much as 620 fathoms. He concludes that the sperm whales must often swim along the sea floor at these depths and get their jaws entangled in cables whilst ploughing through the sediment in search of food. The cable is nearly always wrapped round the jaw and some-times round the flippers and body as well, as if the whale had got more tied up by its subsequent struggles. It is possible, as he says, that the whales may attack slack coils of cable thinking them to be items of food and so become entangled. Perhaps they mistake them for the coiling arms of octopus or squid?

Here I must say a word or two about that strange waxy substance ambergris which is obtained from the intestine of sperm whales or may sometimes be found floating in large lumps on the surface of the tropical seas or washed up on the beach. It is rightly regarded as treasure trove for it is still used in the scent industry as an essential fixative for perfumes and so fetches a high price, up to 25/- an ounce; its use in this respect is said to date from very early times in the Orient where it is also used to give flavour in elaborate cookery. It has been commonly stated, as for example by Beddard (1900), "to be pathologi-cal . . . , for those individuals (whales) in which it was found were dead or sickly"; and it was generally supposed to be caused by an irrita-tion of the intestinal wall by the sharp horny squid beaks which are frequently found embedded within it. Dr. Clarke, however, who is making a special study of ambergris, described (1954b) the finding of two exceptionally large masses of it, one weighing 926 lbs. and the other 340 lbs., in the intestines of whales which "had food in their stomachs and were both in good condition." He quotes Schwediawer writing in the *Philosophical Transactions of the Royal Society* of 1783 (Vol. 73, p. 226) as saying: "We may therefore define Ambergris as the praeternaturally hardened dung or faeces of the Physeter Macrocephalus, mixed with some indigestible relics of its food." Clarke then says:

"By the examination of these two great masses, and of smaller finds, and by descriptions in the literature, I am led to a similar conclusion. Local increase in water absorption by the large intestine, and the chemical transformations enacted by the resident intestinal bacteria, probably each play their part in the formation of ambergris from faeces impacted around some matrix of indigestible matter."

FIG. 112. *a*, Bottle-nosed whale, *Hyperoodon ampullatus;* (up to 30 feet); *b*, a small narwhal, *Monodon monoceros* (but they grow to 16 feet); *c*, the white whale or beluga *Delphinapterus leucas* (up to 18 feet but generally less). Sketched from casts in the whale gallery of the British Museum.

He then goes on to speculate on the possibility of producing ambergris in the laboratory for the perfume manufacturers by incubating sperm whale faeces in suitable conditions.

The so-called pigmy sperm whale or lesser cachalot, *Kogia*

*breviceps*, has not yet been recorded on the British coasts, but it must almost certainly come into our waters for specimens have been reported not so long ago from Brittany and Holland. Unlike the larger sperm whale it has a big, well-defined and curving fin half-way down the back. The bottle-nosed whale, *Hyperoodon ampullatus* (Fig. 112, p. 285), is much commoner, and forty-six strandings on our coasts since 1913 have been reported. The old males are larger than the females in a ratio of thirty to twenty-four feet. It can hardly be confused with others because of its bulging 'forehead' rising up just above its well-marked beak. Cuvier's whale, *Ziphius cavirostris;* Sowerby's whale, *Mesoplodon bidens,* and True's beaked whale, *M. mirus,* are rare whales with very much reduced dentition: a single pair of teeth in the lower jaw exposed in

FIG. 113. Skulls and tusks of two narwhals seen from above: a normal one with only one tusk developed and a rare example with two tusks. Drawn from specimens in the whale gallery of the British Museum.

the males but concealed below the gums in the female. The narwhal *Monodon monoceros* (Fig. 112) is an arctic species, but has been recorded five times on our coasts since the middle seventeenth century, including two records in the Thames estuary in 1949. The female is usually toothless but the male is characterized by one enormously enlarged tooth on the left side of the upper jaw which grows out into a very long and perfectly straight tusk with spiral grooves around it, reminding one of the traditional horn of the mythical Unicorn; indeed the narwhal's tusks were sold for large sums as 'unicorn horns' in the middle ages for their supposed property of being an antidote, when taken in powder form, against any kind of poison. No one seems to have put forward a reasonable suggestion as to the function of this amazing organ. It can hardly be used for spearing prey, for it is difficult to see how the victim, once impaled, could be removed from the spike; and no one appears to have seen rival males using them in

Plate XXXI. (above) a. A common dolphin (*Delphinus delphis*) leaping clear of the water; note the blow-hole showing at the top of the head (*D. Snow*). (below) b. A freshly-shot common porpoise (*Phocaena phocaena*)     (*Douglas Wilson*)

*Plate XXXII.* Rare visitors from the north. (*above*) *a.* a walrus (*Odobenus rosmarus*) photographed by Mr. Bruce Forman on the Aberdeenshire coast in February 1954. (*below*) *b.* A Greenland-type Kayak found off the mouth of the Don, Aberdeen, about the year 1728; in it was an Eskimo who died after being brought ashore. The man beside the canoe is 5 ft. 5 in. tall. The photograph is reproduced by kind permission of the Aberdeen University Anthropological Museum where the kayak is exhibited.

combat. But the tilting matches, if any, may take place well below the surface or only at night.

Very occasionally a narwhal may be taken with a pair of such tusks[1], as shown in Fig. 113, and then we have an extraordinary example of asymmetry; instead of the spiral grooves on the two tusks going in opposite directions to be 'mirror images' of one another in true symmetry, as in the spiral horns of an antelope, they both go in the same anticlockwise direction. There is a very curious asymmetry also in the skulls of many of the toothed whales and D'Arcy Thompson (1942) has connected this and the spiral grooves of the narwhal's tusk with the supposed swimming action of these animals giving the body a twisting motion. He thinks there is a lagging behind, or an incomplete response, in the fore-part of the body to the rotating impulse of the parts behind, or, as he says, "in the words of the engineer: a *torque of inertia*." The heavy rigid narwhal's tusk, he believes, exhibits such inertia and tends to lag behind the oscillations of the body; as it is growing and being formed at its roots, this inertia shows itself as a gradual rotation of the tusk in relation to the jaw; thus the grooves which are formed by the socket of the jaw tend to move round in a spiral in relation to the tusk and so give the rifling effect. Not everyone, I think, would accept this very ingenious explanation. What evidence is there in fact that these small whales when swimming oscillate more to starboard than they do to port?

The white whale or beluga, *Delphinapterus leucas* (Fig. 112), is another arctic and very rare species in our waters; it is similar in size to the narwhal, from twelve to sixteen feet and, like it, lacks a dorsal fin. Having no 'unicorn' tusk it might perhaps be mistaken for a female narwhal, but it has none of the mottling of dark spots of that species, being white or cream-coloured all over. Yet another northern species, but one common round the Shetland and Orkney Islands, is the pilot whale, blackfish or caa'ing whale, *Globicephala melaena* (Fig. 114). This is a larger animal, growing up to twenty-eight feet; it is black like the bottle-nosed whale, and has a very similar bulging 'forehead', but may be distinguished from it by its very short beak, long narrow flippers and much larger curving fin, placed almost half-way down its back. These whales often occur in large schools of a hundred or more, and in the Faeroe Islands are sometimes killed (for their oil) in large numbers by being frightened and driven ashore by a line of boats cutting off their retreat, when they have entered a narrow

[1]D'Arcy Thompson (1942, p. 907) records that the whalers say that the two-horned specimens are all females, and he also states that the famous two-horned skull in the Hamburg Museum is known to have belonged to a pregnant female.

bay or sea-loch. Risso's dolphin, *Grampus griseus*, is very similar in form to the pilot whale but smaller, with a less pronounced bulge to its head and no beak at all; it has a more southerly distribution in the Atlantic, as is shown by the fact that most of the forty-four strandings recorded on our coasts since 1913 were on our south and west coasts. The killer or grampus, *Orcinus orca*, occurs throughout the world and is as common in the Antarctic as in the north; it has been recorded stranded on our coasts twenty-five times since 1913. It is easily identified by its very striking black and white colouring which has the pattern shown in Fig. 114 opposite; the males grow up to thirty feet and the females to only fifteen. It is the most ferocious of all toothed whales and is the only one to feed largely upon other warm-blooded animals. Seals, and porpoises are taken in preference to fish and it is said that a school of killers will attack a large whale and tear it to pieces like a pack of wolves—but perhaps they can only so attack an old whale or one in poor condition. In polar regions they have often been seen to swim upward under an ice floe on which seals are resting in order to tip them into the water or actually to break up the ice. Ponting describes how on Scott's last expedition he had a narrow escape from such an attack whilst photographing on a piece of ice which was broken up under his feet; it was only by jumping from fragment to fragment that he escaped with his life. The false killer, *Pseudorca crassidens*, is entirely black and might perhaps be mistaken for the pilot whale, except that its head is more evenly rounded and its lower jaw does not extend so far forward as its snout; it has no beak at all. It is a whale with a curious history in British waters. Before 1927 it was regarded as one of the rarest of whales, being known only as a sub-fossil skeleton from the Cambridgeshire fens. It is evidently an oceanic species which only very occasionally comes into coastal waters; when it does, it is apt to get stranded in very large numbers if a school takes the wrong turning in unfamiliar shallow waters. Some 150 of them ran ashore in the Dornoch Firth in 1927, and there have since been other but smaller schools stranded on the coasts of South Wales in May 1934, and along the North Sea from the Tay to Lincolnshire in November and December, 1935.

The common porpoise, *Phocaena phocaena*, is by far the commonest of our cetaceans as well as our smallest.[1] The photograph on Plate XXXI, (p.286), shows its general form; it is black on its back, shading through grey to white on its belly. It grows to a length of six feet and is almost half that length at birth. It can readily be distinguished from the dolphins by lacking any trace of a beak, having a much less pronounced back fin and a shorter more rounded flipper. It is a fish-eater

[1]The smallest cetacean known is the tropical river dolphin.

FIG. 114. *a*, the killer whale, *Orcinus orca*, and *f*, the pilot whale or blackfish *Globicephala melaena;* and our five species of true dolphin all drawn to the same scale (see above): *b*, the white-beaked dolphin, *Lagenorhynchus albirostris; c*, the white-sided dolphin, *L. acutus; d*, the common dolphin, *Delphinus delphis; e*, the euphrosyne dolphin, *Stenella euphrosyne;* and *g*, the bottle-nosed dolphin *Tursiops truncatus*. Drawn in the whale gallery of the British Museum.

and, judging from the contents of the stomachs that have been examined, preys largely upon herring and whiting.

Lastly we come to the true dolphins, of which there are five species in our seas. The common dolphin, *Delphinus delphis*, also on Plate XXXI, is the second most abundant cetacean in our waters, judging by the number of strandings which have occurred since 1913. It can grow up to eight feet, but is more usually six feet in length. It is more slender, and so more graceful, than any of the other species; it has also a much longer beak than any other except the very rare euphrosyne dolphin, *Stenella euphrosyne,* of which only three specimens have been recorded from our coasts. These two species are very much alike but may be distinguished by their colour patterns. In Fig. 114 overleaf, the form and colouring of the five species of dolphins are compared to enable them to be more readily recognized. The common dolphin is very widely distributed in temperate and sub-tropical waters, being particularly common in the Mediterranean; the British Isles are on the northern edge of its range and it is much more common on our south and west coasts than it is to the north and east. Its food consists mainly of fish, such as mackerel, herring and pilchards, and also squid. Each jaw is provided on either side with a row of some forty to fifty sharp, slender conical teeth. The bottle-nosed dolphin, *Tursiops truncatus,* comes next in abundance to the common dolphin and is somewhat larger, up to twelve feet; its beak is much shorter and its body rather more robust. It is widely distributed in the North Atlantic. The white-beaked dolphin. *Lagenorhynchus albirostris,* may, as its name implies, be distinguished by its white beak from all others and particularly from its close relative *L. acutus,* the white-sided dolphin, which otherwise is very similar in shape, although different in colour.

The dolphins are among the most beautiful of animals to watch; either when they appear to be at play, turning this way and that in graceful curves and leaping free of the water in sheer abandon, or when, as so often seen from a ship, they form up in a line like a platoon of soldiers and for hours at a time glide along in front of the bows with what seems to be the minimum of effort. The splendid photograph of a common dolphin leaping clear of the water was taken by Dr. David Snow on the Oxford Exploration Club's expedition to the islands in the Gulf of Guinea.

Leaving the whales we pass to those mammals which are in the process of returning to the sea; to the seals or Pinnipedia (L. *pinna,* a fin; *pes, pedis,* a foot); they are an important sub-division of the large order Carnivora which contains the flesh-eating mammals such as the dogs, cats and bears. Incidentally, among the bears, of course, we see the polar bear spending much of its time in the water hunting fish and seals; it is the scarcity of food on the snow and ice bound land of the polar regions and the wealth of life in the sea that has drawn so many of the terrestrial animals back to the water for a livelihood. The polar bear is as yet little modified in structure, but by habit and behaviour it is a wonderful swimmer. The seals have gone far in bodily adaptation, but not yet so far as the whales; their limbs have become flippers and the hind ones, being stretched backwards to act as a tail fin, can no longer be used for locomotion on the land. And to the land they must return for breeding. Like the whales, the true seals have lost their external ears which would spoil their streamline form for swimming; the sea-lions and fur seals have not gone so far in this respect, they still have small ears showing.

There are only two species of seal which are truly British, breeding on our coasts, and in some places they occur in large numbers: the grey (*Halichoerus grypus*) and the common seal (*Phoca vitulina*). A year or two ago I should have said they were entirely coastal forms and should thus not be mentioned here at all; quite recently, however, an unexpected discovery was made by marking grey seal pups on the Farne Islands off the Northumberland coast. A year after marking one was caught on the coast of Norway and another on that of Denmark; they must then occur at times far out in the open sea. They will not be further discussed because they too have been so fully treated by Dr. Matthews; it was he who organized the marking experiments and told me of these remarkable journeys.

Very occasionally the walrus, *Odobenus rosmarus,* may be carried to British shores from its far away home—the ice floes of Greenland. Here indeed is a traveller across the sea. I am fortunate to be able to include in Plate XXXII (p. 287), the excellent photograph taken by Mr. Bruce Forman, of Aberdeen University, of a specimen which landed at Collieston on the Aberdeenshire coast on 24th February 1954. It was at first seen on shore a mile to the south of the village and then put off to sea again and came in later to the north of it, where it was photographed in the late afternoon. Mr. Forman (1954) states that it was almost certainly an immature female; he estimates that it was about 7 feet in length and weighed nearly half a ton. It was very much alive and charged the observers when they got to within fifteen feet of it. It disappeared during the night and was not seen again. Professor James Ritchie (1921) gives a list of 24 records of the walrus in the British area from 1815 to 1920: 9 from Shetland, 10 from Orkney, 3 from the Hebrides, 1 from England (mouth of Severn, 1839) and 1 from Ireland (mouth of Shannon, 1897); since then there have been two other records: Shetland, October 1926, and Gairloch, May 1928. In earlier times when the walrus was more abundant in the Arctic regions it was a much more regular visitor to our islands; since then it has been so much persecuted for its ivory and oil that it is now only to be found in the more remote parts.

Higher than the whales and seals in the marine community there is only man. Man the fisherman we have already dealt with, and man the ecologist will form the subject of the next and final chapter. There is, however, another way in which man figures in the natural history of the sea, and to that I shall now refer. Just as we have seen so many

F&F—U

different animals forced off the land to seek their living in the sea, so too has primitive man been forced by competition to go more and more to the sea for food; particularly is this so in the Arctic where conditions on land are so severe and the sea so rich in life. In the far north the eskimos form part of the wild marine community, living almost entirely off fish and seals, and eating their flesh raw. To-day no doubt many of them are coming under the influence of civilization; but only a little time ago they were men still in the wild, clothed in skins and hunting with spears and harpoons of bone and ivory. Having mentioned the vagaries of the moving waters in bringing at times turtles and walruses to our coasts from far off seas, I must also refer to the possibility that from time to time in the past Eskimos have been carried out of their way to reach our northern shores. Francis Douglas in his *A General Description of the East Coast of Scotland from Edinburgh to Cullen,* published in Paisley in 1782, refers to a Kayak in the museum of Marischal College at Aberdeen as follows:

" . . . a canoe, taken at sea, with an Indian man in it, about the beginning of this century. He was brought alive to Aberdeen but died soon after his arrival, and could give no account of himself. He is supposed to have come from the Labrador coast, and to have lost his way at sea. The canoe is covered with fish skins . . ."

Dr. W. Clark Souter (1934) quotes another account of the same thing from the unpublished diary of the Rev. Mr. Gastrell of Stratford-on-Avon (who figures in Boswell's Johnson) who made a tour of Scotland in 1760 and in his account of his visit to Aberdeen writes:

" . . . in the Church, which was not used, . . . was a canoe about seven yards long by two feet wide, which about thirty-two years since, was driven into the Don with a man in it who was all over hairy and spoke a language which no person there could interpret. He lived but three days though all possible care was taken to recover him."

The "all over hairy" most likely refers to his clothing of furs. Whether the kayak at that date was in a church and later removed to Marischal College, or whether he was confused as to where he saw it, the fact remains that the kayak is there to-day in the College museum for all to see; and it is undoubtedly of Eskimo type. I show a photograph of it in Plate XXXII (p. 287).

Mr. Ian Whitaker has recently (1954) published a most interesting review of this and other similar occurrences. He quotes from a *Description of the Isles of Orkney* written by the Rev. James Wallace, Minister of Kirkwall, in 1688:

"Sometime about this Country are seen these Men which are called *Finnmen*. In the year 1682 one was seen sometime sailing, sometime rowing up and down in his little boat at the south end of the Isle of Eda, most of the people of the Isle flocked to see him, and when they adventured to put out a Boat with men to see if they could apprehend him, he presently fled away most swiftly: And in the year 1684, another was seen from *Westra,* and for a while after they got few or no Fishes; for they have this Remark here, that these *Finnmen* drive away the fishes from the place to which they come.

These *Finnmen* seem to be some of these people that dwell about the *Fretum Davis* (Davis Straits) . . . One of their Boats sent from *Orkney* to *Edinburgh* is to be seen in the Physitians Hall, with the Oar and the Dart he makes use of for killing Fish".[1]

He further quotes from the Rev. John Brand's *A Brief Description of Orkney* of 1701:

There are frequently Finnmen seen here upon the coasts, as one about a year ago on *Stronsa,* and another within these few months on *Westra* . . . His boat is made up of seal skins, or some kind of leather, he also hath a Coat of Leather upon him, and he sitteth in the middle of his Boat, with a little Oar in his hand, Fishing with his Lines: And when in a storm he seeth the high surge of a wave approaching, he hath a way of sinking his Boat, till the wave pass over, lest thereby he should be overturned . . . "

Did these men really come all the way from Greenland—no doubt via Iceland and the Faeroes—or did they perhaps come from Lappland where it is said in former times they made sea-going skin boats? Or again, since there are accounts of Eskimos being taken with their clothing and kayaks from Greenland to be exhibited at the Court of Copenhagen, is it possible that some of these could have escaped and come here on an attempt to get back to their homeland? It is a pretty problem, because it has been generally believed that kayaks become

[1] Whitaker later refers to a minute of the College of Physicians in Edinburgh for 24 September, 1696 recording the transfer of such a boat to the University, which is stated as already having the oars of the boat and the "shirt of ye barbarous man yt was in ye boat." In 1865 the University gave a number of ethnographical specimens to the Royal Scottish Museum including two kayaks which are still there, but which, if either, is the one from Orkney is not certain.

waterlogged after about 48 hours in the water. The shortest direct distances linking Greenland, Iceland, the Faeroes and Orkney are 180, 275, 185 and 200 miles respectively. Whitaker, in spite of the difficulties, is forced to the conclusion that the 'Finnmen' were in fact Greenlanders (the modern designation for the Eskimos of Greenland) making the journey from their homeland."

CHAPTER 16

# THE ECOLOGISTS AND THE FUTURE

SOME people seem to think that the word ecology is just a more modern name for what they have always called natural history, and indeed there are zoologists who like to speak of their natural history observations as 'ecological studies'. There is, however, I believe a valuable distinction between the two; and since ecology[1] is a comparatively modern term, it is well to be clear as to what we mean by it.

I would define ecology as that branch of science which deals with the relations between living things and their surroundings; and in their surroundings we must include not only the physical environment but all the other living things, both animals and plants, within it. Natural history, as the words imply, is the description of nature. Ecology goes further; as a *science* it records organic inter-relationships in quantitative terms—it measures them—and in analysing the factors involved in their relationships it may use the experimental method. When we record that a particular kind of fish is confined to warm oceanic water and feeds upon various kinds of shrimps, that is simple natural history. When we can determine the temperatures and degrees of salinity which limit its distribution, and by a vast number of post-mortem examinations work out the average percentage constituents of its food at different times of the year and at different ages, we are then beginning to learn a little of its ecology.

Ecology is converting natural history into science, but in saying this I do not mean to say that ecology is superior to natural history which is, of course, basic to it all. While we do well to acclaim

[1] Originally spelt oecology (Gk. οικος, a house).

the advance of exactitude, let us not under-rate the contributions of the naturalists who, in the spirit of explorers, have revealed for us the marvellous multiplicity of animal life and, by their descriptions, have given us the facts of their structures and habits. Discoveries by observation may be just as fundamental as those made by the experimental method. We do well to remember that there is plenty of descriptive natural history in chemistry and physics, that, for example, dealing with the properties of the elements and compounds or the colours of the rainbow.

The aim of ecology, however, is not simply to express the inter-relationships of organisms with their environment in numerical terms; that in itself would be just a tedious refinement. It is from this quantitative analysis that the ecologists hope in time, step by step, to discover more of the laws operating in the world of living things. Some people seem to imagine that biology in the field cannot be more than natural history. 'By all means', they say 'get your ideas for research from nature, but you must then bring your hypotheses and material into the laboratory to be tested'. I once heard a well known zoologist say "Ecology only becomes really interesting when it turns out to be something else!" Certainly a great many hypotheses can only be tested in the laboratory; this must apply to nearly all problems whose solutions lie in the fields of physiology, biochemistry and micro-anatomy. Much of what is exciting in ecology does indeed reach its climax within the fields of laboratory research, but by no means all. In ecology experiments will come to play as big a part outside the laboratory as inside it, as the students of animal behaviour are so brilliantly showing.

The idea that science belongs to the laboratory, and that which lies outside is natural history, springs I think from the belief, held by many zoologists, that all biology will ultimately be explained in terms of physics and chemistry: that physiology, biochemistry and bio-physics are the scientific core of the subject. These indeed do at present appear to make up the science of the organism as analysed from within; but just as important is the science of the animal as a whole looked at from the outside as a living unity in relation to its surroundings. I believe that one day all science will be shown to be one; but I do not believe that all of biology will be reduced to the branches of science which we now know as physics and chemistry. Just as these branches are based upon statistical laws concerning the behaviour of electrons, atoms and molecules, so ecology is a science *in its own right* based upon the statistical study of the inter-actions of organisms as living wholes. Ecology could exist as a true science if the laws of physics and chemistry had not yet been discovered, although it would be a sadly limited science. Any one branch of science is handicapped without support from other branches; our ecology will be so much richer in the future when it gets more help from the rapidly developing studies of animal behaviour. To suppose that all the world is composed of nothing but the things of physics and chemistry is to my mind jumping to an unwarranted conclusion, and is altogether too naive a view. But I am straying into philosophy; I must return to the biological fold.

The ecologists in their science aim at building up a framework of knowledge which will eventually be exact enough to enable predictions to be made. They may still have far to go, but they are well on the way and in the foregoing pages I have already cited several examples of successful fishery forecasts being made.

Let us briefly remind ourselves of some of the difficulties in the path of the marine investigator; he is faced with two major handicaps which we do not usually meet with ashore. Firstly he is working in three dimensions. In most regions, forests being an exception, the land ecologist can think of his domain in plan; the extensions of life into the atmosphere and underground are slight, so that he need usually only consider the distribution of his animals in relation to the earth's surface and can plot and think about them on a two-dimensional map. In the sea one must take into account not only the horizontal movements of animals but also the extensive vertical ones they often make. And the environment itself is not stationary; in relation to the sea-bed the water is always on the move and it carries the drifting life which is the all-important food supply. A dense patch of plankton may be here to-day but gone tomorrow. What would the land ecologist say if his woods and meadows changed position over night? The second difficulty is more obvious and yet more formidable than the first: the marine ecologist, as we have already stressed, is working entirely in the dark, feeling for his facts in a world he cannot see.

Considering these obstacles, it does seem, at first, a rather curious fact that *animal* ecology has made much greater progress in the sea than it has upon the land. Only just now are a few ecologists beginning to put the study of the food and feeding habits of some of our common birds and mammals on a truly quantitative basis; at present we know far more about the food-relations of a number of marine fish than we do about those of any terrestrial animals. We have a better idea of the population density, per unit area, of different molluscs on many parts of the sea floor than we have of the snails of our countryside; our knowledge of the numbers of small crustacea per cubic metre of water in many seas of the world is far in advance of such information regarding the insect numbers on land. I think it possible that we know more about the ecology of the Dogger Bank and its overlying waters, than we do about the ecology of any English county.

It was Victor Hensen, I believe, who founded marine ecology when he began his quantitative plankton studies at Kiel in the eighteen nineties. By the later decision to divide my book into two volumes, after it was originally planned as one, I have inadvertently separated this main reference to his work from the volume specially dealing with plankton; this is unfortunate because it was, of course, Hensen who introduced the very word plankton for this drifting life. By using specially designed collecting nets of known filtering capacity, and hauling them up vertically at standard speeds, he estimated the number of plankton organisms per cubic metre of water under different parts of the sea. A photograph of his type of net is shown in Plate XXIV of our first volume (p. 289). By comparing the abundance of planktonic life in one area with that in another and at different times of the year in the same position, he and his colleagues made the first attempts at measuring organic production in the sea. In the earlier volume (p. 64) I referred to his famous plankton expedition of 1889 in which he first showed that the polar and temperate seas are richer in life than those of the tropics. Hensen also attempted to estimate the stocks of fish in the southern North Sea by measuring the number of floating eggs found per cubic metre of water in different areas; he was not, as some people thought, attempting to assess the number of fish which would grow up from the eggs, but, knowing the average fecundity of the principal species, he calculated the size of the stocks which would produce the quantities of eggs found. Hensen's methods are well described by Johnstone (1908). While he carried his estimations to far greater refinements than were warranted by his method of sampling, in view of our later knowledge of the patchiness of the plankton, he was the great pioneer of all the quantitative plankton work that was to follow.

Early in this century C. G. J. Petersen was beginning those comparative studies of the animal communities on the sea-bed of the Baltic to which we have already referred (p. 123), actually measuring the populations of the various species per square metre of the bottom in different areas. These too have led to quantitative studies of the benthos all over the North Sea and in many other parts of the world.

A study of the periodic fluctuations in the fish populations was well under way before the first world war; and as early as 1907 Johan Hjort was advocating the application of the statistics of life-insurance to the understanding of fishery problems. Let me quote from a remarkable lecture he gave in that year, one which was translated and published in Edinburgh (1908):

"I will proceed to draw a comparison between this Fishery Research and a science which is much more generally understood. I mean the science of Vital Statistics.

In all expositions of the science of vital statistics there are three prominent features which attract our chief consideration: 1. Birth rate. 2. Age distribution. 3. Migration. It is customary to study these questions by the help of what are called representative statistics. A certain number of individuals are selected that are supposed to stand for the mass of the people, and attention is directed to them. We ascertain from this source their average length of life, their wanderings, their increase or decrease, and whether sickness, war, disaster, or emigration play any appreciable part in reducing the population.

It seems at first sight a bold suggestion to propose the study of the fish supply on lines like these. A population can be counted; but who knows how many fishes are in the sea? And yet it appears to me a project great in possibilities, to regard the discoveries of fishery research from a similar standpoint to what has been adopted in the science of vital statistics."

He at once proceeded to put his ideas into effect with remarkable results. With the help of his able assistants—Dahl, Damas, Lea and Sund—he began a thorough statistical study of the stocks of the Norwegian herring and cod. By 1910 the extensive liberation of marked plaice and their subsequent recapture by fishermen—organized by Garstang and his team at Lowestoft—had already told us the main facts of their migrations, their growth-rates, and the size of their stocks in the North Sea (see p. 161ff.).

The reason why this new science of ecology has been developed so much further in the sea than on the land is not really far to seek. Man lives mainly on cultivated crops, on the flesh of domesticated animals and upon fish. In the same category as the fish we may put the whales which give us our oil for margarine; sea fish and whales are alone unfarmed and still hunted in the wild. It is, of course, the economic urge to find out more about their life and habits, so as to make their exploitation more efficient, that has encouraged the governments of many countries to support fisheries research—a research which is essentially ecological.

If only cattle, sheep, pigs and poultry had never been domesticated, and we were entirely dependent upon wild animals for our meat, what a wonderful series of terrestrial ecological investigations we might have had by now to enable us to conserve the stocks of wild game and exploit them to the best advantage. It is well to remember the contrast between the lives of wild and domesticated animals when considering the relative progress of agriculture and fisheries research. Some people seem to imagine that, in a very few years after the start of a programme of research, we should be able to bring about some practical improvements in a fishery. This is usually a much too optimistic hope. In agriculture we can try different fertilizers for various types of land, and breed new races of plants and animals to give higher yields under particular conditions; positive results may be achieved in a relatively short time. We have mentioned (p. 172) the possible future transplantation of stocks of young fish to richer feeding-grounds, which is akin to farming; but, with this exception, the problems of fisheries research are *at present* radically different from those of agriculture and they cannot be compared. The time may come, as I shall presently suggest, when this may change.

The greater part of our volume has been taken up with the results obtained by these fishery ecologists. Let us now see them in action.

Throughout the year the two fishery laboratories, Lowestoft and Aberdeen, each have two or more research vessels at work. These are usually steaming over a large area, traversing it backwards and forwards, perhaps on parallel lines, to cover the sea with a series of points of observation (or stations, as such points are called) where the ships stop to take samples or readings. The purposes of the cruises will vary. Sometimes they will be for a hydrological survey; taking temperatures, and sampling the water at various depths for analysis to determine its general saltness, as well as its content of particular salts, such as phosphate and nitrates, so important for plant-growth. Sometimes they will be making a survey of the plankton with various types of tow-net, either hauled horizontally or vertically, made of fine or coarse mesh silk, according to the nature of the work. At other times they will be mapping the production of young fish with special kinds of net, sampling the benthos with dredge or grab, or using a full-sized commercial trawl in a survey of adult fish. Often one cruise may combine two or more lines of work. The ships steam on their way between stations, day and night, to cover as much ground as possible in the time available, often racing against the clock as bad weather threatens to cut a programme short. It is hard going for the scientists. If stations are twenty miles apart, and the ship goes at nine knots, there will only be two and a quarter hours between them. On stations there is continuous activity as water-sampling bottles or plankton nets go up and down; in the time between stations the samples collected will want considerable attention before being put away for future study, the scientific log must be entered up, and meals and sleep taken. One station seems hardly over before another comes. It is the broken sleep night after night that is so tiring; sometimes it may be possible for the scientists to take watches during the night, turn and turn about, but more usually there is so much to be done at stations that this is not practicable, and sleep must be made up at odd times between stations during the day. The same scientists, of course, do not go continuously on cruises, but each will make several a year; and this, incidentally, gives them more than enough material to keep them fully occupied with analysis and working up the results in the laboratory for the rest of the time.

It is a life full of interest and sometimes excitement—but in rough weather it is not always an easy one. Apparatus, especially when of metal, becomes very difficult to handle with cold wet fingers in the biting wind of a winter's night, as the ship rolls and pitches in the darkness. What an aggravation an accident can be; the sudden lurch of the ship as the samples are being carried along the deck may cause one to be lost and then the whole process must be gone through again, for a gap in the lay-out of the observations may spoil the value of the whole set. How bitter, too, may be the disappointment of having to give up work before the end of a cruise, because a storm makes it impossible to carry on; perhaps the vital bit of a story in tracing the movement of young fish from the spawning ground is lost until another opportunity will occur next year. Those scientists who always work in the shelter of a University or Institute laboratory should remember the difficulties of research at sea, when they may be inclined to be critical of some contributions from the marine ecologist. Why didn't he do this or that?—what an opportunity he surely missed there? The answer often is, that what seems such an obvious thing to have done was simply impossible at the time under the conditions prevailing. There are times, too, when the motion of the ship, although not producing actual sickness, may curiously curtail the initiative and vision of those who seem most brilliant ashore; an insidious mental lethargy appears to creep over some and stifle the fires of enthusiasm which burnt so brightly when the seas were calm.

However it is the difficulties of the work, and the problems of getting round them which make it such a fascinating game; there is something of the luck of the chase about it—the chasing of elusive facts among the hazards of unpredictable seas. It is this unusual combination of sport and research which makes it so unique an occupation. It was my good fortune, from 1921 to 1924, to spend the first three years of my zoological career as Assistant Naturalist at the Fisheries Laboratory at Lowestoft; during this period I spent much of my time at sea on that splendid old research trawler, the *George Bligh*—with the best of captains, the late Commander W. H. Stewart, R.N.R.—and I would not have missed a minute of it. Since I myself have gone on to other spheres of work I can, I think without lack of modesty, seize this opportunity to "take off my hat" to the fisheries scientists of many nations who continue to grapple with their problems in the North Sea and the Arctic.

We must not forget the important part played by the captain of a research vessel and his officers and crew. A ship is not just a thing of steel and iron; she has a soul—the spirit of the ship's company—and that matters far more than the details of her design. In a commercial fishing craft the crew have their livelihood to make by their own efforts; they have the zest of the hunter. If the crew of a research ship have not a real interest in their work, the efficiency of that ship will only be a fraction of what it might be; if, on the other hand, they can be given some idea of the importance of what they are doing and be made to feel that they are playing a part in the discoveries being made, then the ship may achieve the almost impossible. I have seen the stokers coming up on deck, when not on duty, to ask if they could help in working the nets because they knew we were trying to push through a programme against heavy odds; they were as much concerned in the stokehold to see the line of stations finished as we in the deck laboratory. That is the spirit that gets results. I have worked with some splendid crews—if any of my old shipmates read this I would like them to know that I have not forgotten them and the grand service they gave to fishery science. A lot depends on the Captain; but also a lot depends on the scientists letting everyone on the ship know what they are really driving at.

Too often the scientist is afraid of giving any indication that there is something really exciting about what he is trying to discover; with what he thinks is appropriate modesty he likes to make it appear just a routine daily job—something quite unromantic. Without his realizing it, that is rather a selfish attitude. He forgets that he himself, if he is a real scientist, has the passion of the investigator which is rather like that of the artist. It is that that drives him on, although he may try to hide it. To be satisfied with life the ship's officers and crew must also be given some share of this spirit of discovery. They have not got the reward to look forward to of seeing their work crowned by acceptance in a scientific journal. If they are told nothing of the object of what they are doing, the taking of net hauls here, or water samples there, is just so much 'messing about'—a frustration, a denial of the opportunity for pride in their craftmanship and achievement. The simplest plankton survey can be made exciting to the crew if they know what it's really for—perhaps to map the food of the herring, to study the path of some ocean current or to estimate the varying crop of tiny plants in different parts of the sea. Whatever its object may be it is possible to keep the crew informed of how the work is going: a rich area here, a surprisingly poor area there, and so on to make them feel that in working the gear—and in the stoke-hold and galley too—they are helping to unfold a picture from the hidden sea. How often have I heard them ask with real feeling at the end of a voyage: "Have we done well this trip, Sir?"

The work of the marine ecologists is only in its infancy, but already we see how many bits of the puzzle are beginning to fit together; their work will assume even greater importance as the years go on. There was a clear warning for us, of things to come, in the last two chapters. When the vertebrates conquered the land they went on multiplying till competition became so great that several lines of reptiles were forced back to the water for a living; with the later birds and mammals it was the same, and they replaced the less efficient reptiles in the sea, as they did on land. Who can doubt, with the rising populations in the world of man, that he too will be forced to turn more and more to marine life for additional sources of food?

We have seen in our chapter on over-fishing that we could increase the yield from the sea with a more reasonable fishing rate and with some husbandry in the transplantation of stocks. Both these require international co-operation. The future must bring, sooner or later, the replacement of private competition by a planned social effort. It is a pity for those of us who like individual enterprise; but if we allow the population of the world to increase beyond what the land can support we shall have to get the maximum possible from the sea. At the risk of having my book placed by the libraries on their shelves labelled 'science fiction', I will express my belief that the time will come, within a century or two, when vast stretches of the continental shelf will be truly farmed to increase our supply of fish.

If we look back to Chapter 6 (p. 137) we find Dr. Gunnar Thorson saying "we must recognize the amazing fact that only 1 or 2 per cent of the fish food is actually eaten by fish; the rest is taken by invertebrates." I then asked 'will future farmers of the sea be able to eradicate some of these pests and so step up the quantity of fish which may be carried on a given area?' I believe that is just what man will eventually do. If Thorson's calculations are correct, and if man could eliminate just a quarter of the pests and so allow the fish to have some 20, instead of 2, per cent of the potential food supply, then he could make a given area support 10 times the quantity of fish. How are such pests as starfish to be eliminated? I believe that, just as we harrow and roll the land in addition to reaping our crops, we shall in time systematically drag some combing or other devices over the sea floor at intervals to weed out the creatures that take the food from the more valuable fish; and the pests themselves may well be ground into meal to feed poultry ashore. It will require much more ecological research to determine just which of the animals we can do with in smaller numbers.

Shall we always fish and farm the sea from ships at the surface—dragging bags below us out of sight? I doubt it. Before we explore the moon in space suits, as I am sure our great-great-grandchildren will, I believe men, with improved diving apparatus, will be working on the sea-bed. Perhaps, working in two hour shifts from a mother ship above, they will be driving pressure-proof submarine tractors down below powered by atomic energy: rounding up the fish in nets of novel design or whirring backwards and forwards over the bottom pulling the latest starfish eradicator. The tractors, driven by propellers in the water, will of course have buoyancy tanks so that they are light enough to skim the bottom on their mud-shoes without sinking in. They will all be in wireless communication with one another and with the parent ship; their positions will be accurately pin-pointed for them on some new kind of portable navigation screen. With a bill for labour and fuel less than that for three or four trawlers, one mother ship may perhaps operate a fleet of tractor-trawls advancing in line across the Dogger Bank below her; with the tractors remaining on the sea-bed for long periods, the men and their bags of fish will be drawn up at intervals through an opening into a well at the bottom of the ship, just as whole whales are drawn today into the hull of a floating factory . . .

There is no need to let imagination carry us any further—our details will be wrong, as many new inventions will have come to us by then; who can doubt, however, that in time man will be forced under the sea again as surely as the ichthyosaurs and whales have been before him? There will not be a separate race of submarine men, but a craft of under-water farmers who will think no more of spending several hours some fifty fathoms down than did miners in the past think of spending eight or more hours burrowing a mile or more below the surface of the earth. And the naturalists will be there too.

Certainly, in the days to come, even if my flights of fancy do not materialise, the work of the marine ecologist must increase in importance as the demand for sea-food becomes greater than to-day. All the discoveries of the marine biologists, both of the fishery and independent laboratories, however remote they may now seem from practical issues, will be required in their different ways for a full understanding of the life in the sea and its more rational exploitation. Plankton and hydrological surveys, such as were discussed in the final chapter of our first volume, must come to play an increasing part in the forecasting systems of the future. There will be more and more scope for those with a bent for natural history and ecology.

I will end by recording a fact which is surely stranger than fiction: one of those curious anomalies which have arisen as an accident of history and remained undisturbed. In the first chapter of this volume (p. 15) I referred to the beginnings of fishery research by the two government departments: first by the Fishery Board for Scotland (now the Scottish Home Department, Fisheries Division) and later by the English Board of Agriculture and Fisheries (now the Ministry of Agriculture, Fisheries and Food). As the reader will have gathered I have nothing but praise for their achievements and admiration for their present work in hand; nevertheless I must ask the question— are they making the best possible progress by being separated into two quite independent organisations? I know well that there are inconvenient political difficulties in bringing about a unification; but I wonder if those concerned with these aspects are fully aware of the fundamental difference between fishery research and that concerned with agriculture and forestry which they take to be the model. We are not dealing with research on plants or stocks of animals grown in either England or Scotland, but with stocks of fish which are moving about the waters fished by the fishermen of the two countries.

I think many scientists in high positions are not really aware of this extraordinary state of affairs. I believe perhaps they think, as did one leading zoologist who said, when I raised the question, "there are surely advantages in two scientific approaches to a problem of common interest." I should heartily agree with this view if the two scientific approaches were each looking at the whole problem, but they are not. The Scottish department investigates the northern North Sea and the English department the southern area; yet the stocks of fish they are investigatng are common to both, and one general flow of water, and its changing planktonic content, circulates round both areas. Neither party sees the whole picture. The English scientists are now going much to the Arctic to investigate the cod fisheries in the region of Bear Island; the Scottish scientists have also got a new Arctic research ship, but by agreement they will be investigating an area separated from the English area by a line of longitude. Can natural phenomena really be studied efficiently under such political limitations? Do the stocks of fish and the factors controlling them arrange themselves conveniently within such boundaries? Of course not, as a glance at Figs. 6, 26 and 98 (pp. 13, 65 and 223) will show.

Suppose that in Oxford and Cambridge some ancient custom was still maintained by which the zoologists of one would study only the anterior half of any animal and those of the other the posterior half— I will not suggest which way it might be—should we not laugh at such a preposterous situation? I believe, since the North Sea and its stocks of fish form one large natural system, that the idea of dividing its ecological investigation into two by a purely political tradition is an equal folly. Let us look at it the other way. Suppose it was one unified investigation is there any scientist who, in his senses, would advocate its being divided as it now is? Let there still be the two laboratories, Aberdeen and Lowestoft—for some fish, like the haddock, are better studied from the north and others, like the plaice, from the south—but let there be more collaboration between them and let their two fleets of research vessels work to a common plan.

Since the last war I have acted as chairman of a Herring Research Group organized by the Development Commission; at this the English and Scottish herring research workers meet twice a year for a discussion of their common problems and an interchange of ideas. For the first time one group knows what the other is doing and they can benefit by each other's experience. But is it enough to meet occasionally and only in regard to the herring? I am sure from my experience of these meetings that the whole of fishery research would proceed much faster and more economically if there were one united effort covering the whole marine front. It will I suppose come eventually; but in the meantime let us not be disappointed by what has been achieved in our own characteristic and quaintly unmethodical way.

# BIBLIOGRAPHY

LIKE that of Part I, this bibliography cannot be more than a list of references to the books and papers which have been mentioned in the text; anything like a comprehensive catalogue of the works dealing with the natural history of the fish, whales and benthos would in itself take up several volumes. It is impossible in the space available to give the original source for every fact recorded.

A number of important papers have been omitted if their findings have been brought together in later works which are included and are more readily accessible to the general reader; this applies, for example, to many records of fishery research which are so well summarised, with references, in the Buckland Lectures, such as those by Hodgson (1934), Hickling (1934), Graham (1948) and Wimpenny (1953).

From the further references in the publications included, the student will be able to follow any particular trail which may attract him; he should also consult the invaluable three volumes of *A Bibliography of Fishes* (B. Dean et al., 1916–1923) and the annual issues of *The Zoological Record* (1864–). All the abbreviations used are those given in the *World List of Scientific Periodicals*.

AFLALO, F. G. (1904). The Sea-fishing Industry of England and Wales. London, E. Stanford.

ALLEN, E. J. (1899). On the Fauna and Bottom-Deposits near the Thirty-Fathom Line . . . *J. Mar. biol. Ass. U.K., 5,* 365–542.

ALWARD, G. L. (1911). *The Development of British Fisheries,* Grimsby.—(1932). *The Sea Fisheries of Great Britain and Ireland.* Grimsby, Albert Gait.

ARNOLD, D. C. (1953). Observations on *Carapus acus* (Brünnich) *Pubbl. Staz. Zool. Napoli, 24,* 153–67.

ATKINSON, G. T. (1908). Notes on a Fishing Voyage to the Barents Sea in August 1907. *J. Mar. biol. Ass. U.K., 8,* 71–98.

BALMAIN, K. H. and SHEARER, W. M. (1956). Records of Salmon and Sea Trout caught at Sea. *Freshwater and Salmon Fisheries Res. Scot.,* 11.

BALLS, R. (1946). *Fish on the Spotline,* London, Marconi Int. Mar. Comm. Co. Ltd.— (1952). Echo Sounders in Commercial Fisheries. *World Fishing, 1,* 75.

BATESON, W. (1890). The Sense-organs and Perceptions of Fishes . . . *J. Mar. biol. Ass. U.K., 1,* 225–256.

BEDDARD, F. E. (1900). *A Book of Whales.* London, John Murray.

BENHAM, W. B. (1901). The Platyhelmia. In Lankester's *Treatise on Zoology,* Part IV, London, A. and C. Black.

BERTIN, L. (1956). *Eels: A Biological Study,* London, Cleaver-Hume Press Ltd.

BEVERTON, R. J. H. and HOLT, S. J. (1957). On the Dynamics of Exploited Fish Populations. *Fish. Invest. Lond., Sec. II, 19,* 1–533.

BIGELOW, H. B. and SCHROEDER, W. C. (1948). *Fishes of the Western North Atlantic, Part I, Lancelets, Cyclostomes and Sharks.*—(1953). *Ibid, Part II, Sawfishes, Guitarfishes, Skates and Rays, and Chimaeroids.* New Haven, Sears Foundation. Yale University.

BLAXTER, J. H. S. (1953). Sperm Storage and Cross-Fertilization of Spring and Autumn Spawning Herring. *Nature, 172*, p. 1189.

BLEGVAD, H. (1914). Food and Conditions of Nourishment among the communities of invertebrate animals found on or in the sea bottom in Danish waters. *Rep. Dan. Biol. Sta., 22*, 41–78.—(1916). On the Food of Fish in the Danish Waters within The Skaw. *Ibid., 24*, 17–72.—(1925). Continued Studies on the Quantity of Fish Food in the Sea Bottom. *Ibid., 31*, 27–56.

BORLEY, J. O. (1912). Report on the Transplantation of Plaice to the Dogger Bank 1904–08. *North Sea Fisheries Investigation Committee Report (Southern Area), 4*. London, H.M. Stationery Office.—(1916). Review of English Plaice Marking Experiments in the North Sea. *Fish. Invest., London*, Ser. II, *3*, No. 3.—(1923). The Marine Deposits of the Southern North Sea. *Ibid., 4*, No. 6.

BOWMAN, A. (1933). Plaice-marking experiments in Shetland Waters. *J. Cons. int. Explor. Mer., 8*, 223–29.

BROWN, M. E. (1957). *The Physiology of Fishes* (Edited by), New York, Academic Press. 2 vols.

BUCHANAN-WOLLASTON, H. J., see under WOLLASTON.

BUCKMAN, A. (1952). Vorlaufige Mitteilung über Fütterungsund Wachstumsversuche mit Schollen im Aquarium. *Kurse Mitt. Max Planck-Instit., Meeresbiol., 1*, 8–21.

CARRUTHERS, J. N. (1950). An Attitude on "Fishery Hydrography". *J. Mar. Res., 10*, 101–118.

CARRUTHERS, J. N., LAWFORD, A. L. and VELEY, V. F. C. (1951). Fishery Hydrography: Brood Strength Fluctuations in Various North Sea Fish, with Suggested Methods of Prediction. *Kiel. Meeres., 8*, 5–15.

CHANG, H.-W. (1951). On *Callionymus reticulatus* C. & V. and its Distribution in European Seas. *J. Mar. biol. Ass. U.K., 30*, 297–312.

CLARK, R. S. (1922). Rays and Skates (*Raiae*) No. 1. Egg-capsules and young. *J. Mar. biol. Ass. U.K., 12*, 577–643.—(1926). Rays and Skates; a Revision of the European Species. *Fish. Scot. Sci. Invest., 1926*. No. 1.

CLARKE, R. (1954a). Open Boat Whaling in the Azores. *'Discovery' Rep., 26*, 281–354.—(1954b). A great haul of Ambergris. *Nature, 174*, 155.—(1956a). Sperm Whales of the Azores. *'Discovery' Rep., 28*, 237–298.—(1956b). A giant squid swallowed by a sperm whale. *Challenger Soc. Abstr., 3*, VIII, 31.

COOPER, L. H. N. (1952). The Boar Fish, *Capros aper* (L) as a Possible Biological Indicator of Water Movement. *J. Mar. biol. Ass. U.K., 31*, 351–62.

CORBIN, P. G. (1947). The spawning of the Mackerel . . . and the Pilchard . . . in the Celtic Sea in 1937–39. *J. Mar. biol. Ass. U.K., 27*, 65–132.—(1950a). The occurrence of the Smooth Sand-Eel *Gymnammodytes semisquamatus* (Jourdain) in the Plymouth Area . . . *Ibid., 29*, 83–95.—(1950b). *Ammodytes immaculatus*, a New Species of Sand-Eel Found in European Seas. *Nature, 166*, 525.—(1958). A new British fish: *Gobius forsteri; Nature, 181*, 1659.

CORBIN, P. G. and VIDYA VATA (1949). The post-larval Sand-Eels (Ammodytidae) of the Celtic Sea . . . *J. Mar. biol. Ass. U.K., 28*, 287–313.

CUSHING, D. H. (1952). Echo-Surveys of Fish. *J. Cons. int. Explor. Mer., 18*, 45–60.—(1955). On the Autumn-Spawned Herring Races of the North Sea. *Ibid., 21*, 44–60.—(1957). The Interpretation of Echo Traces. *Fish. Invest. Lond. Ser. II, 21*, No. 3.

CUSHING, D. H. and BURD, A. C. (1957). On the Herring of the Southern North Sea. *Fish. Invest. Lond. Ser. II, 20*, No. 11.

CUTTING, C. L. (1955). *Fish Saving*. London, Leonard Hill.

DADE, E. (1933). *Sail and Oar (A North Sea Sketch Book)*. London, Dent and Sons.

DAMANT, G. C. C. (1921). Illumination of Plankton. *Nature, 108*, 42.

DAVIS, F. M. (1923a). An Account of the Fishing Gear of England and Wales. *Fish. Invest. Lond.*, Ser. II, *5*, No. 4.—(1923b). Quantitative Studies on the Fauna of the Sea Bottom, Part I. *Ibid., 6*, No. 2.—(1925). Part II. *Ibid., 8*, No. 4.—(1934). Mesh Experiments with Trawls. 1928–1933. *Ibid., 14*, No. 1.

DAWES, B. (1930). Growth and Maintenance in the Plaice. Part I. *J. Mar. biol. Ass. U.K., 17*, 103–174.—(1931). Part II. *Ibid., 17*, 877–975.—(1946). *The Trematoda*, Cambridge, University Press.—(1947). *The Trematoda of British Fishes*, London, The Ray Society.

DAY, F. (1880–84). *The Fishes of Great Britain and Ireland*. London, Williams and Norgate.

DEAN, B., et al. (1916–1923). *A Bibliography of Fishes*. 3 vols. New York, American Museum of Natural History.

DERANIYAGALA, P. E. P. (1938). The Mexican Loggerhead Turtle in Europe. *Nature, 142*, 540.

DOUGLAS, F. (1782). *A General Description of the East Coast of Scotland . . .* Paisley.

ELLIS, R. N. and JONES, R. (1956). The Whiting in the North Sea. *Mar. Res. Scot., 1956*, No. 2.

FISHER, J. (1952). *The Fulmar*. New Naturalist Series. London, Collins.

FISHER, J. and LOCKLEY, R. M. (1954). *Sea-Birds*. New Naturalist Series. London, Collins.

FORD, E. (1921). A Contribution to our Knowledge of the Life-Histories of the Dogfishes landed at Plymouth. *J. Mar. biol. Ass. U.K., 12*, 468–505.—(1923). Animal Communities of the Level Sea Bottom . . . adjacent to Plymouth. *Ibid., 13*, 164–224.—(1937). *The Nation's Sea-Fish Supply*. London, Arnold.

FORMAN, B. (1954). Walrus on Aberdeenshire Coast. *Scot. Nat., 1954*, 56.

FORSTER, G. (1777). *A Voyage Round the World in H.M. Sloop "Resolution"*. London.

FORSTER, G. R. (1953). The spawning behaviour of the plaice. *J. Mar. biol. Ass. U.K., 32*, 319.—(1954). Preliminary note on a survey of Stoke Point rocks with self-contained diving apparatus. *Ibid., 33*, 341–44.

FRASER, F. C. (1934, 1946). *Reports on Cetacea stranded on the British Coasts*. Nos. 11 and 12. London, British Museum (Natural History).—(1937). Common Dolphins in the North Sea. *Scot. Nat., 1937*, 103–5.

FRASER, F. C. and PARKER, H. W. (1953). *Guide for the Identification and Reporting of Stranded Whales, Dolphins, Porpoises and Turtles on the British Coasts*. London, British Museum (Natural History).

FRASER, F. C. and PURVES, P. E. (1954). Hearing in Cetaceans. *Bull. Brit. Mus. (Nat. Hist.), 2*, 103–113.—(1955). The 'Blow' of Whales, *Nature, 176*, 1221.

FULTON, T. W. (1891). The comparative fecundity of sea-fishes. *9th Rep. Fish. Bd. Scot.*, Pt. 3. 243.—(1893). Migrations and the rate of growth of the food-fishes. *11th Rep. Fish. Bd. Scot.*, 176.

GARSTANG, W. (1905). Reports on Experiments with Marked Plaice and Transplantation, I. *North Sea Fisheries Investigation Committee (Southern Area), 1*. London, H.M. Stationery Office.—(1912). Part II. *Ibid., 4*.—(1930). Frank Buckland and Fish Culture, *Nature, 125*, 653.

GAWN, R. W. L. (1948). Aspects of the Locomotion of Whales. *Nature, 161*, 44.

GOODE, G. B. and BEAN, T. H. (1895). *Oceanic Ichthyology*. Washington, Smithsonian Institution.

GOODRICH, E. S. (1909). Vertebrata Craniata: Cyclostomes and Fishes. In Lankester's *Treatise on Zoology*, Part IX. London, A. and C. Black.—(1930). *Studies on the Structure and Development of Vertebrates*. London, Macmillan.

GORDON, W. J. (1902). *Our Country's Fishes*. London: Simpkin, Marshall, Hamilton, Kent & Co.

GRAHAM, M. (1931). Some Problems in Herring Behaviour. *J. Cons. int. Explor. Mer.*, *6*, 252–65.—(1934). Report on the North Sea Cod. *Fish. Invest. Lond.*, Ser. II, *13*, No. 4.—(1935). Modern Theory of Exploiting a Fishery, and Applications to North Sea Trawling. *J. Cons. int. Explor. Mer.*, 10, 264–74.—(1943). *The Fish Gate*. London, Faber and Faber.—(1948). *Rational Fishing of the Cod of the North Sea*. London, Arnold.—(1956). *Sea Fisheries: Their Investigation in the United Kingdom* (Edited by), London, Arnold.

GRAHAM, M. and Collaborators. (1924). The Annual Cycle in the Life of the Mature Cod in the North Sea. *Fish. Invest. Lond.*, Ser. II, *6*, No. 6.

GRAHAM, M., CARRUTHERS, J. N., and GOODCHILD, H. H. (1926). The Distribution of the Pelagic Stages of the Cod. *Fish. Invest. Lond. Ser. II, 8*, No. 6.

GRAY, J. (1953a). *How Animals Move*. Cambridge, University Press.—(1953b). The Locomotion of Fishes, in *Essays in Marine Biology*, (*Richard Elmhirst Memorial Lectures*), Edinburgh, Oliver and Boyd.

GUNN, N. M. (1941). *The Silver Darlings*, London, Faber and Faber.

GÜNTHER, A. C. L. G. (1880). *An Introduction to the Study of Fishes*. Edinburgh, A. and C. Black.

HALDANE, J. B. S. (1927). *Possible Worlds*. London, Chatto and Windus.

HANCOCK, D. A., DRINNAN, R. E., and HARRIS, W. N. (1956). Notes on the biology of *Sertularia argentea* L., *J. Mar. biol. Assoc. U.K.*, *35*, 307–325.

HARDY, A. C. (1924). The Herring in Relation to its Animate Environment, Part I, The Food and Feeding Habits of the Herring. *Fish. Invest. Lond.*, Ser. II, *7*, No. 3.—(1951). Towards a Programme of Herring Research. *Rapp. Cons. Explor. Mer.*, *128*, 9–18.

HARDY, A. C. and GUNTHER, E. R. (1935). The Plankton of the South Georgia Whaling Grounds and Adjacent Waters, 1926–27. '*Discovery*' *Rep.*, *11*, 1–146.

HARDY, A. C., HENDERSON, G. T. D., LUCAS, C. E. and FRASER, J. H. (1936). The Ecological Relations between the Herring and the Plankton Investigated with the Plankton Indicator. *J. Mar. biol. Ass. U.K.*, *21*, 147–291.

HARMER, S. F. (1914–27). *Reports on Cetacea stranded on the British Coasts*. Nos. 1–10. London, British Museum (Natural History).—(1928). The History of Whaling. *Proc. Linn. Soc. Lond.*, 51–95.—(1931). Southern Whaling. *Ibid.*, 85–163.

HARRIS, J. E. (1936). The Role of Fins in the Equilibrium of the Swimming Fish, Part I. *J. Exp. Biol.*, *13*, 476–493.—(1938). The Role of Fins . . . Part II, *Ibid*, *15*, 32–47.—(1953). Fin Patterns and Mode of Life in Fishes, in *Essays in Marine Biology* (*Elmhirst Memorial Lectures*). Edinburgh, Oliver and Boyd.

HART, J. T. (1948). The Distribution and Biology of Hake. *Biol. Rev.*, *23*, 62–80.

HARVEY, E. N. (1952). *Bioluminescence*. New York, Academic Press.

HEEZEN, B. C. (1957). Whales caught in deep-sea cables. *Deep-Sea Research, 4*, 105–115.

HENDERSON, G. T. D. (1957). Continuous Plankton Records: the Distribution of young *Gadus poutassou* (Risso). *Bull. Mar. Ecol.*, *4*, 179–202.

HERON-ALLEN, E. and EARLAND, A. (1912). On Some Foraminifera from the North Sea . . . *J. R. micro. Soc.*, *1912*, 382–389.

HICKLING, C. F. (1925). A New Type of Luminescence in Fishes. *J. Mar. biol. Ass.*

*U.K.*, *13*, 914–29.—(1934). *The Hake and the Hake Fishery.* London, Arnold.—
(1945). The Seasonal Cycle in the Cornish Pilchard . . . *J. Mar. biol. Ass. U.K.*, *26*, 115–38.

HJORT, J. (1908). *Some Results of the International Ocean Researches,* Edinburgh, Scottish Oceanographical Laboratory.

HODGSON, W. C. (1934). *The Natural History of the Herring of the Southern North Sea.* London, Arnold.—(1950). *The Herring Atlas.* Cons. int. Explor. Mer.—(1956). The great herring mystery. *New Scientist*, Nov. 29, 1956, 15–17.—(1957). *The Herring and Its Fishery.* London, Routledge and Kegan Paul.

HODGSON, W. C. and RICHARDSON, I. D. (1949). The Experiments on the Cornish Pilchard Fishery in 1947–8. *Fish. Invest. Lond., Ser. II, 17,* No. 2.

HOLDSWORTH, E. W. H. (1884). *Deep Sea Fishing and Fishing Boats,* London.

HOLME, N. A. (1949). A new bottom-sampler. *J. Mar. biol. Ass. U.K., 28,* 323–32.—(1953). The biomass of the bottom fauna . . . off Plymouth. *Ibid., 32,* 1–49.

HOLT, E. W. L. (1892–94). North Sea Investigations. *J. Mar. biol. Ass. U.K., 2,* 216–19, 363–93 and *Ibid., 3,* 78–106, 123–42, 169–201, 288–291.—(1895–97). An Examination of the Present State of the Grimsby Trawl Fishery, with special reference to the Destruction of Immature Fish. *Ibid., 3,* 339–446; and *4,* 410–414.—(1898). On the Breeding of the Dragonet (*Callionymus lyra*) . . . *Proc. Zoo. Soc. Lond.* for 1898, p. 281.

HOMANS, R. E. S., and NEEDLER, A. W. H. (1946). Food of the Haddock. *Proc. Nova Scotia. Inst. Sci., 21,* 15–49.

HUNT, O. D. (1925). The Food of the Bottom Fauna of the Plymouth Fishing Grounds. *J. Mar. biol. Ass. U.K., 13,* 560–99.

HUXLEY, T. H. (1881). The Herring: a lecture delivered at the National Fishery Exhibition at Norwich, April 21st, 1881. *Nature, 23,* 607–13.

JENKINS, J. T. (1920). *The Sea Fisheries,* London, Constable.—(1925, Second Edition, 1936). *The Fishes of the British Isles,* London, F. Warne & Co.

JOHNSTONE, J. (1908). *Conditions of Life in the Sea,* Cambridge, University Press.—(1905–12). Internal Parasites and Diseased Conditions of Fishes. *Trans. Biol. Soc. Liverpool, 19,* 98–120; *20,* 151–185; *21,* 170–203; *23,* 87–100; *24,* 16–37; *25,* 16–50; *26,* 33–74.

JOHNSTONE, J., SCOTT, A. and SMITH, W. C. (1924). Report on . . . Parasites and Diseases of the Cod. *Fish, Invest. Lond. Ser. II, 6,* No. 7.

JONES, R. (1954). The Food of the Whiting . . . *Mar. Res. Scot., 1954, No. 2.*

KABATA, Z. (1955). The Scientist, the Fisherman and the Parasite. *Scottish Fisheries Bulletin,* No. 4.

KENNEDY, M. (1954). *The Sea Angler's Fishes,* London. Hutchinson.

LANKESTER, E. (Ed.) (1846). *Memorials of John Ray,* London, The Ray Society.

LEBOUR, M. V. (1918–20). The Food of Post-Larval Fish. *J. Mar. biol. Ass. U.K., 11,* 433–69; *12,* 22–47; 261–324.—(1918). Feeding Habits of some Young Fish. *Ibid., 12,* 9–21.—(1921). The Food of Young Clupeoids. *Ibid., 12,* 458–467.—(1922–23). The Food of Plankton Organisms. *Ibid., 12,* 644–677; *13,* 70–92.

LISSMANN, H. W. (1951). Continuous Electrical Signals from the Tail of a Fish *Gymnarchus niloticus* Cuv., *Nature, 167,* 201.

MACKINTOSH, N. A. (1942). The Southern Stocks of Whalebone Whales. '*Discovery*' *Rep., 22,* 197–300.—(1946). The Natural History of Whalebone Whales. *Biol. Rev., 21,* 60–74.

MACKINTOSH, N. A. and WHEELER, J. F. G. (1929). Southern Blue and Fin Whales. '*Discovery*' *Rep., 1,* 257–540.

MATTHEWS, L. H. (1950). Reproduction in the basking shark *Cetorhinus maximus.*

(Gunner). *Phil. Trans.*, *234B.*, 247.—(1952). *British Mammals*. New Naturalist Series. London, Collins.

MATTHEWS, L. H. and PARKER, H. W. (1950). Notes on the anatomy and biology of the basking shark. *Proc. Zool. Soc. Lond.*, *120*, 535–76.—(1951). Basking Sharks Leaping. *Ibid.*, *121*, 461–62.

MENZIES, W. J. M. (1949). *The Stock of Salmon: Its Migrations, Preservations and Improvement*, London, Arnold.

MENZIES, W. J. M. and SHEARER, W. M. (1957). Long-distance Migration of the Salmon. *Nature*, *179*, 790.

MINCHIN, E. A. (1903). The Sporozoa. In Lankester's *Treatise on Zoology* Part I, 2nd Fasc. London, A. and C. Black.

NORMAN, J. R. (1929). Note on a Sailfish (*Istiophorus americanus* Cuvier and Valenciennes) new to the British Fauna. *J. Mar. biol. Ass. U.K.*, *16*, 67–71.— (1931; 3rd Edit.: 1947). *A History of Fishes*. London, Ernest Benn.

NORMAN, J. R. and FRASER, F. C., (1948). *Giant Fishes, Whales and Dolphins*. London, Putnam.

ORKIN, P. A. (1950). A History of the Opah *Lampris guttatus* (Brünnich), *Scot. Nat.*, *62*, 129–141.

OSORIO, B. (1912). Une propriété singulière d'une bactérie phosphorescente. *C.R. Soc. Biol. Paris.*, *72*, 432–433.

PARKER, H. W. (1939). Turtles stranded on the British Coast 1938–1939. *Proc. Linn. Soc. Lond.*, *151*, 127–129.

PARKER, H. W. and BOESEMAN, M. (1954). The basking shark *Cetorhinus maximus* in winter. *Proc. Zool. Soc. Lond.*, *124*, 185–194.

PARRISH, B. B. (1949). Haddock Stocks in the North Sea during 1948. *J. Cons. int. Explor. Mer.*, *16*, 74–84.—(1950). Brood fluctuations in the North Sea haddock population. *Challenger Soc. Abstr.*, *3*, 18.— *The Haddock* (*Buckland Lectures* for *1956*). London, Arnold. (In the press).

PENNANT, T. (1769). *British Zoology*, (Ed. 2) *3*, London.

PETERSEN, C. G. J. (1913). Valuation of the Sea II. The animal communities of the sea-bottom and their importance for marine zoogeography. *Rep. Dan. Biol. Sta.*, *21*, 1–68.—(1915). On the Animal Communities of the Sea Bottom in the Skagerak, the Christiania Fjord and the Danish waters. *Ibid.*, *23*, 1–28.—(1915). A Preliminary Result of the Investigations on the Valuation of the Sea. *Ibid.*, *23*, 29–32.—(1918). The Sea Bottom and its Production of Fish Food. *Ibid.*, *25*, 1–62.

PETERSEN, C. G. J. and JENSEN, P. B. (1911). The Valuation of the Sea. I. The Animal Life on the Sea Bottom: Its Food and Quality. *Ibid.*, *20*, 1–79.

POULTON, E. B. (1890). *The Colours of Animals*. London, Kegan Paul.

PURVES, P. E. (1955). A wax plug in the external auditory meatus of the Mysticeti. '*Discovery*' *Rep.*, *28*, 295–302.

PYEFINCH, K. A. (1952). Capture of Pre-Grilse Stage of Salmon. *Scot. Nat.*, *64*, 47.

RADCLIFFE, W. (1921). *Fishing from the Earliest Times*. London, John Murray.

RAE, B. B. (1956). The Food and Feeding Habits of the Lemon Sole. *Mar. Res. Scot.*, *1956*, (3).

RAE, B. B. and WILSON, E. (1952–56). Rare and Exotic Fishes Recorded in Scotland during 1951, 1952, 1953, 1954 and 1955. *Scot. Nat. 64*, 102–11; *65*, 141–53; *66*, 1–16; *68*, 23–38; *68*, 92–109.

RAE, K. M. (1957). Continuous Plankton Records: A Relationship between Wind, Plankton Distribution and Haddock Brood Strength. *Bull. Mar. Ecol.*, *5*, 247–69.

RAITT, D. S. (1934). A Preliminary Account of the Sandeels of Scottish Waters. *J.*

*Cons. int. Explor. Mer.*, *9*, 365–372.—(1936). The Haddock Stocks of the north-east Atlantic, 1916–1935. *Sci. Invest. Fish. Scot.*, *1936*, No. 1.—(1939). The rate of mortality of the haddock in the North Sea stock. *Rapp. Cons. Explor. Mer.*, *110*, 65.

RAVEN, C. E. (1942). *John Ray, Naturalist*, Cambridge. University Press.

REES, C. B. (1951). First Report on the Distribution of Lamellibranch Larvae in the North Sea. *Hull Bull. Mar. Ecol.*, *3*, 105–34.—(1952). The Decapod Larvae in the North Sea, 1947–1949. Ibid., *3*, 157–84.

RITCHIE, J. (1921). The Walrus in British Waters. *Scot. Nat.*, *1921*, 5–9 and 77–86.

ROTHSCHILD, M. and CLAY, T. (1952). *Fleas, Flukes and Cuckoos: A Study of Bird Parasites*. New Naturalist Series. London, Collins.

RUSSELL, E. S. (1931). Some Theoretical Considerations on the Over-fishing Problem. *J. Cons. int. Explor. Mer.*, *6*, 3–20.—(1942). *The Overfishing Problem*. Cambridge, University Press.

RUSSELL, F. S. (1934a). Tunny Investigations made in the North Sea on Col. E. T. Peel's Yacht, "St. George" Summer 1933. Part I. Biometric Data. *J. Mar. biol. Ass. U.K.*, *19*, 503–519.—(1934b). The Tunny, *Thunnus thynnus* L. An account of its Distribution and Biology. *Sci. Progr. Twent. Cent.*, *1934*, 634–49.

SAMUEL, A. M. (1918). *The Herring; its effect on the History of Britain*, London, John Murray.

SAVAGE, R. E. (1931). The Relation between the Feeding of the Herring off the East Coast of England and the Plankton of the Surrounding Waters. *Fish. Invest. Lond.*, Ser. II, *12*, No. 3.—(1937). The Food of North Sea Herring, 1930–1934. Ibid., *15*, No. 5.

SAVAGE, R. E. and HODGSON, W. C. (1934). Lunar Influence on the East Anglian Herring Fishery. *J. Cons. int. Explor. Mer.*, *9*, 223–239.

SCHMIDT, J. (1922). The Breeding Places of the Eel. *Phil. Trans. Roy. Soc.* (B) *211*, 179–208.

SCOTT, T and A. (1913). *The British Parasitic Copepoda*. London, The Ray Society.

SHELBOURNE, J. E. (1953). The feeding habits of plaice post-larval in the Southern Bight. *J. Mar. biol. Ass. U.K.*, *32*, 149–59.

SMITH, G. (1906). Rhizocephala. *Fauna et Flora d. Golfes v. Neapel*, *29*.

SOUTER, W. C. (1934). *The Story of our Kayak* . . . Aberdeen, University Press.

STEPHENSON, T. A. (1928, 1935). *The British Sea Anemones*. London, The Ray Society.—(1944). *Seashore Life and Pattern*. (King Penguin Books) London.—(1947). The colours of marine animals. *Endeavour*, *6*, No. 24.

STEVEN, G. A. (1930). Bottom Fauna and the Food of Fishes. *J. Mar. biol. Ass. U.K.*, *16*, 677–705.—(1931–33). Rays and Skates of Devon and Cornwall, I, Methods of Rapid Identification . . . , Ibid., *17*, 367–77; II, A Study of the Fishery . . . , *18*, 1–33; III, The Proportions of Sexes in Nature . . . , *18*, 611–25.—(1936). Migrations and Growth of the Thornback Ray (*Raia clavata*, L.) Ibid., *20*, 605–14.—(1948–52). Contributions to the Biology of the Mackerel *Scomber scombrus* L, I: Mackerel Migrations in the English Channel and Celtic Sea, Ibid., *27*, 517–38; II, A Study of the Fishery in the Southwest of England . . . , *28*, 555–81; III: Age and Growth, *30*, 549–68.

STORROW, B. (1912–13). The prawn (Norway Lobster, *Nephrops norvegicus*) and the prawn fishery of North Shields. *Dove Mar. Lab. Rep.*, *N.S.*, *1*, 10; 2, 9.

SWINDEN, H. (1772). *The History and Antiquities of the Ancient Borough of Great Yarmouth*. Norwich, J. Crouse.

SWINTON, W. E. (1954). *Fossil Amphibians and Reptiles*. London, British Museum (Nat. Hist.).

TÅNING, A. V. (1934). Marking Experiments with Plaice in east Icelandic Waters.

*Rapp. Cons. Explor. Mer., 72,* 5.—(1949). On the Breeding Places and Abundance of the Red Fish (*Sebastes*) . . . *J. Cons. int. Explor. Mer., 16,* 85–95.

THOMPSON, D'A. W. (1917) On some of the scarcer fishes in the Aberdeen market . . ." *Scot. Nat., 1917,* 235–249.—(1942). *On Growth and Form.* 2nd Ed. Cambridge, University Press.

THOMPSON, H. (1923). Problems of Haddock Biology . . . , *Sci. Invest. Fish. Scot., 1922,* No. 5.—(1928). Haddock Biology IV, The Haddock of the North-Western North Sea. *Ibid, 1927,* No. 3.—(1929). Fluctuations in the North Sea haddock stock. *Rapp. Cons. Explor. Mer., 65,* 35.—(1930). The possibility of effecting and utilising accurate estimates of haddock fluctuations. *Ibid.,* 68, 27.

THORSON, G. (1946). Reproduction and Larval Development of Danish Marine Bottom Invertebrates, . . . *Medd. Komm. Danmarks Fisk. Havunders, Ser. Plankton, 4,* 1–518.—(1950). Reproduction and larval ecology of marine bottom invertebrates. *Biol. Rev., 25,* 1.—(1958). Parallel Level Bottom Communities, Their Temperature Adaptation and their 'Balance' between Predators and Food Animals. In *Perspectives in Marine Biology,* Univ. of California Press.

TOSH, J. R. (1895). Report on certain Salmon Investigations . . . *13th Ann. Rep. Fish. Bd. Scot. Part II, Rep. Salmon Fisheries.* 47–66.—(1896) Results of Salmon Investigations. 14th *Ibid.* Part II. 62–85.

TODD, R. A. (1905–1907). First and Second Report on the Food of Fishes, (North Sea, 1904–05). *North Sea Fisheries Investigation Committee (Southern Area), 1 and 2* (Part I). H.M. Stationery Office.—(1915). Report on the Food of the Plaice. *Fish. Invest. Lond.,* Ser. II, *2,* No. 3.

TUCKER, D. W. (1949). New British Records of Two Rare Deep-Sea Fishes: *Oxynotus paradoxus* Frade and *Aphanopus carbo* Lowe. *Nature, 164,* 930.—(1955). The Long-finned Tunny *Germo alalunga* (Bonnaterre) in British Seas. *Ibid, 175,* 174.

TUCKER, D. W. and NEWNHAM, C. T. (1957). The blue shark *Prionace glauca* (L) breeds in British Seas. *Annals and Magazine of Nat. Hist.,* Ser. *12. 10,* 673.

TURNER, W. (1905). On *Pennella balaenopterae* . . . *Trans. Roy. Soc. Edin., 41,* 409–34.

VAILLANT, L. (1898). Sur la presence de l'Anguille commune en haute mer. *C.R. Acad. Sc., 126,* 1429. Paris.

VEVERS, H. G. (1951). Photography of the Sea Floor. *J. Mar. biol. Ass. U.K., 30,* 101–11.—(1952). A Photographic Survey of Certain Areas of Sea Floor near Plymouth. *Ibid., 31,* 215–21.—(1956). Observations on feeding mechanisms in some Echinoderms. *Proc. Zool. Soc. Lond., 126,* 484.

WALLACE, W. (1907–11). Age, Growth and Maturity of the Plaice. *North Sea Fisheries Investigation Committee (Southern Area), 2,* (Parts I and II) and *3.* London, H.M. Stationery Office.—(1915). Report on the Age, Growth and Sexual Maturity of the Plaice in certain parts of the North Sea. *Fish. Invest. Lond.,* Ser. II, *2,* No. 2.

WALMSLEY, L. (1932). *Three Fevers,* London.

WENT, A. E. J. (1946). The Irish Pilchard Fishery. *Proc. R. Irish Acad., 51,* 81–120.—(1951, 1953). Movements of Salmon around Ireland. *Proc. Roy. Irish. Acad., 54B,* 169–201; *55B,* 209–223.

WHITAKER, I. (1954). The Scottish Kayaks and the 'Finn-men'. *Antiquity, 28,* 99–104.

WHITE, E. I. (1946). *Jamoytius Kerwoodi,* a new chordate from the Silurian of Lanarkshire, *Geol. Mag., 83,* 89–97.

WILSON, D. P. (1935). Life of the Shore and Shallow Sea, London, Nicholson and Watson.—(1937). The Habits of the Angler-fish *Lophius piscatorius* L. in the Plymouth Aquarium. *J. Mar. biol. Ass. U.K., 21,* 477–96.—(1947). The Portuguese Man-of-War *Physalia physalis* (L.) in British and Adjacent Seas. *Ibid.,*

*27*, 139–72.—(1948–54). Several papers on the Settlement of Larvae. *Ibid.*, 1948, *27*, 723–60; 1953, *31*, 413–38; *32*, 209–33 and 1954, *33*, 361–80.—(1952). The Influence of the nature of the substratum on the metamorphosis of the larvae of marine animals . . . *Ann. Inst. Oceanogr. Monaco*, 27, 49–156.—(1953). Notes from the Plymouth Aquarium, II, *J. Mar. biol. Ass. U.K.*, *32*, 199–208. —(1956). The Courtship of the Cuckoo Wrasse. *The Illustrated London News*, May 26 (Supplement).

WIMPENNY, R. S. (1953). *The Plaice* (Buckland Lectures for 1949). London, Arnold. Arnold.

WOLLASTON, H. J. B. (1915). Report on the Spawning Grounds of the Plaice in the North Sea. *Fish. Invest. Lond.*, Ser. II, *2*, No. 4.—(1923). The Spawning of the Plaice in the Southern Part of the North Sea in 1913–14. *Ibid.*, *5*, No. 2.

WOOD, H. (1930). Scottish Herring Shoals: Pre-spawning and Spawning Movements. *Fish. Scot. Sci. Invest.*, *1930*, No. 1.—(1936). Race Investigation of the Herring Population of Scottish Waters. *Ibid.*, *1936*, No. 3.—(1937). Movements of Herring in the Northern North Sea. *Ibid.*, *1937*, No. 3.

WOOD, W. (1911). *North Sea Fishers and Fighters*. London, Kegan Paul.

YONGE, C. M. (1937). The Biology of *Aporrhais pes-pelecani* (L.) and *A. serresiana* (Mich.). *J. Mar. biol. Ass. U.K.*, *21*, 687–703.—(1948). Bottom Fauna of the Sea, *Research*, 1. 589–95.—(1949). *The Sea Shore*, New Naturalist Series, London, Collins.

## ADDENDUM

Just as the book is going to press comes the exciting news that Dr. and Mrs. A. J. Southward, of the Plymouth Laboratory, have found members of that remarkable group of animals, the Pogonophora, in British seas (1958: *Nature*, *181*, 1607; *J. Mar. biol. Ass. U.K.*, *37*, 627–632). These animals live in muddy bottoms in deep water down the edge of the continental slope. They are long and exceedingly thin worm-like creatures secreting transparent horny tubes in which they live; so long and thin are these tubes that they might easily be mistaken for strands of twine (and may well have been in the past) when brought up in the dredge. They were first discovered by the late Professor Caullery among material brought back by the Siboga Expedition from the Pacific Ocean. More recently twelve species have been found by Russian expeditions in the north-west Pacific and described by Dr. Ivanov; and in the last two years specimens have been found in the Skagerak and off Greenland. They collect suspended particles of food with their long ciliated tentacles, but then, according to the account of Ivanov, they appear to be unique among free-living animals in having no alimentary canal; they seem to digest their food in little glandular grooves and hollows between small processes on the tentacles and then to take it in *through their outer surface* instead of through an inner lining of a gut cavity. The Southwards have recorded three species, dredged from deep water down the continental slope off the entrance to the English Channel; two of these are new to science, *Siboglinum atlanticum* and *S. inermis*, and the third, *S. ekmani* Jägersten, is the species recently discovered in the deeps of the Skagerak. They will shortly be giving us an account of the biology of these strange animals, for they have now succeeded in bringing them back alive. They tell me that they have now seen them produce a larva resembling that of *Saccoglossus* which is closely related to *Balanoglossus* (p. 116) and to late larval stages of the latter; this confirms a suspected relationship with the proto-chordate stock.

# GLOSSARY

THE Zoological names of different groups of animals are given in the index where the first page cited is that on which they are described. Where technical terms are explained in the text, and used more than once, the page references to such explanations are given below; those which are explained in the text and not used again are not included.

*Amphipod\*:* a small shrimp-like crustacean of the order Amphipoda
*Antipatharian:* p. 97
*Benthic:* referring to life on the sea-floor (the *benthos*)
*Chitin:* horny substance forming the outer cuticle of many animals
*Cilium* (pl. *cilia*): p. 99
*Ciliate:* a protozoan animal, provided with cilia for locomotion or feeding, of the class Ciliophora.
*Copepod\*:* a small crustacean of the order Copepoda
*Cumacean\*:* a shrimp-like crustacean of the order Cumacea
*Demersal:* living near the sea bottom
*Denticle:* p. 32
*Detritus:* particles produced by breakdown of animal and plant bodies, or by erosion of rocks or soil
*Embryonic:* relating to early stages in the development of an animal
*Euphausiacean\*:* a shrimp-like crustacean of the order Euphausiacea
*Flagellum* (pl. *flagella*): p. 107 (footnote)
*Flagellate:* a protozoan animal (or a small plant) provided with a flagellum (or flagella) for locomotion
*Larva:* a young form of an animal which undergoes metamorphosis to become of adult type
*Metamorphosis:* the change of form of an animal during development
*Mysid\*:* a shrimp-like crustacean of the order Mycidacea
*Nematocyst:* p. 95
*Neoteny:* a process whereby some animals may become sexually mature at an earlier stage of development than usual
*Notochord:* p. 18
*Pelagic:* of the open sea
*Radula:* (of mollusc) p. 128, footnote; or sometimes used to denote the rasping tongue of the lamprey.
*Sac:* a sack-like structure as part of the body of an animal.
*Spicule:* a fine needle-like skeletal structure of an animal, *e.g.* of a sponge.

\* These animals are described in some detail in Part I of *The Open Sea*

# INDEX

Numbers in heavy type refer to pages opposite which photographic or coloured illustrations will be found.